LOVE YOUR
It's Keeping You Healthy

John Harrison, M.D.

PEACOCK BOOKS

Published by
PEACOCK BOOKS
7/22, Ansari Road, Darya Ganj, New Delhi-110002
Phones : +91-11-40775252, 23273880, 23275880, 23280451
Fax : +91-11-23285873
Web : www.atlanticbooks.com
E-mail : orders@atlanticbooks.com

Branch Office
5, Nallathambi Street, Wallajah Road, Chennai-600002
Phones : +91-44-64611085, 32413319
E-mail : chennai@atlanticbooks.com

Peacock Books is an imprint of
Atlantic Publishers and Distributors (P) Ltd.

Printed in India at Nice Printing Press, A-33/3A, Site-IV, Industrial Area, Sahibabad, Ghaziabad, U.P.

Preface

Thirty-five years have passed since I wrote the original version of *Love Your Disease*.

In that time, the thesis that we are the primary agents of both the cause and cure of our own diseases has been supported by scientific advances in the fields of psycho-neuro-immunology, cellular biology and epigenetics. In addition, the evolution in physics has allowed for a greater appreciation of healing phenomena that are not observable using the mechanistic view of health favored by conventional medicine.

This edition of *Love Your Disease* continues to explore inquiry and innovation in personal well-being, as well as taking into account shifts in community attitudes over the past thirty-five years.

The benefits of self-led well-being have been confirmed by the multitude of people who, since *Love Your Disease* was first published, have been willing to risk the known in order to heal themselves. This edition is a testament to the courage of all those people who were willing to enter unknown territory in their quest for health and happiness. Thank you all.

The book *Highway to Health* from the same author, continues the journey of exploration begun with *Love Your Disease*, offering a road map towards accepting ourselves, as we are.

Life heals us, if we let it.

John Harrison

Acknowledgements

To Kar Fung Santaro-Wu I give thanks for my early acupuncture teaching, but more importantly, for her personal unaffected demonstration that balance and beauty are really possible. She didn't teach me yin and yang, but then, she lived it.

Dr. John Rudolfer spent four years treating me, deprogramming me from ten years of medical school, teaching me dietetics, and refusing to accept standard notions of cause and cure. From him I learned to shift my frame of reference and to risk doing something different. Although we now differ in our respective treatments, we share a fundamental understanding of people's needs, the most basic of which is the need for love.

When I was still searching, I found Graham Andrewartha and Susan McPhee to help me through the transitional phase of unwillingness to accept personal responsibility; through them I was introduced to the family of psychotherapies: transactional analysis, Gestalt, radix, bodywork, encounter, hypnotherapy, and psychological-level communication, among others. For the psychological theory that I've applied to the cause and cure of physical illness, I thank Eric Berne and, before him, Sigmund Freud. My teachers have included Kristyn Huige, Bob and Mary Goulding, George Thomson, Steve and Carol Lankton, Harry and Laura Boyd, Jeffrey Zeig, and the aforementioned Graham and Susan.

I've taken the paradox of yin and yang and applied it to the psychotherapies, concentrating more on physical illness than on psychological states. In order to cure a disease, we need to understand its value. From my exploration of the field of self-created well-being has come a personal perspective on the value of the psychotherapies and, perhaps more significantly, when to quit them.

I'm indebted to Humphrey McQueen for his enthusiasm about the original idea and his reading of the manuscript, to Geoffrey Farr for his criticism of the theory and for his fearless confrontation of my own issues confusing it, and to Josephine Emery for her support and assistance with the dialogue.

I would also like to thank my fellow members of my clinical-training group, who have shown interest in discussing the ideas I've presented here: in particular Peter West for his comments on the manuscript. Finally, I'm grateful to Llyn Smith, who not only provided an intellectual springboard for many of my ideas over the years of the book's formulation but cared for our son while I was writing it.

Contents

Section III:
The Treatment of Illness

Section IV:
The Prevention of Illness and the Creation of Wellness

Introduction

[My disease] went away of its own accord after some years, and I've never had an itch of it since. And I know why. Because I have no further use for it.

—My Mask, Norman Lindsay

Disease is both self-created and self-cured. How and why we give ourselves illnesses will be examined in great detail in this work. After establishing the ways in which we contribute to the development of our own diseases, we will then go on to investigate the ways in which we can minimize our discomfort and, if we so desire, eliminate our disease entirely. The decision is ours.

The delightful thing about such a concept is that you, the patient, can once again assume stewardship over both your disease and your destiny. When we become familiar with our investment in developing diseases, we'll see that we alone can influence whether to maintain a disease process, allow it to progress, or end it. We'll examine the reasons that some people are too scared to become self-responsible, and we'll see how healing ourselves can be great fun—not only fun but an opportunity to reorganize our whole lives, learn about ourselves and our environment, understand our children, and, perhaps most importantly, prevent disease in both ourselves and our offspring. In doing so, we'll have practiced true preventive medicine and understood the most fundamental principles to govern health and disease.

Illness is the physical and psychological result of unresolved needs, not the malfunctioning of a machine that is caused by unknown or external factors. The client is needy, rather than sick, and has exercised an honorable option that was available to him or her to take care of himself or herself as best he can. (I will alternate genders in examples from now on in order to avoid this kind of gender-related awkwardness of language.) How different an approach to the practice of medicine this is! Rather than attending a medical practitioner with a specific complaint or set of symptoms that we wish to be removed, we can use the presence of the disease to learn about ourselves and to learn why we've found it necessary at this particular point in our lives to become ill. We then make use of our existing illness to prevent others from developing.

When we're prepared to understand why we've made ourselves ill, we'll have taken that first giant leap toward the resolution of our problem. We make use of symptoms, for they are the physical expression of our problem; to remove them indiscriminately is to dispose of valuable evidence. When we do this, new physical symptoms will simply replace those that we've hastily removed without referring to the underlying needs that created them. Removing the symptoms does not deal with the needs. We'll discover the advantages that will come our way from having a disease—and understand our reluctance to part with it. The following brief example will serve to introduce this idea.

Peter Walker consulted me complaining of migraine headaches. He reported that they were worse at home, in the evenings and on the weekends. For years he'd been unsuccessfully treated with medication and, more recently, with acupuncture and chiropractic. He was a gentle sort of man with a job in the forestry department. His hobbies focused on plants and wildlife, and he spent as much time as he could engrossed in journals and books on the subject. His wife was by nature more gregarious than he was and was generally annoyed by his wish to be alone. She tended to pursue conversations and would only desist when Peter was clearly in pain. For this purpose his migraines proved ideal. When Peter learned that he was paying for his wish to be alone by having migraine headaches, he resolved to tell his wife what he wanted instead. He no longer needed the headaches, so he removed them. In turn, she decided to stop feeling guilty about going out and enjoying herself; later, having satisfied her need for social interaction, she reported a favorable change in their relationship at home.

When we've established our investment in creating and maintaining our disease, we can decide to achieve the disease's advantages; these may include attention, solitude, love, respite from work, and, perhaps the major reason, our attempt to confirm our existing beliefs and attitudes about ourselves, others and life, in less painful and less damaging ways. We can learn to get what we want without needing a disease to justify getting it.

Were a patient to go to a doctor and be given a drug, or to a surgeon and have an organ removed, she would be temporarily free of symptoms but none the wiser and upon the return of the disease, or the development of complications, as impotent as before. The treatment of disease by powerful suppressive drugs and by surgery guarantees the development of further disease.

Later we'll examine the reasons behind the "quick-fix" symptom-removal therapy of today.

In order to see the mechanisms behind the prevention, development, maintenance, and treatment of disease, we'll need to look at developmental psychology. In doing this we'll trace those factors that influence our health starting from our conception through pregnancy and childbirth, childhood (the period of diminished responsibility), the transition period (denied responsibility), adulthood (self-responsibility), and parenthood (shared responsibility).

In accompanying me through these pages, you're invited to become aware of the role you're playing in your own health, join in the anticipation and excitement of self-discovery, heal your own body, and finally rejoice at a celebration of yourself.

SECTION I:
THE NATURE OF DISEASE

1

FACTORS THAT INFLUENCE DISEASE

This book concerns itself with the most significant and the most ignored cause of illness—us. We're not the only cause. Paradoxically, we make ourselves ill in order to take care of ourselves as best we can. The fact that disease is largely under our influence—and is a physical response to our internal needs—doesn't deny that other factors are involved. Of course they are. The following chapter examines some of these other factors and shows how even they are partially under our influence. Although these other factors are potentially damaging, it's we who determine, usually subconsciously, whether we'll fall prey to them. In discussing them, I don't dismiss them but instead place them in a position secondary to our own investment in being ill or well. We can either use them to facilitate our disease or we can protect ourselves against them.

GENETICS

Many textbooks are available on the subject of genetics, so a discussion of all but the most elementary concepts is beyond the scope of this book. Some diseases are passed from generation to generation with mathematical certainty. One such familial disorder is classic hemophilia, where half the sons of carrier mothers will have the disease. Females are usually unaffected, as are the sons of affected males. The daughters of affected males will all be carriers. Even for people with this classically inherited disorder, the degree of bleeding has been lessened during dental extraction using hypnosis, which indicates that genetic factors are not the only factors involved. Many diseases appear to be inherited. Some of these are governed by the laws of genetics with greater or lesser mathematical certainty and predictability (as with hemophilia); in these cases, parents can be informed about their chances of producing affected offspring. As a preventive measure, they may elect not to take the risk of having an affected child.

Many more diseases that afflict families are not governed by the laws of genetics. Some of the more commonly known chronic diseases—for example, arthritis, hypertension, asthma, and breast cancer—are in this category. If the disease is common among the adults in a family, then their children will run a greater risk of developing it. For example, if a mother had asthma as a child and hay fever as an adult, then her child may develop the same maladies. The likelihood of this occurring will be heightened if the father also suffers from these diseases. Why is this?

The answer is to be found within the living and eating habits of the family as well as in the role that disease plays in the family psychodynamics—that is, how diseases facilitate social interaction among members of that family. The myriad factors that affect genetic transmission are referred to as the "epigenome". Increasingly, research shows that the epigenome is as important as the genome in the body's development of, and the protection from, disease. Numerous researchers have also examined the mechanisms involved in how the epigenome affects the cellular functions of the organism. Take the following example of family circumstances contributing to the development of asthma.

Mrs. Cason brought her eldest son, Peter, aged twelve, to see me because he was suffering from chronic asthma. She was enthusiastic in her praise for the fortitude he'd displayed in dealing with what she described as "a very debilitating disease for a young man to have to bear". During the interview, he sat quietly and spoke briefly of his desire to go into the air force like his father had, and showed the usual physical signs of asthma. Mrs. Cason had been a nurse before marrying and felt most wanted when she was helping others. Her own uncle had suffered badly from asthma, and the whole family would take turns nursing him in the days before bronchodilators. Peter's brothers—Simon, eleven, and Andrew, five—had no sign of the illness. While his father was away, which was often the case, Peter would sit at his father's place at the table and take over his chores (such as cutting the grass); he would often keep his mother company while his two brothers played. During these times, Peter would often develop asthma. This suited his mother, who liked to care for her eldest son while he was ill. She was frightened of the tenderness of her feelings toward the boy, whom the local butcher had referred to only last week as her "second husband". She had laughed at the time and had been proud to note how he was certainly turning into a fine young man.

Asthma in the Cason family was an acceptable disease. For generations it had enabled some members of the family to care for others. It enabled Mrs. Cason to express her love for her son, who was missing his father. She was evidently afraid of her sexual attraction toward the boy and felt safer when he was ill. He took care of his mother by providing her with a sick patient to care for—the thing she did best. Everybody had an investment in the disease's continuation. The father reinforced the asthma by praising his son for looking after his mother while he was away. In this case, the family psychodynamics maintained the disease process.

We'll see later in the book how children's personalities are influenced by their parents and how, in most cases, parents give children the same messages that they themselves were given. Thus certain personalities are encouraged within families, and illnesses, we will come to learn, are an integral part of personalities.

In addition to psychosocial factors, diet and lifestyle tend to be passed from generation to generation. The diet of the parents is generally the diet of the children, although in recent times this has changed in the Western world, with the advent of universal fast food.

Predispositions to diseases are often not passed on in a physical sense—that is, through the transmission of genes—but rather through the messages that parents give their offspring and the living habits and diet they pass down to them. As noted earlier, the set of factors that affects the expression of genes is termed the epigenome. The medical profession spends much more time and effort in investigating the physical aspects of disease than it does the psychological factors. This is as true of the transmission of diseases as it is of the orthodox profession's mechanical view of cause and cure. It seems that laboratory data is much more acceptable to contemporary Western scientific thinking than psychological profiles. Personality and behavior are passed most assiduously from parents to their offspring. Given long enough time, the components of personality, if reinforced sufficiently, may find physical expression within the structure of genes and may eventually be inherited, like blue eyes. All of nature is a cycle. Psychological states can alter the physical body, and physical characteristics will be reflected within the psyche.

An angry individual has a raised adrenaline level. If such a person fails to resolve her anger, she'll alter her external appearance. Her face will show discontentment and may be ruddy in complexion. She'll walk and talk like an angry person. The unresolved anger will also have internal consequences, such as chronic elevation of the blood pressure (hypertension) and a shutting down of the blood vessels in the hands and feet (peripheral vascular disease). All systems and organs of the body are affected by one's psychological state. The testes (in men) and ovaries (in women), which carry the genetic information, are two such organs. After a time, they may subtly adjust to the interior milieu of their hosts, thereby passing components of the parents' psychological states to their children. Anger then becomes inherited.

The concept of biological feedback or cybernetics introduced here in simple form will be referred to continuously as we examine how we can use those diseases that currently cause us anguish, to assist us. Paradox, continuous evolution, and the learning available to us in our suffering, are all elements of the *Love Your Disease* philosophy of health.

CONCEPTION

Many factors influence the ability to conceive; many others influence the ability to conceive healthy offspring.

Art Rosenbloom, in his 1977 book *The Natural Birth Control Book*, has documented that in some peoples, females do not conceive, despite having multiple partners over a ten-year period, until they've married and it becomes socially acceptable for them to conceive. During this interval they use no contraception. Such a situation highlights the fact that conception and contraception are influenced by mental states. Women in Western society have largely lost this control. Many women do believe, however, that they'll conceive when the time is right for them, and they do. These women are more in harmony with nature's cycles, often ovulating and menstruating in accordance with the moon. When such a woman does not wish to become pregnant, she influences her body chemistry to such a degree that conception becomes impossible. If conception does occur, then spontaneous abortion may follow.

Such a circumstance needs to be distinguished from one in which the woman professes not to want a child and becomes pregnant anyway. I've found in interviewing such women that they were fulfilling parental messages to become pregnant at that particular time. These influences are very powerful and may override even the most unsuitable current social circumstances. Thus large families may continue to get larger in circumstances of poverty or, occasionally, when the mental state of either parent seems least able to accommodate it.

Similarly, we all know of cases where a woman is unable to conceive despite years of trying, and both she and her spouse have been given a clean bill of health. In these cases there's nothing physically amiss with either partner, but the woman may have a deep-seated fear of pregnancy. She may feel, for example, that to conceive a child would detract from her femininity, that she would cease to be attractive to her husband, and that he might then leave her. If she's been told by her mother that when a woman has a child she becomes unattractive or less sexy, she'll most likely have selected a husband who shares those views. The threat of him leaving will then be quite real, thus reinforcing her decision in childhood that having babies threatens marriages. Under these circumstances, it's unlikely that the woman will conceive, even with all the latest medical technology. Therapy for such women then focuses on resolving the fear of the social consequences of childbearing.

For those women who are desperate to conceive and for whom the example above is meaningless, in order to enhance your own chances of pregnancy, please continue reading.

I've also found many examples in my medical practice of women who fail to conceive until they've spent several months on a dietary regimen preparing themselves to carry a child. They're afraid to produce offspring whose health, they argue, may be adversely affected by their smoking cigarettes or by drinking tea, coffee, and alcohol. After several months on a diet designed to eliminate toxins from her body and supply the necessary vitamins and minerals, a woman often feels confident of conceiving a healthy baby and becoming pregnant. In these cases, despite clearly wanting a baby, she's fulfilling an inherent need to become very healthy herself before conceiving.

Any system in the body needs to be exercised appropriately to function properly. This is as true for the digestive system, where underuse in prisoner-of-war camps, for example, often causes later problems, to overuse of the musculoskeletal system, which results in muscle strain or torn ligaments. In a similar way, the reproductive system can be improperly exercised. In the male, sexual excess in the form of overly frequent ejaculation may deplete the stores of viable sperm or deplete the physical reserves of the man so that abnormal sperm become more prevalent. Conversely, an ambitious man may so concern himself with the worries of business that high anxiety levels, combined with a lack of sexual stimulation, may cause a low sperm count. In either case, infertility may result.

In the case of females, psychological stress often results in an inhibition of ovulation or a complete suspension of menstruation. In many others, the regularity of the menstrual cycle is upset by emotional factors. Nearly all women will have experienced the effect of anxiety on the regularity and the nature of the menses. Often periods are more painful (dysmenorrhea) or the blood loss is greater (menorrhagia) at times of emotional stress. Those women who have unresolved tensions concerning femininity, sexuality, or conception will often experience an increased level of anxiety immediately prior to menstruating. This is the much-written-about but little-understood "premenstrual tension". Physical changes certainly do take place in the tissues, which are consequences of the woman's own attitude toward her menstruation. I don't intend to expand on this detailed topic here, other than to include the topic of menstruation in those factors that affect women's ability to conceive (or to conceive a healthy child). Failure to conceive is dealt with at length in section II, "Finding the Cause".

A woman needs to be in a state that is physically and mentally conducive to conception. It is necessary, for example, that her sexual functioning be active. To enhance this activity, she might surround herself with sexually attractive males and females who are unafraid of their own sexuality and who'll accept hers. She might have sexual intercourse with or flirt with people who arouse her sexual desire. She will have orgasms from masturbation and mutual masturbation, and just prior to the ejaculation of her male partner she should become readily aroused and have sufficient vaginal lubrication not to require artificial lubricants. The joy of orgasm ensures the correct muscular contractions of the pelvic muscles and the correct electrolyte balance throughout the organs of conception. These matters require attention many months before a woman plans to conceive, and they all contribute to the organs of conception functioning at their peak at the time pregnancy is required. They represent correct functioning of a system that needs to be exercised like any other. (Who would deny the sense in an athlete training to peak physical condition before an important event?)

In addition to the female achieving a well-functioning reproductive tract, she needs to alleviate many of the usual burdens of living for several months prior to conception as best she can. Financial matters and business problems should be minimized. She needs to feel confident that, having eliminated other commitments, she'll be able to cope with motherhood. Ambivalence at the time of conception results in the mind and body not acting as a unified whole, and may decrease the chances of a desired outcome.

Before attempting pregnancy, the woman in particular, but also the man—both to help his partner and for healthy sperm production—need to be on a specifically formulated diet. This diet convinces the woman that she's physically fit to become a mother (as we've seen in the cases cited earlier) and balances the body chemistry. Expectant mothers must pay particular attention to the elimination of drugs: for example, nicotine from cigarettes, caffeine from tea and coffee, tetrahydrocannibol from marijuana, and artificial colorings and flavorings. In the male, alcohol, caffeine, and nicotine have all been shown to decrease sperm quality. Patients should also be instructed about which foods will supply the necessary proteins, carbohydrates, and fats.

Expectant mothers and their advisors must pay attention to mineral input, especially calcium, and to the fat and water soluble vitamins. The diet needs to be interesting and appealing to the taste and well presented. Much of this commonsense diet will continue into the gestation period.

PRENATAL ENVIRONMENT

Once conception has occurred, the environment within which the fetus will spend the next nine months of her life becomes a major factor shaping her health. Cradled within the womb, the fetus is extremely sensitive to both the physical and emotional state of the mother.

In the first three months of gestation, referred to as the organogenetic period, the cells of the embryo are dividing and multiplying so rapidly that small changes in the blood chemistry of the mother may cause significant changes in the direction of fetal growth. During this period of rapid growth, the conventional medical profession advises caution in the administration of any drugs, but they still prescribe antinauseants in large doses to thousands of women, despite the disaster of thalidomide. When, by their own incomplete assessment, a drug appears to cause no obvious fetal abnormalities, they feel able to recommend its use, although we have neither the biochemical expertise nor the long-term statistical evidence to support or denounce the use of many drugs that are currently used during pregnancy. My belief is that when the medical profession's tests become more sophisticated, we'll be able to demonstrate side effects from all drugs that are taken during pregnancy. I believe that no discretionary drugs should be administered during pregnancy, particularly within the first three months. Included within this category are antinauseants, caffeine (tea and coffee), nicotine (tobacco), tetrahydrocannibol (marijuana), narcotics, antihistamines (for hay fever), or any others. I believe that even drugs that cannot be shown to cross the placental barrier between mother and child still have an effect on the developing fetus. They do this by altering the maternal hormones that do cross the placenta, as well as by interfering with placental function. In addition, many of the complaints of early pregnancy, such as morning sickness, may be effectively treated by natural methods without recourse to drugs. Many other factors affect the biochemistry of the mother and, indirectly, the child.

A prudent diet can improve the likelihood of conception and is no less important during the period of gestation, particularly during the early months. Because this is the period of rapid growth or change, the fetus is vulnerable. Common sense is the element lacking in most dietary regimens. It doesn't make sense to ignore the vitamins and minerals available in nature and take a pill instead. The general dietary regimen in pregnancy needs to provide a balance of vitamins, minerals, proteins, carbohydrates, and fats while augmenting those substances that the fetus makes special demands on, particularly calcium and iron.

Eating extra dairy products is not the best way to increase a pregnant woman's calcium intake. Drinking twice as much milk to account for the baby's needs often upsets the mother's digestion, which then causes bowel and liver disturbances. In turn, the extra calcium in the food is not digested. Some authorities would argue that people who eat few or no dairy products have similar calcium levels to those who consume a great deal. A more radical minority (namely, Curtis Shears, 1976 *Nutritional Science and Health Education*) suggests that dairy products, which are themselves high in calcium, may actually *remove* calcium from the body. Many cooked vegetables offer an abundance of calcium, including cabbage, spinach, broccoli, kale, parsnips, and dandelion and turnip greens. Nuts, pulses (soybeans, lentils, lima beans, and red kidney beans, for example), freshly fertilized hen's eggs, and raw oats—indeed any whole grains—also contribute significant amounts of available calcium, while rhubarb, dates, apricots, raisins, oranges, prunes, peaches, and figs generally contain lesser but worthwhile amounts. Goat-milk products (milk, yogurt, and cheese), with some cow's milk, may be used sparingly.

Vitamins must be taken in the form of a great variety of raw vegetables and, to a lesser extent, raw fruit. The greater the variety, the greater the chance of including all the required vitamins and minerals. Green raw vegetables cannot be successfully replaced by vitamin pills, fruit, or any other substance, since the chlorophyll is required in a fresh state to maximize its benefits. The crisp and colorful vegetables give pleasure to the mother and foster her desire to create and nurture the fetus.

Substances that are living (for example, freshly picked vegetables and fruits) and those foods that are capable of growing (for example, brown rice and pulses) are more likely to nourish the developing fetus. If a substance is capable of supporting itself—plant a grain of brown rice and it grows, for example—then it's capable of providing the unique combination of vitamins and minerals necessary to sustain us. If a food rots when planted (like white rice), then it cannot support itself and is unlikely to offer humans the range of essential ingredients we require.

The mother needs to be mentally stimulated by her food. It must be appetizing and well presented. By consuming a very large variety of foodstuffs, not only are the various food categories better balanced, but the maternal digestive mechanisms are fully exercised. This means that the fetus develops within a fully functioning human being whose fluctuations in adrenaline, insulin, endomorphins and other hormones guarantee its own capacity to be fully functional.

In addition to the mother's diet and the drugs she consumes, other chemicals may affect the fetus. Industrial gases, deodorants, perfumes, soaps, toothpastes, the water supply, dyes in clothes, sunscreen applications, washing detergents, carbon monoxide from motor vehicles, and so on may all be absorbed into or onto the mother and affect the developing baby.

Electrical stimulation from computers, radio, television, microwaves, tablets, smartphones and overhead power lines may also be significant. The fetus must also contend with many other hazards in the environment. All these may promote disease on the one hand and promote health on the other, depending on the amount or dose. Posology, or dose, is a vital consideration in medicine and many other aspects of life. The word "balance" just about covers it: what Buddhists refer to as the "middle path".

As an example, small amounts of brewer's yeast—one-eighth of a teaspoonful twice a week—supply the B-group vitamins, but a tablespoonful taken every day may cause excessive fermentation in the intestine and can actually remove vitamin B from the body. The fetus can easily deal with controlled exposures to substances; this exposure can help it to overcome a larger dose next time. An overdose of the substance may cause damage and can lead to disease developing in childhood or much later in life. But appropriate exposure to environmental stresses, both physical and psychological, guarantees quality of life, since we flourish in proximity to those things that are potentially dangerous to us.

Factors that affect the developing fetus that emanate from the psychological state of the mother fall within an area that hasn't received a great deal of attention in the past. Sophisticated monitoring of fetal heart rates, hormone levels, and states of sexual arousal shows that the fetus is reacting to the emotional climate. An increase in fetal heart rate accompanies maternal anxiety. If this is prolonged and severe enough, the newborn child will already have a stress problem, which may cause it to seek stress situations in the future because of its physiological familiarity with high adrenaline levels. People become hooked on adrenaline just as they become hooked on tea. Such a situation, if perpetuated or expanded by parental messages in childhood, may have consequences for the long-term health of the individual.

Photographs taken in utero have shown males with erections. This may be a response to maternal sexuality, mediated via placental hormones, maternal hormones, or direct nervous-system stimulation. Physiologists will no doubt provide the answer one day. In the meantime, we may reflect on how a mother who feels sexual about pregnancy, childbirth, and breastfeeding will affect her son's or daughter's sexuality. This is neither good nor bad. Whether it will be a positive or an adverse influence will depend on the "dose" and the method of delivery.

If the mother is truly delighted to be pregnant, watches in awe and excitement as her abdomen and breasts grow, and expresses a full range of emotions while carrying the fetus, the baby has a great chance of being born without abnormalities and will already be "well adjusted".

The father's role in the in utero psychological environment is also significant. By providing assistance, love, care, and physical comfort to his partner, he can help her to feel safe and well. Another woman can also fulfill this role. In addition, the partner of the pregnant woman can, by speaking softly and reassuringly, accustom the fetus to his or her voice. During childbirth and early infancy, this may be of great value in comforting the infant.

Similarly, both parents can openly express anger, fear, sadness, and joy before the fetus is born. These are all natural, healthy emotions, and if expressed rather than suppressed will acclimatize the growing fetus to a series of muscular stresses, hormonal states, and sensory stimuli that will facilitate the child's own developing ability to deal healthily, both physically and mentally, with a full range of emotions. Having experienced its mother in a full rage, and having witnessed this state passing into a state of calm, the fetus is learning the value of emotional expression while still in the womb. As the fetus develops and experiences its mother in all four major emotional states of anger, sadness fear and joy, the fetal systems become capable of responding to emotional demands. This will be valuable during delivery and will provide a measure of emotional flexibility with which to deal with the joys and traumas of infancy.

Similarly, sexual activity during pregnancy is beneficial. Intercourse, until discomfort or womb instability dictates otherwise, may be continued. Partners must avoid venereal disease. Masturbation, either with or without a partner, will accustom the infant to the particular movements and sounds associated with orgasm. A later chapter will discuss how a full range of emotional expression is a necessary prerequisite of a healthy body.

If, as is often the case, the mother is in a state of anxiety during pregnancy, the baby will be affected. Misinformation will often cause a young mother to be apprehensive about childbirth. An unsatisfactory relationship may result in the mother being in a constant state of anger about her pregnancy. In these cases the fear and anger aren't healthy contemporary emotional states, but "leftover" feelings that aren't healthy for the fetus. This is because the emotions are not fully expressed but rather are dealt with internally by the mother, resulting in changes in her muscles and organs. A chronic state of tension leads to a wide range of bodily complaints. In the case of a pregnant woman, blood flow or metabolic transfer across the placenta may be altered, which can jeopardize the well-being of the fetus. There may be no obvious physical abnormalities in a child born to a mother who has been under great stress in pregnancy, but, as time goes on, various behavioral difficulties that seem to have no explanation may arise. These can often be traced back to the emotional state of the mother during pregnancy.

If her partner's voice initiates a chronic fear or anger response in the mother, so too will it affect the fetus. Similarly, a loving partner's voice will be a source of comfort to the developing fetus. The mother's pleasure in relating to other people will condition the emerging infant to do likewise and will significantly affect the child's ability to socialize. A mother who feels and shows joy toward her developing child by massaging her abdomen lovingly and by speaking in soothing and welcoming tones will be encouraging her child to be born. When combined with her partner's positive attitude toward the pregnancy, the result will be a child who has no doubts about her right to exist. Cradled for protection inside the womb, a child grows secure in the knowledge that she's loved and wanted. This knowledge is the greatest gift that parents can give. Without it, the tendency to develop diseases is virtually guaranteed.

CHILDBIRTH

Imagine what it must be like to come from the security, warmth, darkness, and comfort of the womb into the noise, bright lights, confusion, and harshness of a delivery suite. Most of us did that; if we could recall it, we would say that it was the single most traumatic event of our lives. If the experience was a particularly severe one, as in the case of a forceps delivery or a difficult breech birth, or if the conditions of the delivery environment were very unsympathetic, the fear associated with our own birth may be concealed in our subconscious thereafter. We'll see later how the power of conditioning depends on both the impact and the frequency of the experience. In the case of childbirth, while the experience isn't repeated, at least not physically, the degree of trauma involved may be enough to affect our personalities. Therapies such as rebirthing and primal therapy provide ways in which to "relive" the birth trauma and, by reexperiencing the fear, neutralize it.

Any emotion is legitimate. Any emotion that is suppressed (or not allowed expression until naturally exhausted) will remain embedded within the psyche of the individual and will cause both physical and psychological changes. Childbirth under natural circumstances would leave no lasting impression on the child. The fear of birth and the sadness and anger at leaving warm, known surroundings will disappear within the arms and at the breast of a loving mother. The reassurance of a voice fondly recalled from intrauterine times will ease the fears of the newborn and will reassure him of continued support. If a child's fears are not allayed by his parents, the child may decide that life is unsafe. Where circumstances prevent immediate contact between the child and his mother following birth, he may make a very early childhood decision that his needs will never be met, initiating a lifetime of anxiety.

"Soft birth" is justified by the appearance of less traumatized babies. These babies appear to have less adjustment problems: that is, they're more emotionally expressive, more content, and surer of their right to exist than other children. The major factors are a positive expectation on the part of the mother, which is a balance of fear and excitement and may vary according to the number of previous children the woman has had. Many books have been written on the subject of birth without violence, some of which are listed in the bibliography.

The existence of warmth and soft lights, the giving of warm support from the woman's partner, the placing of the child on the mother's breast, the cutting of the cord after pulsations have ceased, and the decision not to violate the child with suction hoses all contribute to the impression of this new world as a nice place to be. A newborn's fears about being able to survive in the new and frightening environment will be allayed, and a major decision for health will have been made: the decision that life is welcoming and full of love.

2

THE CHILDHOOD BASIS OF DISEASE

Most commentators—psychologists and the public alike—agree that the period of early childhood up to the age of six years is the most important in the shaping of an individual's personality and destiny. Within this period, the first three-year period is probably the most significant. The messages a child receives in the first six years of life will largely determine whether the person is a dancer or a dietitian; is married or single; has four children or no children; has diabetes, cancer, or dandruff; is homosexual or heterosexual; plays football or smokes a pipe. The parents are more important in the early years while the influence of siblings, peers, relatives, friends and the media increases later on. Decisions the child makes in these early years will also directly or indirectly influence every other aspect of that individual's character and lifestyle, determining even old age or an early death. Such is the vulnerable and impressionable nature of early childhood. As this book is about health, we'll be concentrating on those messages that promote either well-being or illness. These same messages affect our social lives and the ease with which we achieve peace and happiness.

Those people who are generally happy to be themselves and who satisfactorily resolve childhood conflicts (often inadvertently) will be healthy. People who are less able to accept themselves and who live with guilt, fear, anger, anxieties, doubts, and sorrows will eventually develop physical diseases.

An infant's mind is virgin territory. Every single incident is unmodified by experience, and therefore profound. As we become older and more experienced, individual incidents have less impact on us because they're modified by those that have come before them. Factors that affect personality, health, disease, and the curing of illness have their greatest impact during periods of change. During gestation, childbirth, and early childhood, we're in a major state of change, and these times become crucial periods of development. Why are children so impressionable during those early years? Children are unsure that they can survive, and therefore they adapt to the wishes of the big people in their lives who are capable of keeping them alive.

Consider the following: You're reading a book entitled *Love Your Disease*. It's keeping you healthy. You've found the opening remarks to be interesting, and you're looking forward to uncovering more reasons why you may be continuing to make yourself ill. You decide to settle down comfortably for a couple of hours and keep reading, since the book is very readable, and you know that in two hours you'll have covered much of it and will have understood its relevance for you. The benefits appeal to you.

Now consider this scenario: You begin to feel a little cold, but you can't put on more clothing or turn on the heater. Perhaps you're a little warm, but you can't take off your clothing or turn on the air-conditioning. You're slightly uncomfortable, but you lack the strength or the skills to lift a cushion into place. You're hungry, but you lack the coordination or the mobility to fetch something to eat. You're thirsty, but you're unable to get yourself a drink. You're scared, because you can't keep yourself alive and you want somebody to hold you. Let yourself feel what that might be like.

What do you do? How do you get someone to help you? What must you do in return in order that the help might continue? What needs of yours are you prepared to sacrifice to be cared for by those around you who can help? What's the cost to you? What do you decide to do in the future?

The baby faces such needs, inabilities, fears, pressures, and decisions every day. Because the child is inexperienced, she won't know what's safe, and because she's unable to care for herself, she'll make decisions based on what she perceives to be dangerous. In order to feel safe, she's receptive to parental demands; thus, if her father is better disposed toward her when she doesn't cry, she may make a decision not to cry. Of course, her father may not physically harm her if she does cry, but at this stage she doesn't know that.

The incorporation of this early childhood message, "Don't cry," has sown the seed for later psychological imbalance and ensuing illness, for later we'll see how a failure to cry may result in sinusitis.

In the animal kingdom, many of the young can protect themselves (at least to some degree) in the first few months of life. A calf may, by running away, evade a minor predator in the first few hours of life. Other birds and animals may be protected by armor or camouflage. By comparison, human babies have no physical protective mechanisms. Indeed, if a baby were left on her own under the age of two years, she probably couldn't survive. Physically defenseless humans protect themselves, or try to feel safe, by using their intellects. This is as true for the infant who takes great notice of the big people around him and assesses what they require of him (and what he must do to survive) as it is for the mature adult who defends himself against any threat.

The baby, contrary to common belief, is very receptive to parental pressures. She's finely tuned to the emotional state of her parents and other members of her family. She monitors their anger, sadness, fear and joy and, by the age of six months, can be seen checking out many things she does with a quick glance at her caretaker. During this period when the baby is incapable of caring for herself, she needs to be aware of the responses of those who guarantee her survival. The infant's thinking capacity is, however, immature, and so some of those threats will be perceived rather than real. This awareness is much more developed than the baby's physical coordination, which makes the baby appear to be either not reacting to what's going on around her or to be crying indiscriminately. Vulnerability forces the baby to react to parental pressure. This vulnerability has a number of components.

Because she is so small, the infant lacks physical power. Parents are usually at least one hundred times stronger than infants, and, in conjunction with their much larger physical bulk, leave no doubt in the baby's mind as to who would win a physical showdown. Siblings, even though they may only be a few years older than the infant, are nevertheless much more physically competent and able to support their point of view with force if necessary. Fear of physical pain motivates an unconvinced infant to comply with a parental or older sibling demand or attitude. At such an immature stage of development, the infant is unable to handle stress adequately and, in order to avoid stress coming its way from the parents, may choose to behave in certain ways.

If the mother becomes upset when a small girl placed in the bath begins to masturbate, the girl will most likely respond by stopping the practice and taking care of her mother. By taking care of her own caretaker, the child is effectively taking care of herself. The child is in no position to confront much parental behavior and hence acquiesces to the parental viewpoint. The mother may, in order to relieve her own sexual anxiety about masturbation, offer the girl a toy to play with instead. If this situation is repeated often enough, the child may decide that masturbating is wrong or harmful and will later on experience anxiety in similar situations. In this she has followed her mother. Because masturbation produces such pleasant bodily sensations, the child may believe that her mother doesn't want her to do anything that makes her feel good. This may not be what her mother wishes to convey at all, but, because of the child's lack of experience, that may be her response. This decision could have significant effects in the future, resulting in an individual unable to physically "feel" pleasant sensations.

The resultant lack of stimulation to the surface of the body contributes to an imbalance in the internal organs, a concept recognized in acupuncture and Eastern medicine. A belief central to acupuncture is that the internal organs are represented on the surface of the body by meridians or channels of energy. If these body surface points are not stimulated regularly, then an imbalance is set up in the internal organs which that may later result in organic disease: for example, gallstones or stomach ulcer. Similarly, psychology has shown that lack of adequate physical stroking of the infant can result in serious psychological disturbances, both in children and in adults. Thus, for the healthy development of the child, both for the growth of the internal organs and to let the child know he's loved and wanted, much holding and cuddling is advisable. It's also enjoyable for the parents and a critical part of parent-child bonding.

An infant doesn't have the experience with which to balance or quantify a message. An infant doesn't have the information with which to reject certain data. If a child is indirectly told by a parent that she's dumb—for example, by overhearing her father saying to the next-door neighbor, "She's not as smart as her brother"—she may decide, "I'm dumb". As a child, she doesn't understand that her father may have an investment in women being dumb, whereas if she were older and overheard a similar statement, she would have the information to reject it: "That's just the old man's chauvinism speaking," she may think. Lack of information during childhood may result in children accepting information about themselves that they would reject in more neutral situations. They are not, however, in a neutral situation. Their view of the world is adopted from their parents, and, more importantly, their view of themselves is similarly influenced. In these circumstances the child has few options, the best of which is to go along with the beliefs of the parents. Despite the lack of available options, it's still the child who's making the decision to comply or rebel. At a later time, adults may choose to address some of those early childhood decisions in order to cure themselves of disease.

We've considered some of the reasons why children are susceptible to the influence of parents and other bigger people in their lives. The child acts on these messages, both the positive and the negative, and incorporates them into her personality. The combination of these decisions and their related behavior becomes the individual's personality. Because messages need to be repeated and delivered with authority to be incorporated into one's personality, the parents clearly influence the young child most, although the media and other people become increasingly important as the child is able to understand more. Ultimately, multiple inputs into a child's personality occur. Peer groups, the Internet, and social media now influence much teenage behavior, although this behavior is acting on the fertile (or barren) ground of early-childhood conditioning.

We'll next consider the nature of these parental messages as well as the mechanism whereby they're finally transmuted into diseases. To do this, we'll use some of the theory of Transactional Analysis and Gestalt psychotherapy, since these psychological modalities describe the early childhood decisions clearly.

One form of message that comes from the parents is called injunctions. These are described in Transactional Analysis a "a prohibition, or an inhibition of the free behavior of the child". They reflect some of the deepest fears, angers, sorrows, and desires of the parent. They may be given directly or indirectly, verbally or non-verbally. The injunction "Don't be a child" is one commonly given to the first-born child in a family. Inexperienced parents are often frightened of harming babies and are only too happy to see them grow quickly and become more self-sufficient. Such a child may decide he's unworthy of the same love and caring he sees his younger siblings receive from his parents, who now feel much safer about babies. As an adult, he may continue to deny himself love, since he now believes that caring and affection are for others who are more deserving. On the other hand, the last-born child in a large family may be given a "Don't grow up" injunction, often when the mother has enjoyed child-rearing and wants to prolong the experience. Such a person may marry late, remain closely attached to his parents, and choose a partner who treats him like a child. These people frequently suffer acute illnesses, which brings their partner scurrying to their aid, a situation which suits both of them and which they both learned in childhood.

The major injunctions and their opposites, permissions, are:

Injunctions	Permissions
Don't exist	Exist
Don't feel (emotions, sensations)	Feel (emotions, sensations)
Don't think	Think
Don't be close	Be close
Don't be a boy or a girl	Just be yourself
Don't be a child	Be a child when you are a child
Don't grow up	Grow up when you are ready
Don't make it	Make it as you want
Don't do it	Do what you want

The first of these, "Don't exist," is called the primary injunction. The rest are really modifications of it. "Daddy doesn't like you climbing over him dear," Mother may inform young Peter, which is indirectly saying it's only OK for you to exist if you don't climb on Daddy. All of the injunctions are a qualification of the right to exist, which the child interprets as meaning his continued existence is only guaranteed if he satisfies certain parental requirements. In the case of a powerful and often repeated message to not exist, the child may take the decision that death is the best option. He may then exercise that option by having a fatal accident, or by contracting a fatal disease. Of course, not all children who die young have "don't exist" injunctions. The majority do not. The book addresses the psychological element of an individual's health. As mentioned previously, there are many other elements. Many of these may not be as accessible as the psychological element.

In cases where either parent doesn't want the child for any reason and communicates this to the child, that child will grow up with a "Don't exist" injunction. The strength of the injunction will depend on the frequency and power with which the parents express it. A casual comment to the effect that Dad was not altogether ready to become a father when Susy was born will probably be of little import, especially if it's obvious that he now loves her. At the other end of the scale may be a father who continually berates a child for being born and for subsequently ruining his business and social life: "If it weren't for you kids, I'd be wealthy by now." In this case, the child may assume responsibility for his father's unhappiness and decide that his father would be better off if he, the child, were dead. He may act on this belief in a number of ways, consciously or subconsciously, mentally and physically. Alternatively, he may rebel against the injunction.

When a parent says angrily to a child, "I wish you were never born," the child has the option of believing that *Mommy wishes I were dead*, or maybe that *Mommy's upset; she doesn't really mean it.* In the first instance, the child has "furthered his script" (that is, his personal life plan in response to his parents' messages); and in this case has consolidated his belief that he wasn't meant to be alive. In the second example, the child has already decided that it's OK for him to exist, and has rationalized his mother's remark as hasty or ill-conceived.

If someone believes "I shouldn't exist," then certain events are more likely to happen: he neglects to protect himself against dangerous or life-threatening situations. These people may engage in dangerous activities (e.g. extreme sports or daredevil stunts). They may join the armed forces and apply for active duty, or they may become mercenaries. They may become involved in dangerous occupations like illegal drug trafficking or, in some parts of the world, join the police force. Not all people in the above categories are trying to fulfill their parents' messages not to exist, but dangerous occupations do attract people who are ambivalent about living. So do life-threatening diseases.

Most people who decide that their parents didn't want them and who subsequently don't take all available measures to stay alive do not become mercenaries. Instead, they may drive their cars dangerously, fall asleep at the wheel, or drive under the influence of drugs or alcohol. In these ways they put their lives at risk and get a real thrill from flirting with death, often with tacit parental approval. When these people eventually seriously hurt or even kill themselves, we all cry, "What bad luck to have a fatal accident at such a young age!" But often that was no "accident". Why did the young woman, apparently enjoying life and with a successful career, fail to notice the bald tire on her car, or, if she did notice it, why didn't she take the time and effort to have it changed? Why did the handsome young lawyer fail to notice the oncoming bus as he stepped from the curb? These people weren't trying hard enough to stay alive. In other words, they'd manifested their early childhood decision to "not exist" and exploited available hazards to put that decision into effect. This is nearly always outside their awareness.

There are other ways to act on the parental injunction "Don't exist". Illness is one of these. An option for everyone is to end their life by giving themselves a fatal illness. Bear in mind that these decisions are mostly taken subconsciously. A person rarely says, "Life for me is intolerable, I'll give myself cancer and die." However, if the mind is giving the body too few messages of the "keep healthy, stay alive, stay sane" kind, then the potential for physical illness increases. How does this happen?

Various glands in the body (adrenals, thyroid, ovaries, testes) are under the control of hormones produced by a gland in the brain called the pituitary. These glands in turn produce substances that profoundly affect the functioning of the body. The pituitary gland is affected by our psychological state. When we're afraid, the adrenal gland produces adrenaline, which dilates the pupils, increases the heart rate and causes us to sweat. This prepares the body for "fight or flight." What's happening to us emotionally will be simultaneously affecting us physically. Imagine the physical effects upon the body during a lifetime of these chemical substances (hormones) circulating in response to us thinking and feeling about ourselves in certain ways. Their physiological effect is increasingly understood. On another level, the work of Bruce Lipton shows how our thoughts and feelings affect our cellular biology by directly impacting the cell membrane.

All of us are able to look at another person's face and see anger, joy, sadness or fear, which in some cases has been so longstanding as to cause permanent changes in the facial features. This may happen at quite a young age, so that the person may look like an "angry young man." Emotions that are left over from childhood and go unresolved ("racket" feelings is the term used in transactional analysis) are as capable of altering the internal organs as they are the facial muscles. "Racket," by the way, has an unfortunate pejorative ring to it, and the term fails to recognize that everyone always does the best she can, whatever the circumstances and whatever her early childhood decisions. We incorporate longstanding feelings (or our denial of them) into our "second natures" — "Oh, it's become second nature," we say — which of course begs the question, "What's first nature?" — a term which is rarely, if ever, heard.

Eventually, the physiological effect will cause anatomical changes, that is, the psychological state is transformed into physical disease. So what's new? Most people believe that anxiety contributes to stomach ulcers (bacterial involvement not withstanding) and emotional upsets result in intestinal upsets. But this thesis goes beyond stress, for here I'm explaining both the origins and the advantages of stress. Acting on the messages that we receive in childhood, we see ourselves as someone with an unqualified right to exist, a qualified right to exist or no right to exist. Over a period of time, our mental attitude affects our body chemistry (physiology) and keeps us healthy or, in the case of those with a powerful "don't exist" injunction, eventually kills us. That is, we kill ourselves. Hence people may develop a lifethreatening disease such as cancer or prolong an otherwise innocuous disease like hepatitis, until they die from it. As in the case of road "accidents," the fatal illness has dutifully followed their instructions, impacted their physiology, and killed them. This will usually be subconscious. For a person with a heavily qualified right to exist, life becomes intolerable. By dying, he fulfills his most fundamental belief: that he has no right to exist. Not many people have such a powerful "don't exist" injunction but many have modifications of it, injunctions intended to keep them alive but which modify their behavior. We will be looking at these shortly.

As the child becomes an adult, he'll often modify that early childhood decision. He may do this unwittingly, alone, with friends, a spouse, by joining a psychotherapy-treatment program, or in many other ways. One important point about the injunctions is that they aren't usually given in a direct way, and children often more completely absorb indirect messages. When parents give their children indirect parental messages, it becomes more difficult for children to identify and react against them. That's why people who have given themselves life-threatening illnesses, when invited to recall such messages as "We don't want you" are often genuinely unable to do so. These messages were never given to them directly.

Let's look at a few ways in which parents give their children indirect messages, and we'll see what the children make of them. Take a situation in which the younger of two boys is being bullied by his older brother. The younger child is in real need of physical protection, and the only way available to him is to get someone to look after him. Because of her greater availability, he may choose his mother. She may inadvertently invite the child to become ill or sickly in order to protect him from the older boy, the bully. The illness justifies her repeated berating of the older boy, who is, of course, jealous of his newly arrived brother: "I told you to stop bothering your younger brother. You know he's not as strong as you." Now this message—given not to the boy himself but to others, or even only implied by the mother's protective actions, offers the younger child the option of being protected by being weak. As he grows older, he may be less anxious when he has some ailment than when he's perfectly well, since when he's in good health he may feel unprotected and vulnerable. The role of illness in this case is to invite the protection of other people.

Those messages that define or label a person are called "attributions." They're very powerful, because children are presented with a statement about themselves in which they have no say: a fait accompli. "Oh yes, he's not as sturdy as his brother," a mother reports to an inquiring neighbor, thereby recommending frailty to the child. Many people are of the view that attributions (statements made about the child indirectly, or often simply implied by the parents' actions) are the most powerful of all parental messages. An example many of us will be familiar with is the common admonishment: "You're just like your father/mother."

The whole family may contribute to the disease process in one or more members of that family. Our young boy mentioned above who became ill to get his mother's protection was pressured into doing so by his older brother, invited to use that option by his mother, and covertly supported by his father, who chose not to intervene. The interaction between members of a family will often initiate and maintain both health and disease. In some families, disease is simply unacceptable. In others, family members have permission to suffer "nervous breakdowns" but no physical diseases. The ongoing interaction between members of a family is referred to as "family psychodynamics."

The role of parents is not only to protect, love, and raise children but also to prevent the excesses of their partners' parenting being passed unfettered to their children. Consistent, supportive parenting, providing role models, and modifying the parenting of our partner are all part of natural parenting.

Other categories of messages are given by parents to their children. Some of these are called "drivers." These are messages that restrict the child's free behavior; they often represent messages that parents give their children when they want to make their children's behavior socially acceptable (and therefore help the children to be successful in life). As such, they're often effective, resulting in successful business people, for example. At the same time, they may lead to much anguish if the person struggles to maintain a lifestyle based on those messages. Illness is often a consequence of these drivers, as demonstrated in the following example.

A forty-three-year-old man was to be transferred to a new appointment in a city some eight hundred kilometers away from his home. His wife wasn't happy about leaving her friends, and she voiced strong opposition to the move. Not wishing to upset his employer, the man agreed to go but was suddenly struck down with gout—a condition that he'd suffered only once before, some ten years previously. Because the new position involved increased travelling, the employer sent a younger man instead. By giving himself gout, which was the physiological result of his wish to be immobilized, the man justified staying where he was rather than following his driver of "Please me" and continually seeking promotion, as his father had wished.

This example shows how effectively illness can result from, and then be used to break, early childhood messages, rather than the individual taking personal responsibility for breaking them. The matter of personal responsibility in illness will be taken up later.

The opposites to drivers are "allowers," as follows:

Drivers	Allowers
Be perfect	Be yourself
Hurry up	Take your time
Try hard	Do it
Please me	Consider and respect yourself!
Be strong	Be open and get your needs met

The child is coerced by fear into following the driver directives. The child perceives parental disapproval for not following the drivers to be a threat to his own existence. What the parent is saying or implying to the child is that he's OK only so long as he's perfect, hurries up, tries hard, pleases the parent, or is strong. If the child does not fulfill these parental wishes, then he risks loss of parental love and support. To a young child, this is life-threatening. We've spoken before of the balance of power between infants and adults, and I think it bears repeating, since only by understanding the pressures on the child to conform is it possible to see why people are prepared to give themselves diseases. When they do this, they're following decisions that they've taken in childhood at a time when it was prudent to do so. It's essential for anyone who's ill to acknowledge that they've decided, at some stage, and in some way, to contribute to his or her disease. That decision may not be obvious. Only then do people assume their power over removing the disease. If, at the outset, the role we've played in our illnesses isn't obvious to us, we can commit ourselves to an inquiry as a way of identifying and releasing hidden contributors to our dilemma. The "m3health inquiry," available at www.m3health.com, is just such an inquiry.

The m3health inquiry signposts participants through a gentle and forgiving journey into the role they're playing in the creation, and the recovery from any disease or problem from which they're suffering. The inquiry is taken at the person's own pace and is very forgiving, re-inforcing the fact that everyone always does the best he or she can in any particular set of circumstances – always.

As we get older, many of the responses we made in order to be looked after as best we could as children are no longer relevant. We can now look after ourselves and need neither our parents' approval nor support to do what we want, nor an illness to justify breaking an earlier parental directive.

Many of the drivers are messages that, if the child takes them up, will result in successful people. Those who possess the personality traits of perfection, strength, and urgency often make excellent professionals, business people, public servants and trades people. If they fear losing parental love should they "fail," they'll often be unhappy and eventually may give themselves a serious disease. This is a consequence of both the physical impact of fulfilling the directives and the advantage of contracting a disease in order to justify breaking those directives. Such is the paradoxical nature of the cause and cure of disease: we're attracted to illness in order to fulfill the early childhood directives, and at the same time, our suffering signposts those elements of our lives we need to explore if we're to cure our diseases.

It's possible for parents to raise successful children who *aren't* driven by fear. Allowers, as the name implies, are a category of parental attitudes that facilitate self-determination in children. They're listed earlier opposite their driver counterparts. Allowers encourage children to do things for their own benefit, rather than for the benefit of their parents. This removes the urgency of achievement and the fear of failure and, in so doing, promotes mental and physical health.

The development of disease from driver behavior is interesting. Before we examine that, however, we need to understand how the personality of the individual develops from these various messages—the injunctions, attributions, drivers, permissions, and allowers. An injunction or attribution is incorporated into the personality only when the child decides that she'll accept it—that is, the child decides to not exist, to not be close, to be a member of the opposite sex. The child makes this decision under duress and mostly out of awareness. Nevertheless, it's still the child who is making the decision. When the child makes this decision, she incorporates the injunction or attribution into the script. As alluded to earlier, a "script" is a personal life plan that an individual decides on at an early age in reaction to her interpretation of both external and internal events.

Injunction / Attribution + Decision   =   Script
[Given by parents and others]   [Taken by child]

The child may decide to incorporate the drivers and allowers into her belief system. This series of decisions then becomes the "subscript." Hence:

Driver / Allower + Decision   =   Subscript
[Given by parents and others]   [Taken by child]

The script and subscript usually mutually support each other and form the basis for thoughts and feelings about self that promote the development of health or disease.

This may be the time to discuss the notion of a "decision." Does the child really make decisions under the duress of her parents? Perhaps not in the same way a grown woman may look at a decision that she makes and that she's fully aware of. It may be more accurate to say that the child responds to her parental messages, and those responses then consist of thoughts, feelings, and actions. These elements constitute the "decision." The child makes the decision to attract parental caring. The mechanism of disease development from driver behavior varies, because no two people have the same script or subscript, even though there may be familiar patterns. When genetic factors, environmental factors, age, and other variables are taken into account, it might become clear that a strong "Be perfect" driver may result in a heart attack in one patient, a stomach ulcer in another, and a PhD in yet another. Often this is because families or communities have given certain diseases a degree of acceptability. Heart attacks, for example, are common among the males of some families but uncommon in others, who may instead consistently suffer gout.

Diseases, like table manners, are modeled by grown-ups. If, as a child, a boy hears about Grandpa, who "worked himself to death" in the family business, and Uncle James, who had a "mental breakdown" and was forced to retire, the boy may decide that if work becomes too onerous for him, disease would be an acceptable way out. If the family scripting or modeling is coupled with a "Be perfect" driver, then the boy may end up giving himself a disease: "We had such high hopes for Trevor—he had distinctions in both years of his economics degree—but now that he's been unfortunate enough to become schizophrenic, who'll run the company?"

At a later date, should the disease become sufficiently irritating, the discomfort may motivate the person to face the fear of, and then break, the original decision. When he decides to be well for himself and not simply to remove the discomfort, he'll no longer need the illness, and in this state of self-responsibility he can attain good health. Using one's current illness is a good place to start the healing process and constitutes the transitory advantage of disease.

There is another component to driver behavior. People incorporate drivers into their subscripts because of a fear of parental reproach if they don't. The only way to alleviate this fear is to continue to drive yourself. This, as we've seen, alters the body physiology and eventually causes physical changes. Disease may result from unresolved fear, anger or sadness. We'll examine this more fully in section 2, chapter 6. Drivers are often associated with societal values. In his 1974 book *Scripts People Live*, Claude Steiner says: "The subscript is an acquiescence to the cultural and social demands that are transmitted through the parent."

Disease must be looked at in a cultural as well as a personal and familial setting. In contemporary Western society, disease is commonly an end result of a script. People who remain "in script" are struggling to assume personal responsibility, since they're continuing to observe parental directives. They don't believe they can, as adults, please themselves, and similarly they don't believe they can protect themselves from physical diseases that they, like society generally, attribute mainly to bad luck. Having suffered the disease, they may then use it to stop pushing themselves. If they assume responsibility for contributing to the original condition and decide to stop making themselves ill, they'll have changed their script and started on the road to health.

Consider the following sporting "accident": I ruptured my Achilles tendon playing squash. If it hadn't been for this injury, I'd have been a champion. Now I won't be able to realize my full potential. Of course, if my full potential wasn't as good as my parents had hoped, then I'm at risk of being a failure in my own eyes. I may or may not have been a failure in my parents' eyes, depending on whether or not my childhood perception that I needed to be perfect in order for them to love me was correct. This injury serves to relieve the anxiety of not being perfect. Now I can enjoy my squash at a much lower level that is more consistent with my ability.

"Be perfect," you will recall, is a driver. Such people strive for success until eventually they do themselves physical and psychological harm. And, of course, if a person always strives for more, she'll never content with what she has, irrespective of her achievements. A person with a "Be perfect" driver is trying to achieve or retain her parents' love by being a perfect person.

There are, of course, gradations of "Be perfect." For example, I could have prevented this injury by deciding to play at a lower level of stress, thus avoiding giving myself an injury.

Illness is a physical and psychological consequence of the script and subscript, and it involves any permutation of drivers, injunctions, and attributions. Illness is prevented by the allowers and the permissions. These are the personal causes of illness. In addition, illness has numerous external causes, including genetics, diet, womb environment (physical and psychological), childbirth, environmental pollutants, diet, physical activity. Some of these are under our control, some we can influence, others we can't. We can deploy many of them in making ourselves ill. The act of taking responsibility for our diseases and our lives, *is* the mechanism of healing.

The physiological processes responsible for converting psychological states into physical disease are being increasingly studied. Research conducted at the University of Sydney by a psychobiologist, Dr Dale Atrens, in 1980, produced some interesting information. Obese people who attempt major weight reduction by dieting are often frustrated after an approximate 5 per cent weight loss. This is because the brain resets the circulating blood levels of thyroxin and adrenaline at a lower level, thus reducing the basal metabolic rate and preventing further weight loss. This is an automatic response of the body to maintain the pre-existing weight and has been dubbed the "hibernation response" because it mimics hibernation.

I believe these individuals subconsciously decide to remain obese, even though they may be dieting. Subconsciously they instruct their pituitary hormones to maintain the old weight until such time as they feel safe enough to be slimmer. Then they lose weight with minimal or no dietary change.

Physiognomy, the diagnosis of psychological states by facial appearance, is practised effectively by all of us. One of the least true things my mother told me was that people can't help what they look like, in reference to someone I found unattractive. People's faces reflect their personalities exactly.

The physical consequences of scripting can reasonably be expected in the internal organs in much the same way as they can be seen in the face and body. Script issues may find expression in disease if left unchanged. I believe a man who as a boy has decided to be non-sexual (different from a "don't be a boy" injunction), will often have a smaller penis than his father. Similarly, small breasts or amenorrhea may be indicative of a sexual injunction in a woman. These things can be modified.

The injunctions "don't feel emotions/sensations" may lead to a person who fails to spontaneously express fear, anger, sadness or joy, and this in time affects body physiology. The injunction may only cover some of the emotions.

Some parents are very happy to have their children express joy but not anger, for example. It's interesting that in Traditional Chinese Medicine, suppressed anger is claimed to cause liver dysfunction and suppressed fear is said to result in kidney malfunction. Imagine the downturned mouth of a person who's unhappy all the time being reflected in a downturned liver, spleen, kidneys or heart.

Visualize for a moment a dog experiencing the joy of his master's return. The furious wagging of the tail and the movement of the whole spine stimulates the central, peripheral, and autonomic nervous systems and balances the internal organs.

A basic tenet of some medical systems is that the well-being of the internal organs depends in part on what happens to the external body. Touching and stroking energize and regulate the function of the liver, spleen, kidneys, lungs, intestines, heart, gallbladder, urinary bladder, pancreas, and the body's thermal and chemical regulators. A person who isn't being touched may be inviting physical disease.

Physiological imbalances may arise as a consequence of not directly expressing emotions. Where rage, for example, is suppressed, there may be a chronic elevation of adrenaline that leads to hypertension, a flushed face, and eventual cardiovascular pathology. Sinusitis, mentioned earlier, is an example of a condition that is often caused by people (usually men) denying their sadness and refusing to cry. The resultant swollen and chronically inflamed mucous membranes would have returned to normal had the person shed tears at the moment of sadness. I speculate that if emotions were spontaneously and totally expressed then body physiology would be temporarily exercised and rapidly return to a state of healthy equilibrium. In a similar way to exercising the biceps, a good cry or yell will keep the body functional.

What are some of the "advantages" of illness? Many people will not address script decisions because the little kid in them is afraid to do so. When the pain or suffering of the disease is greater than the fear of the original adaptation, they may change. That is to say, the pain of illness—itself part of their script—may prompt them to overcome the fear of exploring, identifying, and moving beyond the original script decision. They may make their illness responsible for change.

A person may have specifically incorporated this decision into his or her script or subscript; for example, the child's parents may have considered a heart attack in a businessman with a "Be perfect" driver to be a valid reason to slow down at work. Now that he's made himself aware of this driver, the businessman may decide to make himself responsible for how hard he works and discard illness as a way of giving himself permission to slow down.

The advantages of illness are illustrated in the following: "People become ill to get what they want (caring and the like)" and "People do not get what they want (caring and the like), so they become ill."

We'll explore the prevention of disease, using healthy early childhood messages, in some detail in chapter 20, "Healthy Parenting."

3

WHEN YOU GO
TO THE DOCTOR

A client I was seeing for the first time told me that she'd known of the work I was doing for some nine months before coming to consult me about her medical problems. I found this information surprising, considering the progressive and debilitating nature of her illness.

"Why," I asked her, "did you wait for such a long time when you knew your friend who recommended me had made a dramatic recovery from a similar condition?"

"Because I was scared you'd insist that I change the way I was," was her reply, "and I wasn't sure I wanted to do that."

In the meantime, this woman's condition had deteriorated substantially, yet her fear of change had obviously been such that she preferred to live in pain. Only when her symptoms became physically intolerable did she come for treatment.

This interesting attitude led me to ask all my new clients how long they'd waited before coming to see me. The average time was about four months. Since they'd all heard from whomever had recommended me that I worked on removing the disease by eliciting the personality factors behind it, I assume their reluctance to come indicated that they were afraid to look closely at themselves.

Now, this I can understand. If a person has made a decision in childhood which turns out to be counterproductive later on, they'll have done so because of fear: fear of losing something more important to them than the inconvenience of modifying their original behavior. For example, it may be better not to cry when you fall over and hurt your knee and thereby obtain Dad's love and approval for being brave, than to cry (which is what you'd like to do) and risk disapproval.

The same fear that caused the original adaptation leading to or contributing to the illness will be evoked as soon as somebody (in this case me, the therapist) wants to begin "poking around in the past," as one client expressed it. Such a way of expressing it is significant because it shows the anger which very often overlies the fear of looking back. In general terms, people's physiology becomes disturbed and leads to illness not when they express fear, anger, sadness or joy but when they repress those emotions. In the case of the woman who didn't want her past "poked into," it was fear of the fear that maintained her illness and therapy centered about making her feel safe enough to risk confronting her fears. When she was no longer afraid to do things which directly benefited her, she was on the way to a cure. Because of fear, which is really the infant's fear of not being loved and therefore not surviving, people will push unwanted feelings and thoughts to the backs of their minds and expend an enormous amount of time and effort in doing so. This often leads to the lack of energy that many patients complain of. It's not the result of insufficient sleep, excessive work, poor diet or lack of exercise but a consequence of needing to keep the mind and body hyperactive so as to avoid unwanted thoughts and feelings. The alternative is to express our feelings freely, to laugh heartily when we're happy, cry when sad, yell when angry and have wide eyes, a fast pulse and start to sweat when afraid. To do this has major physiological benefits and is energy-restoring as opposed to energy-depleting.

Anybody prepared to make fearless decisions in their best interests will avoid all major illness and most minor ones as well. Some people, through lack of information, will predispose themselves to problems, for example, eating foods low in fibre, like white bread, and thus suffering from constipation before they discover that fibre is necessary for good bowel function. Most people who suffer from constipation however, are fully aware of the need for dietary fibre but ignore the information. By so doing, they use their illness for other, secondary gains and only allow solutions to their problem to enter their awareness when they no longer need the illness.

This is the way they've learnt to care for themselves best, by using illness, and this isn't a bad thing. A small percentage of people will become aware of the role of illness in their lives, be prepared to risk doing some things differently and dispense with the need for illness altogether. In general, relief of physical constipation will rapidly follow relief of mental constipation. Flexible minds make flexible bodies, capable of adjusting to environmental change.

Two features of becoming or remaining well together provide a balanced approach to whole-person health. The first of these is the willingness to take responsibility for our own safety, while the second is the willingness to take risks. We take care of ourselves by ignoring, selectively suppressing, or simply not noticing those things in ourselves and others that challenge our view of ourselves. For example, if I consider myself an excellent doctor, and most of my clients seem to get well, then I may ignore the fact that people who have difficulty expressing their sadness don't do well under my treatment. The reason for my failing to notice this is that I'm not prepared to look at my own sadness, because I don't feel safe doing so. If I'm unprepared to confront my own sadness, it's unlikely I'll be effective in helping others confront theirs. Now, in this I'm looking after myself, which incidentally is a good primary rule for therapists and clients alike. Those clients who do not get what they need from me will seek out other therapists. It's a cornerstone of my thinking about why so many patients accept bad and ineffective treatment from doctors that people choose the doctor and the treatment they want, that is, they choose for themselves what may seem *to me* bad and ineffective treatment.

We keep ourselves safe on both a conscious and subconscious level. Many people could benefit considerably from a change of lifestyle and diet and, although they know this, choose to continue with their current living habits and are prepared to accept responsibility, and the consequences of their decision. Clearly they view the disease they're suffering from as less of a problem than changing some other aspects of their lives. This is a valid decision and I consider that we all do the same thing, at various times and with varying degrees of awareness. We all have to decide on what "a life well lived" looks like for ourselves. How much we choose to care for ourselves physically at any one time is very flexible and will depend upon our current psychological state. When we explore and release old fears, our minds will instruct our bodies to function harmoniously and beautifully. Before the fear goes we aim to have our adaptations reinforced, and it's in this frame of mind that we may go to the doctor.

The humorist who said, "If surgeons performed the operations on themselves that they perform on their patients, there would be far fewer surgeons and far more patients," had more than a cursory appreciation of the dynamics between patient and doctor. However, the truth is that there are the exact number of surgeons operating that the community is prepared to support. When people decide that they no longer require operations, then the number of surgeons able to make a living will fall accordingly. At any given time, the popularity of various medical practices and philosophies rises and falls. The forces that change medical practice come predominantly from the medical profession reacting to a more general movement in society, not from doctors making unilateral decisions. When an individual doctor such as myself decides that the basis of disease lies in childhood and that we manipulate our state of health rather than the reverse, it's because that doctor has been looking at his or her own life. The methods available for this task are a reflection of the collective psychology predominating in Western society. As such they're effective for those people living in that society at that time and less effective elsewhere. The advances in medicine will reflect the willingness of people to look at themselves and their problems from a different perspective. This inevitably involves some risk-taking.

When people buy goods and services, they enter into a contract with the seller; that is, for an agreed amount of money, the goods change hands or the services are rendered. In the majority of cases, the contract is not written and may not even be verbalized. Nonetheless, the contract is understood by both parties and agreed upon before the transaction takes place. Failure to acquaint oneself with the fine print of the contract, whether it be verbal or written, is often the reason why one party ends up dissatisfied with the transaction and why both parties may end up in court.

We tend to contract in our personal relationships as well, although this is usually done subconsciously. This is not a written contract in the majority of cases or, if it is, as in the case of the marriage contract, only covers the essentials. The main part of the marriage contract is unwritten, is quite different in each marriage and often ends up in disarray through failure to clarify it early on in the relationship. As in the case of goods and services, both parties may become confused or disillusioned with the contract and may end up in court. A contract between long-standing friends may be broken when one has an affair with the other's partner, although this has never been discussed as a clause in the contract and neither has mentioned it as a reason for ending their relationship.

In a similar manner, a contract is drawn up between the patient and the doctor. This contract is generally not stated and is never written. The contract states that the doctor, in exchange for money, will remove the unpleasant symptoms that the patient is complaining of. In much contemporary practice, where a patient refuses responsibility for his own illness, the contract states that the doctor will not remove the disease process by recommending anything disruptive to the patient's chosen way of life, will tell the patient what he wants to hear rather than what might help him, and will guarantee the continuation of the disease process, albeit in an altered form.

The current opioid prescription epidemic in the United States becomes different when viewed through this lens. Instead of regarding doctors and patients as both reprehensible, we can look at the opioid epidemic as doctors responding to the overwhelming loss of control people feel in contemporary society. Only a handful of doctors and patients seem able or willing to resume stewardship of their own lives.

As in the case of the other contracts, this one will last only as long as it suits both parties. If the doctor repeatedly decides that the antibiotic or opioid requested by the patient is not necessary, then the patient will most likely change to a doctor who agrees with him and is prepared to prescribe the requested drug.

Every disease we give ourselves has advantages. The advantages lie in helping us to maintain a belief system about ourselves, others and the world which, although damaging to us in some way, effectively masks more deep-seated and fundamental fears. By becoming ill, we spare ourselves the trauma of examining those aspects of ourselves we've chosen to suppress. When disease is regarded like this it becomes clear that if the doctor attempts to instruct the patient in the true nature of the disease, in most cases the patient will become scared and will resist or redefine the information. If the doctor persists, then the patient will seek alternative advice and the Doctor will lose the patient and the business. Thus in most medical practice the contract between the doctor and the patient covers only the removal or modification of the symptoms. Provided the doctor is effective in removing the symptoms quickly, which usually means using a powerful drug, and provided the patient on his part does some of what the doctor suggests and also pays his account, then the contract remains in force and both parties remain satisfied. This form of treatment guarantees the continuation of the disease because there's been no attempt by either the patient or the doctor to look for the cause.

Let's look at some interactions between patient and doctor that provides evidence of the real nature of the contract between them. I've indicated that the patient is expected to do only some of the things that the doctor prescribes or suggests. A metric measuring drug prescription has been developed which deals with patient compliance, that is, the degree to which the patient actually takes the drugs prescribed. This turns out to be remarkably low. The reality is that virtually no patients comply completely with the doctor's advice. The reasons advanced for this ignore the most obvious reason, that is, the patient doesn't want to be rid of the disease, if the cost to his view of himself and the world is too great.

He does, however, want to be rid of some of the symptoms.

Very few doctors expect their patients to adhere totally to their advice. Experience shows that even when suffering from a particularly irritating and chronic condition, patient compliance is low. Both parties to the contract know that. The doctor says, "Now, Mrs Jones, we haven't been taking our tablets, have we?" with a knowing smile. Mrs Jones responds with a sheepish grin. Both she and the doctor know this means, "No, I haven't been taking all the medication and you can be damn sure that I won't be taking this new bunch, either." The contract for "some of the symptoms to be removed and the illness to continue" having been satisfactorily concluded, both parties leave, agreeing to reconvene the meeting at a later date. At that and subsequent visits, the routine continues until the client decides to get better and therefore breaks the contract or the doctor becomes frightened or disillusioned and sends the patient to a specialist. In these ways much, but not all, of contemporary medical practice is conducted. The five minute consultation, with no chance of really understanding anything of importance about the condition, and the broad categorization of diseases with their standardized drug treatments have all been specifically developed to cater for these sorts of contracts. This is "normal" medical practice.

Looking for the cause of the disease has become the fashionable pursuit of medical practitioners and paramedical practitioners with an eye to the market place. Hence the burgeoning field of "holistic" medicine, which could have been a great leap forward but threatens to become lost in commercialism. In order for the idea of alternative, complimentary and preventive medicine to become fashionable and marketable, people must be able to feel as safe with the new medicine as they felt with the old, with the new requirement that they must feel they've become more closely acquainted with the cause of their problem. The majority of patients are still very reluctant to look at how their personality may be contributing to the disease and at how their reluctance to change some aspects of their behavior is maintaining the problem. Hence, many increasingly popular therapies must appear to be earnestly searching for truths, while the patient's investment in maintaining the disease is ignored by mutual agreement.

This is the reality of many of the alternative or complimentary healing arts when practiced narrowly. I don't believe that diet, homeopathy, acupuncture, chiropractic, herbalism, radionics, naturopathy, osteopathy, chelation therapy, orthomolecular medicine, vitamin therapy, color therapy or any other of the healing arts, when practiced in isolation and without regard for the psychology of the client, are of more than passing value. The same can be said of orthodox Western medicine. All of these alternative healing arts can significantly contribute to the well-being of clients who are in the process of working through their reasons for giving themselves the disease. While in this transition period, which may last from a few hours to several years, symptomatic relief is required by most patients. This is available using any of the modalities listed above, including drugs, and other symptom relieving treatments.

For a system of medicine to contribute to the healing process and support the body in curing itself from within, it must not be too disruptive of body physiology in its efforts to provide symptom relief. In this regard, many of the alternative healing arts are ideal, and much of orthodox drug treatment is akin to working on a piece of fine jewellery with a pick-axe. The curative powers of the body work overtime in an attempt to eliminate the massive doses of antibiotics, opioids, antihistamines, analgesics, diuretics and laxatives administered by doctors too uninformed and frightened to do otherwise, and taken by patients too intent on instant symptomatic relief to consider probing into why they became ill in the first place. While the body is dealing with these artificially introduced agents, it must continue to heal itself. Consequently, a simple complaint that the patient could have eliminated in twenty-four hours is often prolonged by the introduction of a drug. A major reason for the continued success of orthodox medicine is its ability to prolong what could have been a simple minor complaint.

Now that may sound ridiculous but it's the logical consequence of our custom of giving ourselves physically destructive complaints in order to manipulate our environment. We are not ridiculous; we harm ourselves physically in order to protect ourselves psychologically. This book establishes that connection, and offers alternatives.

Orthodox medicine and unenlightened alternative medicine, which together constitute nearly all medical practice in the West, prolong illness. They do this by labeling the patient as ill, rather than needy. Thus the patient becomes someone needing expert medical care, which prolongs the victim status and usually achieves the patient's desired ends, that is, official sanction to ask for help, caring, time off work or other things. Without this official medical sanction, many people will not ask for what they want. They were taught in childhood that capable women and strong men don't do that. Hence the very real need in society for a popular system of medicine compatible with this characteristic of the society, the unwillingness to ask directly for care when it's needed. Disease which is permanently removed by treatment would no longer serve this function, and that's why orthodox drug treatment has perfected symptom relief and basically ignored the causes of illness.

The contract that those members of the public who don't wish to take responsibility for themselves make with the medical profession goes something like this: "I've consulted you to have my need recognized, my suffering validated, my pain removed and my disease retained. In return, I will support you financially and give you status commensurate with the powers I ask you to exercise."

Each part of the contract is necessary to the whole. In order that the expertise and validating power of the doctor may be legitimately sought, people need a disease. This validation is officially recognized by giving doctors far-reaching powers in all manner of things, many of them having little or nothing to do with medical practice. Doctors, for example, may witness signatures for passports and other legal documents, are invariably invited to be members of committees and boards within communities and are offered club memberships and other benefits with no questions asked. All these things are intended to keep doctors on a pedestal, as it's an essential part of healing and the validation of suffering that they be seen to be powerful. And of course, this prominence also serves to make the doctor more vulnerable to attack. The law in many countries has adopted orthodox western medicine as its standard, from which platform orthodox medicine ruthlessly destroys any other contribution to human wellness, however effective.

If the word "disease" is broken into its two parts, it becomes "dis-ease" which means "un-easy" or "un-comfortable." We tend to go to the doctor when we're uncomfortable. Because psychological discomfort is generally not afforded the same status as an obvious physical disease that can be measured in the laboratory, it's similarly less effective in having our need and suffering validated.

Why, one may ask, is psychological dis-ease generally regarded as less valid than physical dis-ease? This is an anthropological question that would take a whole book to answer, but it serves our purpose here to look at the question in the light of contemporary orthodox medical practice.

In general, the scientific principle has been very poorly applied to the humanities. The scientific principle requires that one researcher's experiments be reproducible; that is, if a treatment works with one person or group of persons, then it ought to work, if it's valid, with any person or group of persons, i.e., the results are predictable. While this works in the laboratory, where conditions are standardized, it's highly doubtful that any of nature is identical. This means that even the most scientific of laws are merely descriptive of what is observable most of the time. Human beings seem to me the least standardized of all nature (though no doubt a tree or a cat would disagree with me). Most modern doctors like to think that they're very scientific, because they've been taught laboratory methods of diagnosis and are familiar with the latest advanced technology. Because of this, they welcome measurable physical disease and are frightened by psychological problems. If the patient wants his suffering to be socially ratified, he needs to come up with a physical ailment. Usually the confirmation of illness is a semi-public testament and can be used to demonstrate infirmity when the occasion calls for it.

The orthodox view that medical practice is "scientific" means that an equally "scientific" (and equally fallacious) treatment may be used. This is effective in removing the symptoms but of no help in curing the disease. And therein lies its value, the maintenance rather than the cure of illness, for you'll recall that an integral part of the contract is the need to be able to show a physical disease. If that's a prerequisite for being helped, then removal of the disease is not an advantage.

Evidence based medicine, or EBM, is generally now regarded as the hallmark of acceptable medical practice. EBM relies on clinical trials and meta-analyses of large numbers of trials. It attempts, mostly unsuccessfully, to allow for researchers' self-interest to be identified so that the researchers will not contaminate the results of their trials. The reality is that researchers conduct few trials without bias of one sort or another, such as financial, professional, or career benefits. "Anecdotal" evidence is generally frowned upon, since it relates to an unscientific method or an unrepresentative research group. Anecdotal evidence is actually the only true evidence, however, since nothing has been manipulated to gain a result. It applies to one person only and not to a group. Within the "evidence-based group," in contrast, the conclusions of a clinical trial actually apply to no one.

Compounding the current medical practice of claiming to be scientific is the medical profession's lack of understanding of contemporary science, represented by quantum mechanics, uncertainty, complexity, entanglement, and multiple other concepts that have been discussed for over a century in science but not yet in medicine.

Maintenance of the disease process and removal of the symptoms is neither a bad nor good thing. It's simply what happens a lot of the time when a patient who doesn't want to take responsibility for herself goes to the doctor. Plenty of people can ask for help from others when they need it, make powerful decisions in their best interests, and have no need for illness or the doctor. Many others give themselves relatively minor illnesses and use the ritual of going to the doctor to gain permission to get better, often despite the chemical or drug they take on their doctor's advice. There's also a substantial number of cases in which the person's investment is in being so ill that all the drugs and technology available to modem medicine are required if he's to stay alive. Fifty years ago, these people would have chosen diseases that were just capable of being controlled with the techniques that were available at that time in history.

The doctor has been a powerful person in most cultures. The form of the healing has varied tremendously but if there's one feature common to all medicine men of all ages and cultures, including our own, it's mystique. Without mystique, healers find it difficult to be effective. Mystique is a careful blend of admiration and fear, hung on a framework of "agreed upon fictions." It requires the healer to be powerful and to possess greater knowledge and understanding than the recipient. In the twentieth century, an epoch of incredible scientific advancement, the doctor must be seen to be technologically advanced. As soon as the public becomes familiar with X-rays, the doctor needs to be ordering CAT scans. As the public become familiar with CAT scans, the doctor must order MRIs, then PET scans. As soon as the public becomes familiar with penicillin, the doctor needs to be prescribing clindamycin. "Needs to" because, without the progression of medical practice to bigger and better things, the illusion is lost and without the illusion the doctor is impotent.

There's a mutually sustaining fear in all of this. The fear on the patient's side is something I've already spoken of in depth: the fear of taking full responsibility for who he or she is. The fear of the doctor is the fear of not having the answers and of having his or her system of medicine exposed for the fiction it is. For these reasons, medicine has always been shrouded in mystery. The doctor hides behind technical names and masks of

all descriptions, while the patient disingenuously puts himself
"in your hands, Doctor."

We place the doctor on a pedestal by joint agreement. It's
worth reiterating that all these arrangements can only survive
by joint agreement. As soon as one party breaks the contract,
the system is replaced by another. Because our society is
capitalistic, the doctor has to be well provided for financially
in order, once again, to maintain the illusion of potency. This
system also provides a very convenient avenue for complaining
about the treatment a patient has received or about how the
treatment was ineffective. As a spinoff it also provides an outlet
for aggression for those who are unhappy, and are looking for
someone other than themselves to blame: "Doctors' salaries are
absolutely outrageous!" we exclaim. Those who are capable of
providing the greatest salvation, are also capable of providing
the greatest anguish. This is the basic paradox.

It becomes obvious from the preceding discussion that
the medical practitioner is a highly significant member of
our society. The doctor will be different things to all people,
and people will seek out the doctor whom they want. Some
will use their doctor as a resource center for researching and
understanding mental and physical processes. On a purely
mechanical level, the doctor has a deeper understanding of
pathology than at any other time in history. If the doctor can
be encouraged to impart some of this knowledge, it can be
effectively combined with a client's understanding of his or
her investment in the disease, and help an early resolution of
his illness. Similarly, the doctor's knowledge of symptomatic
drug therapy can be temporarily valuable. An alternative
practitioner of the healing arts can also be of real value to clients
seeking to understand their illness, so that they may assume
responsibility for it.

The Internet has enabled patients to learn more about their
particular conditions than the doctors they attend (should they
elect to do so). Some doctors welcome this development, since
it has the potential to involve patients in their own treatment.
Others find it confrontational when a patient points out clinical
trials that contradict what the doctor has recommended. People

who want to take responsibility for their own health make good use of both the Internet and the doctor.

Those medical practitioners who refuse to take the onus of recovery from the client onto themselves are doing their clients a great service. Some people who have decided to get well may in the early stages require the permission of a parent figure they regard as powerful — namely the doctor — to oversee their recovery. Placing themselves under the umbrella of a practitioner reduces the fear they experience when they start to take responsibility for themselves. In effect, they're using the doctor's authority, status, and protection to override their own parents' messages. I call this stage of their journey to self-responsibility and personal evolution the "transition stage."

Often, however, the doctor is interested only in labeling the disease, without providing any reference to the underlying reasons for it. This will inevitably be a superficial classification based on obvious symptoms, readily elicited signs, and insensitive laboratory data. (Bear in mind that the average consultation with a general medical practitioner takes well under ten minutes.) The administration of a drug that is conveniently allocated to that combination of signs and symptoms guarantees continuation of the disease and the patient's contribution to it. In a similar way, psychiatric diseases are categorized and then treated with drugs with little reference to the underlying psychodynamics that are involved. The American Psychiatric Association's *Diagnostic and Statistical Manual of Mental Disorders* (DSM), which was originally conceived of as a way to communicate between psychiatrists, is running the risk of categorizing much of human behavior as a disease.

This is care and control psychiatry and unfortunately constitutes a large proportion of psychiatric practice. Psychotherapy which orientates clients toward an understanding of why they have made themselves ill and what they can do to heal themselves, is real psychiatry. However, it's way messier than squeezing a patient into a category to which he doesn't really belong and then prescribing a drug for that category which doesn't really work, citing fallacious evidence based trials which just happen to make someone lots of money or advance their career. Hence few psychiatrists are attracted to uncovering the early childhood circumstances contributing to the disease, and those that are, risk being sued by disgruntled patients. Their law suit will be enthusiastically supported by the accused doctor's colleagues, psychiatrists who jump at the opportunity of removing a competitor, abandoning any pretence at impartiality or integrity along the way.

Modern general practitioners are little acquainted with the causes of illness and indeed it would be financially disastrous for them to regard disease as "self-created and self-cured."

In addition, their mechanistic and out of date scientific training leaves them threatened by the mention of the psychological causes of physical illness. In this climate of mutual support for each other's fears, doctor and patient may contract to ignore the patient's contribution to the illness, remove the symptoms and watch helplessly as acute goes to chronic and the disease worsens.

An increasing number of clients are choosing to use the doctor as a resource centre, the healing arts as a means of understanding their illness, and contract with themselves to remove their illness when it no longer suits them, that is, when they no longer need it.

In assuming responsibility for our disease, we assume the power to remove it.

4

DISEASE—MISFORTUNE OR ADVANTAGE?

A notion in our society that is widely held and aggressively defended is that people, through no fault of their own, will from time to time become unwell, may have accidents and may require surgery. Getting ill or staying well is regarded as a matter of chance, misfortune or luck. So deeply rooted in our belief system is the concept of disease as both inevitable and out of our own control that in treating disease we usually look only at the very last point of expression of the disease—the symptoms.

Beneath the symptoms, those irritating and unacceptable aches and pains, is a vast network of interrelated causes and factors contributing to the disease. In all but the most enlightened medical practice, these are ignored. Instead, we concentrate on the tip of the iceberg, forgetting the major features of the illness which are unaffected by the treatment and continue to cause further trouble.

We're all familiar with the idea of treating the cause of the disease rather than treating the symptoms. Despite our familiarity with causes and symptoms, the medical profession is still reluctant to investigate beyond the most superficial basis of disease and the public in turn is equally disinclined to patronize practitioners who aim for a cure rather than an improvement of the disease. And yet to most people the idea of being reluctant to part with diseases is senseless. Because of this, the value of disease in our society needs to be scrutinized.

Why do many people become angry when confronted with the part they play in the development of their own illnesses? Why does the medical profession continue to regard the patient as a victim of disease? Presumably, the idea that we cause our own illnesses must disturb some very fundamental belief we hold about ourselves and our bodies and a challenge to that belief causes great fear. We pass this fear on to our children and they in turn believe that they don't cause their own illnesses.

What are the advantages to us, as a society, in continuing to believe that we "catch diseases" or develop them because of factors beyond our control?

First, disease that afflicts us "out of the blue" exonerates us from taking responsibility for who we are and for what we're doing to our bodies. To put it another way, by maintaining that we're the victims of disease, we reinforce our belief that we're not responsible for our own lives and destinies. If we did accept responsibility for every single event in our lives, including our state of health, how would we feel?

I think many of us would feel very vulnerable and fearful.

It's therefore an attractive proposition to most people that if they become ill, it's not their "fault." I put the word "fault" in quotes here because, along with the word "blame," fault only contributes to the discussion by virtue of us excluding it. Both words carry feelings of guilt and shame. Let me state quite categorically that there's no place in the thesis that we cause our own illnesses for the idea that people with illness should feel ashamed or guilty. Quite the opposite. We give ourselves illnesses in order to "take care of ourselves" psychologically, which is in no way reprehensible. As human beings, our quest for less pain, less anxiety and greater happiness is only admirable. If we give ourselves illnesses, that must be a legitimate way of taking account of greater needs. This book examines how and why we give ourselves illnesses.

I return to why we like to think we're the "victims" of disease, that we can neither cause nor cure disease and why we would be afraid to believe otherwise. The answers to many of these questions are to be found within the experiences of childhood. After all, it's here that our first interpretations are made and our first decisions taken. The child lacks power and therefore makes prudent or expedient decisions given a limited range of options. As we get older, these options expand and our earlier childhood decisions become inappropriate or obsolete. As adults, we can take care of ourselves and no longer need to coerce our parents into caring for us. The need to be taken care of by people more powerful than ourselves leads us into taking some decisions which are damaging to us in the long-term.

Take a simple case such as obesity. A young child has certain food requirements that, given adequate exercise, would result in a standard weight range. In some cultures, parents and other relatives believe that children should have a large surplus of body fat to be healthy. If the children are of average weight, they are fed excessive quantities of fat-producing foods in order to put on weight and to make them overweight. The anxiety of the family is removed by having the child overweight. The child, who is very much affected by tension in the parents and family, will do what she can to lessen stress in both herself and her parents. Thus she takes the decision to be a fat child and will often continue as an obese adult unless she decides to do something different as she gets older. If she's grossly obese, she may increase her risk of heart disease, diabetes and gallbladder disease, for example. Thus her early childhood decision to be fat, which was effective in reducing anxiety in everybody, is now resulting in potential physical disease as an adult.

Now this case has several interesting components. If the fat girl had decided she was solely responsible for her weight and had chosen to ignore her parents' directives to be fat, she would have risked censure, maybe physical punishment, and perhaps imagined losing other necessities in her life which she was incapable of providing for herself such as love, closeness, protection and clothes. Tension in the family may also have increased. As a child, she would be unlikely to handle such tensions. All of the above factors created a situation in which the child decided that to be fat was her best option—and it was.

Children are not responsible for themselves. Parents are clearly responsible for keeping their children alive in the first few years of life. During this period, the child comes to rely on a person more powerful than himself who is capable of solving problems and meeting his needs. Society dictates the rate at which responsibility is handed to children as they tum into adults. Many societies have specific rituals and ceremonies for just this purpose.

Many of our beliefs about ourselves are created in the first few years of life. The belief that we are not solely responsible for ourselves is one; as a child, that's exactly the case. But we may carry the decisions we make in childhood through to adult life, even though they may be harmful to us in some way. We may express the belief that we aren't totally responsible for ourselves and that others will take care of us, by getting ill. Our investment lies in reinforcing our belief that some things are beyond our influence. Society obliges this strategy by accepting illness as being beyond the individual's control. As a child, things *were* beyond our control.

Because even as adults, some things in life are beyond our control, we may use that fact to shoehorn all matters, including illness and accidents, into that category. A balance is achieved by accepting some things as beyond our influence and experiencing the discomfort of that, and addressing those matters which we're able to influence. Moving health from the first to the second category is the aim of this work.

If we do get ill, we hope that we'll be cared for and comforted as in childhood. Childhood was a time of diminished responsibility with the comfort of knowing that there was somebody more powerful to step in and solve the problem. By maintaining our belief that "we couldn't help it," we try to revert to a belief system which existed as a child.

And no wonder we feel afraid when faced with the prospect of being totally responsible for ourselves. As a young child, such a prospect would have terrified us, because it would have meant certain death. If the child had no reason to fear that her needs were not going to be met, she would not fear for her own survival. If, however, her mother doubted her own ability or desire to adequately care for her child, then she would pass this doubt on to the infant. A very young or inexperienced mother may feel inadequate when the baby first arrives. This is to be expected. If these feelings continue over the years, and particularly if they're coupled with ambivalence or outright hostility toward the child, the child may begin to seriously doubt whether or not he can survive. He would most probably decide he couldn't keep himself alive, she couldn't keep him alive, and look for ways to get her or others to take better care of him. Getting ill is one way do this. The depth of this fear can be seen in the fact that people give themselves life-threatening diseases rather than face the fact that they are responsible for themselves.

Many philosophers have written about humankind being ultimately alone. Disease is commonly used by those who won't accept that they are their own final arbiter. In this sense, disease is like a fatalistic religion and anyone who has worked in a general medical practice or a hospital will attest to the comfort many patients feel as a consequence of being ill and therefore getting themselves cared for. For these people, disease becomes a way of life, or a way to death, both elements of everyday existence. Some people put their very life at threat, in order to keep their belief system intact.

There's always the opposite end of the spectrum; those people who take great joy in the power they have over their own lives can fulfill their dreams. These people will be successful in what they want for themselves and will have little need for diseases. They may from time to time suffer acute complaints because of environmental hazards that combine with old childhood messages they've elected to retain, but they will not put themselves at risk for major trauma or serious illnesses. These people have overcome any fears they had in childhood of not being able to take care of themselves. They will live as long as they want to, usually choosing to die peacefully when the infirmities of old age become intolerable to them or when they've simply achieved for themselves what they wanted.

Recall the example of the obese young girl who makes herself overweight in order to facilitate the smooth running of her family. There's a further element to this story, beyond that of an obese adult following now-obsolete childhood messages. The family believed a fat child was a healthy child. That sort of belief doesn't arise overnight, and that family, that village, that society, maybe even that country has probably held that belief for generations. And more likely than not, it was a view with much truth at the beginning, which meant that fat babies were more likely to survive than thin ones. Any number of circumstances may have validated that view. If the seasons were variable and the crops could not be relied upon, then through a bitter winter, indeed the fatter the child the greater the buffer against famine.

The point is this: the family, which was living in the late twentieth century in an affluent society, was following old instructions that were simply no longer necessary. There was no longer a lack of food, nor in the foreseeable future would there be. Therefore, the need to keep babies overweight was no longer unnecessary. Can we make use of this example when we look at why our society still chooses to give itself diseases?

Parental attitudes will generally reflect societal attitudes. As an example, most parents raising children in the 1950s in Western society would have been more antagonistic towards premarital sex, nudity, marijuana, and inflation than parents with young children in the 1980s. In addition to the negative messages parents give to their children on these matters, fewer marijuana-smoking nudist parents who lived out of wedlock would have been around to model these attributes to children. 1950s society was of course far less permissive than the seventies which were more permissive than the climate in which the current millennials were raised. Society changes, sometimes becoming more tolerant, before swinging back to being less tolerant. Many other social attitudes are in a constant state of flux; marriage, childrearing practices, sex, religion and politics all seem to change significantly every 50 years or so.

The reasons for change will be varied; and include the media, economics, politics, the Internet, social media, computer games, and perhaps most significantly, the "Age of Entitlement." The end result is that children now grow up with quite different messages from the ones they received fifty years ago, because societies and the people in them change.

Is the need for illness fading out, like the need to keep babies overweight, or are factors at play that are strengthening the need for illness? It's surely worth asking why both families and society generally contribute to the child's belief that illness is an acceptable, indeed a much-condoned, way to escape the fear of self-responsibility. Put simply, some people kill themselves by disease rather than face their own power to live or die. For these people, dying surrounded by caretakers is preferable to the uncertainty of existence.

Let's look now at the creation of wellness, using the framework we've already established in our discussion of how and why people give themselves illness. If the child were given no reason to doubt his survival, he would believe the world to be a safe environment in which his place was guaranteed. Such a child, surrounded by loving caretakers, would believe in his own power to create favorable circumstances for himself, since from birth his experience had been that his very presence induced happiness and pleasure in those around him. He would have no reason to fear that unless he fulfilled certain parental expectations, his right to exist might be revoked. Instead, he would become confident that things he did in his own interests would, if not directly help him, then at least not harm him.

Now this is the basis for believing that we're in charge of our own lives. We would have no reason to be tentative when doing things in our best interests if our memory of doing just that in childhood was positive. As adults, we would take decisions in our best interests fearlessly. As a matter of course we would keep our bodies healthy and free of major trauma or illness. We would not believe disease was beyond our influence if we had no childhood memories of needing to be ill or helpless in order to be cared for.

Parents who allow children to feel powerful by supporting the decisions their children take in their own interests will foster the belief that the children are powerful and capable of both preventing and curing illness.

5

SELF-RESPONSIBILITY, HEALTH, AND DISEASE

Let's examine what happens when a young child wants something. The newborn cries when she wants to be fed, when she's wet and wants to be changed, when she's cold and wants to be made warm, when she wants to be held and comforted, or for many other reasons, emotional or physical. The object of crying is to attract the attention of her caretaker so that her needs may be met.

In these early years, the response of the adults to the baby's demands will determine how the baby goes about getting her needs met. If the mother responds quickly and consistently to the baby's crying, the infant learns that her needs will be met on demand and as time goes on becomes sure that she'll be able to survive. If the baby's needs are met in a caring way (which is not easy at 3 a.m. when the other children have been awake all night with croup), then the baby is assured that she'll receive both physical support and approval. In other words, the mother and other caretakers approve of her demands and respond to them with love, rather than hostility or resentment.

Now, it will not be all the time that such an idyllic situation occurs. Sometimes Mom, Dad, the kids, or Grandfather will be fed up with caring for the baby. While they'll continue to respond to the basic needs of the infant, they may do so with some annoyance. If this is an irregular event, the child comes to appreciate that at times some of her legitimate needs will not be met immediately or with smiles, but that generally they will be. Such a child will grow assured of her place within the family and assured of the love of the other members. As she grows older, she learns that when her needs clash with the needs of others, she may not get what she wants. Because it's already been established within the family that it's OK to ask for what you want, the child will not feel threatened by demanding for herself and will continue to do so in the face of disappointments. Failure to get what she wants will result in a display of anger and then perhaps sorrow but will not be accompanied by the fear of loss of love. Her parents have established already that they love the child and that they welcome her demands, even though they may not always grant them.

Such a child grows up with a certain attitude toward her own needs and, more particularly, an attitude toward her power to achieve things which she believes are in her best interests. Her own experience has been that needs which she cannot satisfy herself as a child will be treated with love and respect and generally met. Because of this, she believes that it's legitimate to have needs and to ask other people for things. She also has experienced her own ability to get what she wants and needs. As a young baby, she cried and this resulted in people caring for her. She feels powerful. As a young child she asks for what she wants and generally gets it. As an older child she's taught how to do things for herself and how to come for help when she can't manage alone. She grows up believing that she can do things that are in her best interests and that although at times her interests may clash with others, generally she has the power to benefit herself.

Would this girl grow up with a feeling of stewardship over her own life? And furthermore, would she believe that she could influence the course of her life favorably, either by her own devices or with the assistance of others? I think so. This woman would not feel the need to do things against her interests in order to obtain love and attention. In particular, she would not need to become ill in order to get what she wanted, for she would feel able to get those things directly, either by herself or by asking others. She would feel in control of her own body, knowing that she could keep herself healthy. She would be in no doubt that she could influence her physical state in her favor and with such a belief, would look toward her diet and lifestyle with a view to maintaining her health. Such a person would not allow the environmental hostilities under which we all live to create major illnesses within her body. She's accustomed to doing things in her best interests and has always believed she has the power to achieve what she wants. She'd regard her right to good health as a matter of course. In other words, this person has no need for illness.

This woman's positivity toward life and her feelings of stewardship over her own destiny will be subconscious. That is, she would mostly be unable to point to any of the specific psychodynamics discussed above. If, however, we listen carefully to this person's language, we'll hear the metaphor of self-care and self-regard. She may say, "I can do that overseas trip next year if I set my mind to it," or "Last year when we visited India, only two others apart from myself in our party of twenty didn't suffer from diarrhea," or "No wonder Jill's sick all the time with a father like hers."

She'll find herself automatically attracted to like-minded people, namely those who believe in their own capacity to influence their own lives. Most likely she'll marry a man who is similarly healthy. Because she was not raised in a family where a child needed to become sick to get attention, she will neither look for a partner who wants to be taken care of, nor look for a partner to take care of her.

The difference between "taking care of" and "caring for" is important. It's the difference between a belief in non self responsibility and self responsibility. One person may say to another, "I want you to take care of me," meaning, "I want to place responsibility for my life [or this aspect of my life] in your hands." This is the basis of the usual contract that is drawn up between the public and the medical profession. Another person may say, "I want you to care for me," meaning, "I take responsibility for my own life, and within this responsibility I welcome your care of me."

Now, unlike the woman we've been discussing who didn't need to hand over responsibility for herself to another because as a child her parents had encouraged her to develop a sense of her own strength, let's consider a very common arrangement in Western society that has to do with illness and being taken care of.

People in Western society are usually aware that a large proportion of their taxes go toward health-delivery systems and generally learn via the media of new technology, new facilities, and new costs in the area of health. This concern for our well-being is heightened by exposure to information on environmental pollutants in the air and in our food and water supply, so it would be a rare person indeed who remained completely impervious to health information. Because in general we dwell on health matters as a society, we tend to have a good idea of the attitude that potential partners might have toward their own and others' health. In this climate of concern, one might hear a comment such as, "I'd never go out with a smoker" or "If he thinks I'm going to live on the industrial side of town and breathe all that pollution, he's very mistaken." We check out our partners' attitudes about diet, exercise, past illnesses, and health status, so it's no surprise that a person who often gets ill and wants to be looked after finds himself attracted to, and marries a person, who likes to look after sick people.

A personal life plan which limits us in some way but which we chose as the best way to get ourselves looked after as kids is called our script. A man who feels that it's necessary for him to become ill before he deserves caring is fulfilling a script decision taken as a child. In this case he limits himself by not simply asking for the caring he wants. For some reason, his parents disapproved of his demands as a child and he became afraid to ask for certain things unless he could show to his parents' satisfaction that his need was legitimate. In his family illness was considered to be a condition warranting caring and he may have needed to use the device of illness to get what he wanted. As an adult, the man developed illness whenever he wanted to be cared for and will most likely be living with a partner who shares his belief system and who's more inclined to care for him when he's ill than when he's not.

When two people relate to each other in ways which limit both of them they are said to have interlocking scripts. Co-dependency is another way of expressing it. One of the very common interlocking scripts is that of the nurse and the patient. Usually the man is the patient and his wife is the nurse. If he feels unloved, overworked or if the kids are taking up too much of his wife's time, he makes himself ill and she looks after him. If she's been brought up to do this she'll like it and may even encourage illness in her husband. The marriage, revolving around the illness of one member, may go on harmoniously for some time. Then may come a major change. She may get fed up with looking after him and refuse to play the game any longer, in which case he feels hurt and completely unloved and perhaps escalates from a bad back to pneumonia. Or he may decide to not get sick any longer because his life is passing by his bedside and she may respond by feeling unwanted and therefore unloved. She may have an affair with a bronchitic down the street. And so it goes on until, perhaps, both partners decide they have the responsibility of looking after themselves and their children and that within this self-responsibility they can both love and be loved.

We began by following the development of a baby growing up in a family where her needs were generally met promptly and with a smile. This baby was allowed to experience her own power to get her needs met and grew into a woman who subconsciously or with partial awareness took charge of her own life and health. What about the other end of the spectrum?

A baby cries and is not fed. A baby is wet and cold and scared and is not changed, made warm and comforted. How do you think this baby's perception of the world will be different? A mother who can't or won't attend to her baby when he cries will be at the other end of the spectrum from one who slavishly attends to her baby's every need, even at great personal discomfort, and who may end up smothering the child's independence by needing to shower the baby with love and caring beyond his needs. So here we have two completely opposing attitudes. Both provide the extremities of a range of caring for the child, the balanced attitude represented by the woman discussed previously. Let's look at the child whose needs are simply not met.

This unfortunate situation may occur where an unwanted pregnancy, perhaps through ignorance, the law, or other factors, is allowed to result in an unwanted baby. If the mother is coerced into keeping the child against her wishes, or is ambivalent about keeping the baby and yet does so, her child may receive minimal basic caring. When the baby cries he's not fed but is allowed to continue crying, often out of earshot of the mother. Or perhaps the mother is busy with a large family and delegates responsibility for feeding the child to other siblings, often the younger ones who are unable to protest as loudly.

They get fed up with the baby crying and ignore it. Baby may be offered food when he's not demanding and not offered food when he is. He therefore feels he has little control over his situation as nothing he does to indicate his needs seems to have any bearing on whether or not he's fed. The same situation occurs when he's wet and needs changing or when he's crying because he's scared and needs to be comforted. Nothing he does influences the big people around him. He feels powerless, unable to control his surroundings and in this situation, in order to feel safer and better able to survive this hostile world, he begins to adapt.

Since he's been unsuccessful in attracting food, warmth and caring from his mother and the family by crying, he may decide that this behavior is not working and start screaming, having tantrums, holding his breath and turning blue, having fits or any other activity devised in desperation to attract the attention he needs. He's fearful that if his needs are not met he will die. Even though the mother and other caretakers may be fully intending to keep him alive, the baby has no experience or evidence of this. The fear is therefore very great and very real. Now if these new behaviors are equally unsuccessful in attracting caring, he may decide that nothing he can do will improve his lot. He stops crying. He becomes very passive and may attract remarks like, "Isn't he a good baby, so calm, he hardly ever seems to cry." This type of experience will lay the basis for a belief in fatalism, that is, the inability to alter the course of one's life. "What will be will be, nothing I can do will make any difference."

If people believe they're powerless to influence the course of their own life they'll hardly be receptive to the notion that they're responsible for their own illnesses. Rather they'll believe that, "You catch colds because other people give you germs" or "The pollutants in the air, foods and water are so bad that you just can't resist them" or, "There's cancer in the family so I guess I'll catch it as well." In addition, they'll most likely have a high degree of anxiety as a consequence of their early childhood fear about not getting what they want and not surviving, which will raise their adrenaline levels, increase their blood pressure, predispose them to ulcers and colitis and increase their susceptibility to both colds and "accidents." If we believe we're incapable of withstanding these stresses, we sabotage our defense mechanisms and succumb to disease. If the young boy we've been speaking of cried and was responded to with anger rather than not being responded to at all, then he might have decided that to ask for what he needed was dangerous and that he had better not cry. He may have received love and caring provided he didn't make a fuss and give Dad a migraine. The likely outcome of such a situation would be an adult who suppresses his emotions, bottles up anger which he's afraid to express openly and consequently suffers from a range of physical complaints, hypertension being a likely one. If the personality of the individual refuses to allow the healthy and legitimate expression of emotion, then disease is practically guaranteed. We've discussed the girl who, as a consequence of consistently having her needs promptly met, grows up with a faith in her ability to be healthy, and the boy who becomes diseaseprone from fatalism and fear. Let's consider a child who grows up overprotected.

Both Mrs. Jones and her daughter Sally were patients of mine. As the eldest of a family of five children, Mrs. Jones had been given responsibility for looking after some of her younger brothers and sisters from an early age. She'd resented these often confining duties, preferring to have fun playing with other children her own age, but her mother was obviously incapable of managing alone, so Mrs. Jones had stayed home and helped out. In the severe winter of 1981, an epidemic of meningitis had claimed the lives of at least four children in the area, one of whom was her younger sister. Mrs. Jones had felt guilty about her sister's death. It was her responsibility to look after her sister and despite her mother's reassurances, Mrs. Jones had never really forgiven herself for her younger sister's death when they were both children.

When Sally was born after three previous pregnancies had all miscarried, Mrs. Jones had naturally been overjoyed. A boy would have been fine, but a girl! She had to be the happiest mother in the world!

When Sally cried, her mother was there in an instant, offering food, changing diapers, cuddling the child, and making sure the crib was clean and that no harmful germs could come Sally's way. She found herself rather anxious when strangers wanted to hold or even get close to her child, eventually preferring to have the groceries delivered rather than risk Sally catching cold by going outside. If a cat or dog came near the baby she would become really quite frightened, shooing the animal away vigorously. Eventually she noticed that Sally herself would cry whenever an animal or a stranger wanted to be friendly. This she took to be the child's own innate protective mechanisms, confirming her own belief that the situation was unsafe. She really was a devoted mother.

Sally grew up to be an excellent scholar, first at school and later at college. Throughout her teenage years she was a loner who disliked boys, disliked going out, and generally regarded the world as a scary place. Her health was reasonably good, but she did seem to catch more than her fair share of colds and trivial ailments, which confirmed both to herself and her mother that she was "delicate." She scrupulously watched her diet and never ate junk food and as a result had beautiful skin and perfect teeth. She looked angelic and was angelic. When she eventually got married and left home, she began to suffer recurrent vaginal infections. Her husband agreed to be circumcised, since she thought, as did her mother, that this was the cause of Sally's vaginal infections. The condition didn't improve, however, and she also found that she was rarely free of mucus and complained of increasing abdominal problems.

Sally never believed that she was capable of keeping herself healthy. She didn't see that she was responsible for being well because the responsibility for her state of health (or anything else for that matter) had never been handed over to her at the appropriate time in childhood. She'd been attended to well as a baby but hadn't grown beyond her dependence on her mother. When her mother was no longer available, she was defenseless, even though she'd chosen a husband who wanted to take care of her. Sally's unwillingness to take responsibility for herself through fear of the world (as decided upon in childhood) meant she never accepted her own power to be well and as a consequence, she was ill. In this she was not unlike the boy who hadn't been cared for as a baby and had decided he was powerless to help himself.

The cases discussed are not meant to be detailed analyses of often complex family situations. Instead they're intended as simple examples of how early childhood experiences shape the long-term health of the individual. They represent several points along a very broad spectrum.

There are many factors to be considered in examining why people do not take responsibility for their own health, preferring instead to believe that if they become ill they are the victims of bad luck. When confronted with the idea that we give ourselves illnesses, many people react with great hostility, pointing to a wide and varied number of examples from their own lives which are intended to prove that illness is beyond the control of the individual. Here we've restricted our examination of this phenomenon to situations where children never believed they had power over their own lives and therefore as adults, never believed they could prevent illness in themselves.

I hope that it's becoming clear that when I speak of assuming stewardship over one's life that I'm not advocating "controlling" one's life, quite the opposite. No-one can anyway "control" their own life, since we're hurtling around in space at a rate and direction not of our own choosing for reasons beyond our understanding. We're kept warm by a sun we didn't create.

The notion that we "control" our lives is nonsensical. Nonetheless, we are "responsible" for our own lives. This means that we explore, over a lifetime, allowing our bodies and minds to make the most appropriate and complete response possible to any event which comes our way. Our willingness to "respond" frees our immune and endocrine systems to best adapt and to best protect us from harm.

SECTION II:
FINDING THE CAUSE

6

THE FIRST CONTACT

The diagnosis (and often the treatment) of any condition begins at the very first contact between the client and the practitioner. In my case, this happens over the phone, since I make my own appointments. At the conclusion of the usually brief conversation required to effect an appointment, I have roughly assessed the state of health and, more importantly, the healing receptivity of the client. The following is a typical call.

"Hello?"

"Hello, may I speak with Dr. Harrison, please?"

"Yes, this is Dr. Harrison speaking; how can I help you?"

"I'd like to make an appointment to see you."

"Right. It'll mean waiting about two weeks if I haven't seen you before, and you'll be charged the following fees." [An explanation of the exact cost structure and the client's return from an insurance fund follows.]

"Thank you. Actually, I knew the charges already; I've been meaning to come and see you for some time."

"Wednesday, the fifth of October, at four p.m. The consultation will last for an hour and a half."

"Thank you, Doctor; I'll see you then."

My information so far is that I'm dealing with a well-educated middle-aged woman who's taken a decision to come and see me from a position of some power and self-responsibility. She hasn't come immediately but has waited some months before making the appointment, and I therefore know she puts safety first but is prepared to take risks when necessary. No doubt she knows a lot about my treatment from talking with the friends who recommended me. More information about how far she's prepared to take the notion that we give ourselves illness will have to wait until the actual appointment. I know also from the telephone conversation that she's already decided that she's prepared to take responsibility for the financial burden of the appointment. This information has come from the content of our conversation. Tone of voice is equally, if not more, important.

If she sounds angry, I differentiate between anger directed at me or at others. This tells me if I'm dealing with someone who's angry that her professional caretakers, usually the medical profession, have not solved her problem. In these circumstances, I can anticipate the client setting me up to be yet another useless professional who fails to help her. This is valuable information which, if not recognized, can mean a considerable waste of time.

Or the client may have a helpless, breathless voice, which is saying, "I cannot look after myself. If I appear helpless enough surely someone will assist me." And of course most doctors love to be helpers and many will go along with the client and say, "Yes, what rotten luck you're suffering from cancer, let me help you." After the rescuing doctor has been well and truly entangled in his and the client's mutually laid mesh, the client will often, as her condition worsens, accuse the doctor of being hopeless, uncaring or of being a false prophet. The doctor in turn becomes angry at being abused for his efforts and says that the client "doesn't want to get well anyway!" Both end up feeling bad because neither has been prepared to admit that the client is a major contributor to her illness, though neither party at this stage knows how or why. The doctor, for his part, is scared that unless he maintains the illusion of fate as the cause of the disease and unless he can be helpful, he's redundant. It's also dangerous for him to acknowledge the role the client plays in her own illness, because logically that proportion the client admits as "self-caused" will then become available for "self-cure." This he sees as threatening to his livelihood.

Consider instead the following phone conversation.

"Hello?"

"Hello, may I speak with Dr. Harrison, please?"

"Yes, Dr. Harrison speaking; may I help you?"

"Yes; I'm calling to make an appointment for my husband — he's at work right now."

"I'm sorry, ma'am, but I'm not prepared to make an appointment for him through another person. If your husband wants to see me, he'll have to call himself."

"I see. Well, thank you; I'll tell him."

"You're welcome; good-bye."

Except in the case of children, making appointments for relatives is a game, and to accept the appointment will generally get the doctor involved in a situation that uses the illness of one partner for the benefit of both. If the patient calls later, then I've gained some valuable information, and if he's so bent out of shape that he doesn't call, then I've saved myself the trouble of spending an hour with someone who wasn't ready to take a look at himself in the first place. Later he may feel safe to do so.

Upon initial contact, clients will commonly attempt to assess whether the doctor will be an ally in their persecution of the medical profession. This is tantamount to establishing that the doctor agrees that they're not responsible for their own illness. Here's a third phone conversation to consider.

"Hello?"

"Hello, may I speak with Dr. Harrison, please?"

"Speaking."

"Oh, doctor, I'm so glad I reached you—I've been trying for a couple of weeks now, and you never seem to be there." The content is condemnatory despite a friendly, effusive, and somewhat seductive mood.

"I've been here all along; how can I help you?"

"Well, I suffer terribly from arthritis, and my local doctor said there was nothing more he could do. All he does is give me more and more drugs. Even the specialist figured I'd be in a wheelchair by the time I'm sixty, and I hate being a burden on people, especially my poor old hubby, who's not doing so well himself. We're retirees living on a pension, you know: nobody cares about us, the cost of living is so high, you can't even afford fresh vegetables..."

I Interrupt: *"You may know from the person who recommended me that in cases such as yours, I believe diet plays a large part, and the likelihood is that yours will be changed substantially."*

"But doctor, we eat very well given our meager means, and..."

"I'm sorry, but I can't discuss this over the phone. You might consider whether you're prepared to undergo a long and significant dietary prescription; if you decide you are, then I'd be pleased to make an appointment for you." [My tone indicates the end of the conversation.]

"Very well, Doctor, thank you!"

"You're welcome."

This caller may decide that the initial contact was encouraging and come to see me. Having spouted out the usual helpless game and gotten nowhere with it, she may decide I'm capable of helping her after all. In that case, she may do well in therapy, and, while substantially altering her diet, I'll engage her in an examination of the advantages she gets from being ill. She's already indicated that her husband's health is a significant factor, and my guess is that they're playing "I'm sicker than you are!" If she doesn't come to see me, then I assume that what I was offering was unattractive to her, and that she'll continue as she is until the symptoms worsen or she's prepared to risk more. Either way, I've learned something of value in our exchange, and perhaps she has as well.

Many phone conversations will be longer than the ones reported here, but whatever the length or complexity, I follow some basic principles. I take the view that there's a component of the disease, small or large, that's a consequence of the client's own actions. I indicate that this is a good thing as that part of the illness is available for them to cure. I avoid the words "blame" and "fault." I avoid clients who want to fight if I see that my chances of winning are slight. Sometimes I recommend them to other practitioners who I think can help them. I avoid claiming sole ownership of the truth. I'm generally enthusiastic about their prospects. I make good use of the anger, sorrows, frustrations and resentments directed toward people who are supposed to heal them. I never let the client hand me the burden of responsibility for her own illness. This all takes place during the initial telephone conversation, and when I first see the client, I recall what she previously said and how she said it.

The actual appointment time that the client settles is also significant. A businessperson who interrupts a busy schedule to attend has decided that she needs to do something about her condition, even if her day is disrupted. People who argue about the fact that I don't see people outside of office hours will still be at the stage of believing that, because they are the victims of illness, it's unreasonable for them to be inconvenienced by it. I may use barriers that prevent people from getting what they want to prudently assess the form of therapy that will be most effective for them. I'm reminded of an American colleague who would not make appointments for specific times within the day. His clients arrived at 9:00 a.m., and he might not see them until 5:00 p.m. The receptionist arranged activities such as nutrition and antismoking films and walks in good weather. By the time the doctor saw them, they would often have a new perspective on their illness. My colleague argued that since he didn't know what he'd be dealing with until he'd had a chance to investigate the matter, the time required for each appointment might vary from ten minutes to three hours. My own personal "Hurry up" driver and my need for a bit more order would find such an arrangement intolerable!

THE FIRST ATTENDANCE

One of the advantages of not having a large staff and greeting my patients personally in the waiting room is that I see the client before she actually enters my office. By that time, she's already modified her behavior significantly, especially if she has a long history of attending medical practitioners. She feels that she's expected to behave in a certain way. Waiting-room ambience will often be set by the doctor and almost always enforced by the medical receptionist.

The game of "You're privileged to be able to see me," which maintains the patient in a deferential position and keeps the practitioner divorced from the real problem and, most importantly, aims at keeping the patient feeling guilty about being ill and taking up everyone's valuable time, usually begins with the medical receptionist. For this purpose the receptionist is often abrupt, depersonalized and a very hard person to reason with if she's taken it upon herself, or has been instructed, to protect the doctor from his public. In addition, the mood of the client has often altered a great deal by having to run this gauntlet in the reasonable attempt to consult the doctor. This may interfere with the diagnosis.

In figuring out why a child has at this time given himself an earache, it's invaluable to hear the mother or father herding him, along with their other children, into the office. If both parents attend the consultation, which I encourage, it's even better.

"Mom, if the doctor says I'm all right, can I have a chocolate ice cream later?"

"No, you cannot!"

"But, Mom, when Barney went to the doctor last time, you bought him one."

"Yes, but he was sick; the doctor said his ears were very bad."

"Mom, that's not fair!"

"Be quiet; here's the doctor to see you."

The message from Mom to young Johnny here is quite clear. If you want a chocolate ice cream, then you have to earn it, and you do that by being very sick. This rewards illness and penalizes wellness, and believe it or not, is by far the most common way in which families act. It directly descends from the notion that people who get ill have little say in the matter, and are simply the victims of circumstance. Therefore, when they fall ill and are "brave," they're rewarded. You can be very sure that if Johnny's ears aren't bad enough this time to earn a chocolate ice cream, they will be next time!

A family with three children has consulted me since the girl was born. The elder boy was five and had suffered many complaints, all of them minor. The girl, who was three, had been exceptionally well, much to her irritation at times. When she came into the office, I was sure to listen to her chest and look into her ears. She found the attention very exciting, even though there was nothing wrong with her. On these occasions her brother was the patient. The one-year-old boy had been well and, given the very much more relaxed style of childrearing in the family that had come with experience, I expect he always will be. His parents told him that the world was safe, that he could expect to be well, and that there was no need to make himself ill.

One evening while the three children were playing at home in the family room, both parents overheard the elder boy say to his sister, "If you want Mommy to look after you, just get sick—that's what I do!" Remember, this is a five-year-old patient telling his three-year-old sister how to get cared for. When the boy's mother told me this story, I was amazed at the boy's command of the family psychodynamics. It's a mistake to believe that children don't understand what happens in families. They understand very well, and since the children direct their involvement toward being cared for, their perceptions are usually very accurate. Also, because they aren't yet conditioned into secrecy and shame, they'll tell you what's happening, if you ask them. In the case of this young boy, the parents and I now reward him when he's well and not when he's ill. Eventually, when he believes that he'll be cared for without being ill, which was the old pattern, he'll start to be well. His body will also need time to recover from the damage caused by organisms made dangerous by a physiology not directed toward keeping itself healthy.

A three-year-old is introduced to her new brother for the first time.
She does not conceal her apprehension about this intrusion.
She feels excluded; only when she believes her needs will
continue to be met will she warm to the new arrival.

All of this essential information may be lost by not being within earshot when the family is interacting as they come through the door of the building. Until they know you, children will be subdued in the presence of the doctor, especially if under parental pressure. Parents in turn often feel very guilty when their children are ill, and if this isn't dealt with, the children's chances of resolving the need to be ill are reduced.

With children, the next information comes from watching them play with the toys in the waiting room. I often bring the toys into the consulting room so that I can observe them at play while I'm getting the details from the parents. This will usually tell me the pecking order of the family, who chastises who when the younger child has a toy pulled away from him and begins to cry, and what behavior has proven effective in the past for attracting parental attention. In cases where children have been born within two years of each other, I observe the older one's attitude toward the younger.

One of the most common illness dynamics in families is the older of two children of similar ages getting ill for attention. It makes sense. The secure world of the elder child is shattered by the arrival of the new baby (see photo above) and any behavior which results in his receiving more attention will be repeated. There may be an exaggerated caring for the younger sibling by the older child. When mother's attention is diverted, the older child may twist the younger's arm. I wonder whether I'm becoming too cynical when I say that I distrust children caring for those in the family who are only slightly younger than themselves. Such a caring attitude is of course much praised and paraded in front of relatives and neighbors but as new babies are rarely in the best interests of slightly older siblings, I suspect the older children unconsciously want to send the baby back in the first instance. That would be natural.

Adults are just as informative as children—often while trying hard not to be. Usually they have their behavior more under control, and the practitioner must be very observant if she wants to find out the real problem. I believe there's a place for shoe therapists, hat therapists, and clothes, car, ring, and perfume therapists. Each of these accoutrements and many others tell you who you're dealing with. What the person is actually saying may be of secondary importance.

The choice of chair is significant. In the waiting room I have several very different styles of chair. They face different directions and are close to either the books, the plants, or the door. Some can be seen readily as I emerge from the consulting room, while others are well hidden from direct view. The chair the client chooses will be as specific as his choice of clothing and will reflect his prevailing mood.

THE GENERAL APPEARANCE

One of the moments of truth in the process of preliminary diagnosis occurs when the client and the practitioner come face to face for the first time. The look on the client's face may vary from "This was a good idea; I like the look of this guy" to "I'm not too sure about this guy!" There may also be pleasure, fear, excitement, amusement, indifference, or anger—particularly if I remind them of a significant figure in their lives.

In turn, the immediate impression that the client makes on me is lasting. The first whole-body image, or Gestalt, will be an accurate reflection of her most cherished dreams, her greatest disappointments, the way she views herself, her illness, and the world. I see stored-up anger in the flushed face and the red margins of the eyes. The stooped walk and hunched shoulders show the fear that leads to poor kidney function and ear infections, and in the bridge of the nose, the chronic allergy and sinus sufferer reveals her sorrow.

I'm aware of the despair of the chronically ill, or the smugness of a multiple-sclerosis sufferer who's achieved the incapacity she's always wanted. I see the fear of anticipating the long haul back to health and the anger of being confronted by yet another healing professional. Fear, anger, joy, and sorrow are there for all to see. We can all see in others' faces a pictorial history of their lives. There's no hiding, no editing, no mask, for how can a person alter the way she looks? The very attempt is obvious and reflects exactly what she's feeling and thinking at the time. Every line tells of a past experience either satisfactorily resolved or hidden away at the back of the mind, where it continues to smolder.

PHYSIOGNOMY – DIAGNOSIS BY THE FACE

The set of the mouth is vital in establishing why the client has made himself ill. Forced emotions are easily detected, such as the thinning of the comers of the mouth in clients who smile their way through a tragic history, or the clenched-teeth smile of the chronically angry. With the latter no stethoscope is needed, for the diagnosis of hypertension is obvious. The size of the upper lip often reflects the emotional flexibility of the client. A large, full, mobile upper lip is indicative of someone who has smiled a lot from the joys of childhood. Suppression of any emotions results in a thinner upper lip. One must allow for the genetic element, of course, but I've seen these things change in therapy and in people in their forties. Pouting, which occurs when people are dissatisfied with what they have but are afraid to get what they want, expresses itself in a large, protuberant lower lip. This state of chronic sadness and fear will eventually result in internal changes in the body, just as it caused a large lip. If I exercise my biceps for any reason, I'll end up with large biceps. If we repeatedly use the facial and lip muscles to express certain emotions, those emotions will eventually be visible in the face. Similarly, the internal organs will be altered by the chronic stresses of predominant emotions, particularly if those emotions are not expressed but internalized. Disease is made from old emotions that haven't been expressed and forgotten but have been retained through fear. Expressing thoughts and feelings as they occur allows the body to return to a state of resting balance. In such cases the face becomes lively and flexible, expressing myriad expressions.

Chronic anger manifests itself in the structure of the jawline. The powerful chewing muscles at the angle of the jaw enlarge in cases where it was not safe to yell at one's parents. In these circumstances, particularly if the individual was expected to smile instead, she'll learn to smile through clenched teeth. When she gets angry, she won't open her mouth wide and yell but separate her lips and keep her teeth together instead. She'll tend to snarl rather than be openly angry. Such a person will often end up getting what she wants indirectly and in a manner that rarely satisfies her and often leaves others she interacts with feeling uncomfortable. When one yells through clenched teeth, we can think of the anger as bouncing off the back of the teeth and going back deep down inside, from whence it continues to cause further havoc.

To release the muscle tension associated with anger, it's necessary to open the mouth wide and stretch the jaw muscles. The pupils dilate, the adrenaline level increases and the blood pressure rises. When the anger is fully dealt with, all of these physiological reactions return to normal. If someone buries her anger, the blood pressure remains higher longer and eventually becomes chronically elevated. This is hypertension. In addition, the liver (the seat of anger, so the Chinese have claimed for three thousand years) will be healthy if anger is expressed. If the liver is functioning well, the eyes will be clear and bright. According to the theory of macrobiotics, general health is reflected in the position of the iris within the eye socket. The more white showing beneath the iris, the worse the state of health.

The eyes are also invaluable in determining how scared the client is. Chronic fear will result (once again according to the Chinese) in a disturbance of kidney function, which in turn causes puffiness and often a blue discoloration around the eyes. We've all experienced the urinary frequency associated with fear before exams or a sporting event. Sometimes the eyes will be red and the eyelid margins will be both red and swollen. When I see this, I wonder if the client needs to cry but for some reason has been stopping herself. If she's been suppressing other emotions as well, then the odds are she'll be depressed, and I'll expect her to tell me later that she's suffering from either sinusitis or constipation, or more commonly both.

Embryologically speaking — embryology is the branch of science concerned with the development of the body — the skin and the brain come from the same basic tissue, called ectoderm. Because of this early common origin, the skin reflects our emotional state quickly and accurately. Within the practice of dermatology (diseases of the skin), a large number of conditions are generally recognized as having a psychological origin (i.e., they are psychogenic). The skin of the face shows both chronic emotions and acute ones, such as with blushing. The precise texture of the skin may be difficult to see at first and may have to await the formal examination, especially if the person wears makeup. But the general impression of the skin as a significant part of the personality will be obvious. If the skin is either perfect or, alternately, is suffering from acne, dermatitis, psoriasis, or excessive oil, you can be sure that the skin important to the person's image.

If clients haven't liked themselves much in the past, they'll often advertise the fact in their face. By such a mechanism, they declare the world to be an inhospitable place and let others know of their suffering. They may become focused on their skin in order to avoid an alternative, perhaps more difficult, self-inquiry. "If only I had good skin!" they might say, or "Why me?"

People with skin which is blemish-free may be suffering other more serious ailments, but "soldiering on bravely." They may have a need to appear perfect to the world, although suffering both mentally and physically in private. I've found intestinal problems to be common in this group. The skin at the side of the nose is often scaly and inflamed in chronic fear and sadness, and if it is, I'll take more time during the formal examination of the ears, as often the skin will be similarly affected in the external ear canal. The general skin texture is noted for colour and general vitality, but this is within the realm of orthodox diagnosis and much has been made of it elsewhere. My concern is to use the facial anatomy to diagnose the emotional state and from there the physiological disturbance which follows (or vice versa). This is called physiognomy.

BODY SHAPE AND SEXUALITY

I now note other elements of the client's physique and clothing. My attention will be drawn to those areas she's highlighted, either wittingly or unwittingly, and in both cases these will be features which are of significance to the person herself. In addition, my own personal bias will affect the areas of the body that I look at first. My diagnostic abilities are compatible with my personality, so that I pick up some things easily and miss others completely. Those things that are important, but which I habitually ignore, will result in my handling some cases poorly and those people will eventually stop coming to see me. This is inevitable.

I take great note of general body shape. Within the category of body shape or "habitus" I include the person's attitude to his or her own sexuality. Clients may stand erect, a man with his pelvis inclined slightly forward, inviting an appreciation of his genitals, and with his neck and shoulders broad, relaxed, and powerful. A woman may project her breasts forward in sexual display and walk with both grace and fluidity, her more mobile pelvis swaying gently as she enjoys her own body.

In cases where there's been a childhood direction to ignore feelings but where either or both parents were comfortable with their sexuality, I may find an exaggeration of the client's sexuality at the expense of expressing sadness, fear, and anger. She may be at ease with multiple casual relationships but uncomfortable with genuine closeness. In such cases a woman may wear too much makeup and have scarcely concealed breasts. She may rush into premature intimacy.

A man who over-displays his sexuality will have a certain swagger to his walk and a dress sense that is more flamboyant than attractive. On the other hand, a man who continually turns up to appointments in clothing that is drab and shapeless but when undressed reveals a trim, attractive male physique may be attempting to look unattractive.

Between the over and under-dressing is a set of clothes for men that are functional and comfortable, show their masculinity to advantage, and that give an indication that they are sexually potent. Women will be similarly attired, with what they consider their best features highlighted. Teenage girls who are embarrassed by their breasts often walk with a stoop to conceal them or hunch their shoulders if they don't want to lose height. Boys who are testing their fledgling sexuality will make sure that their clothing is provocative but safe enough for retreat if required. Younger children's clothing will reflect the attitudes of their parents, usually the mother.

Suppression or overuse of any bodily system will result in imbalance. If this goes on long enough, exhaustion and disease will result. People who either suppress their sexuality or abuse it will eventually complain of a disease of the sexual organs: the penis and testicles in men; or breasts, ovaries, tubes, womb, and the vaginal area in women. Sexual history will be part of the later, more detailed client history, as will a sexual examination, but at this point of first contact, much of this information is available to the astute observer. General appearance will reflect the later sexual history. Where the appearance and the story conflict, then I question the story.

Sexuality aside, a person's general body shape is equally revealing in other ways. If people stand or walk hunched over and are shabbily dressed, it's reasonable to assume that at the time they regard themselves as shabby, unless they've dressed with the intention to mislead you, which happens sometimes and will be evident elsewhere in the examination. Depression reveals itself in the clothing and the walk; the voice is powerless. Anger will often produce a tight, muscular body with little fluidity, often the shape of professional sportspeople, while sadness is evident in stooped shoulders and irregular breathing. Someone who is afraid will rarely look at you directly, often has darting eye movements as if looking for danger, and breathes in a shallow, rapid manner.

We all have the ability to see these things in others. We do it ourselves every day to avoid situations that may be a problem for us. The avoidance behavior is automatic. It's unnecessary to be conscious of the individual features we monitor. We just know that right now there's something, about another person which makes us uncomfortable and we want to stay away from her.

Diagnostically, however, to overlook the various physical reflections of the underlying psychological states is to ignore the most valuable source of unedited information. A person who stands up straight every day of her life appears quite different from one who normally walks bent over but has straightened out for this occasion. You can tell this by simply looking at her. Dialogue need not cloud the matter. An appreciation of the psychological state begins at the point of first contact and is essential if the practitioner intends anything beyond a cursory and superficial consultation. Offering treatment without this information would be like trying to repair a broken-down car by painting it.

The color, texture, style, and grooming of the hair will provide information on a client's feelings now as well as in the recent and distant past. Premature graying or balding may indicate chronic tension and underlying high blood pressure. Dry, lifeless hair, as described in television advertisements, may reflect a similar state of mind. A friend of mine calls such hair "frayed nerve ends." The grooming of the hair is as helpful as clothing in establishing a person's self-image. Hair has long been used in our society to indicate a person's social and political status. Pop culture, hippies, street gangs,

Eastern religious sects, punk rockers, the business fraternity, and politicians have all used hairstyles to advertise their allegiances. There's obviously a strong genetic element to hair distribution, color, and texture, but it's still a valuable display, particularly since it can be changed quite radically (unlike the face) in a short time.

Because our society associates certain appearances with wealth or poverty, people can dress to appear as if they do or don't have money. If a person who is quite wealthy or has worked hard to improve her financial position continues to dress as if she's still poor or perhaps a student, that's significant. She'll often want to be seen as a loser, and she still regards herself as such. To acknowledge that she's "made it" would arouse in her the fear of contradicting a parent who told her she'd fail in life. Becoming successful threatens the parental attribution, since the child interprets the parent message as being, "I'll only love you as long as you don't make it," or often, "I'll only love you if you don't do better than me." Such an individual will often be suffering from a complaint that won't kill her but will prevent her from achieving her full potential in her chosen occupation. Arthritis is one example. I often hear variations on, "If I didn't have arthritis, I figure I'd have been a better lawyer than Dad. It's so debilitating...."

When I meet a client face to face for the first time, I'm careful to note the tone and the exact content of his greeting. The actual words he uses in this and in any interchange come unedited from his subconscious and more often than not are a true reflection of what he means, as opposed to a hasty alteration. "Hello Mr.—I mean, Dr. Harrison" may indicate a hopeless player ("Help me because I'm incompetent") or a rebellious nature ("Don't put on your doctor's airs with me!"). The first person may be using his illness as a way of being cared for, while the second has not forgiven her parents and may be making herself sick to stay angry with them. If she stays sick enough and for long enough, then surely they'll recognize the error of their ways and will love her as she wants (even though they may have died years ago).

Without addressing these underlying psychodynamics, cure of the disease isn't possible. A willingness to explore them... is the cure.

THE VOICE

Hostility, fear, sadness, and joy are always evident in the voice. There's a certain resonance to a happy person's voice. There's no inflammation of the sinuses, which means that the voice box gives the voice a mellow, powerful quality. In addition, the vocal chords are healthy, suffering neither from abuse nor inflammation. The airstream that the lungs deliver to the vocal chords is steady and strong. The lips and the facial muscles (which help to shape the airstream) are flexible, and the facial expression and the quality of the voice are synchronized. There's a wide range of vocal abilities, which reflects the person's ability to express what she's feeling at the time. A happy person will much of the time be willing and able to sing.

A person who suppresses her anger usually speaks with her mouth partially closed, for fear of exposing her wrath. The small mouth aperture and the limited range of movement of the upper lip, causes the voice to sound "thin." The upper lip in these people is narrow from lack of exercise, as in the abandonment of laughter, and from being continually drawn into a contrived smile. The final shaping of the airstream is therefore affected. The airstream is less steady because there's a permanent battle between the client's angry little kid who wants to scream, and her controlling grown-up. The result is a variable delivery of air to vocal chords already stretched tight by muscular tension. A harsh abrasive voice caused by the vocal chords hitting each other may result. This is called "vocal attack."

Where sadness predominates, the voice will be weak and often breathless. The mouth and vocal chords "wave in the breeze," resulting in a voice with a lack of impact and conviction. The air delivery will reflect indecision about whether to breathe or not, especially in severe depression, and sometimes sighing will be a feature as will speaking while inhaling. A wavering of the voice and a quiver of the bottom lip may be observed in someone struggling not to cry. If crying has been suppressed, there may be chronic inflammation of the sinuses with a muffling of the vocal resonance. The voice may have a nasal quality caused by the chronically swollen lining of the nose and the resultant partially obstructed airway.

I'm listening for two levels of feelings: the immediate (or spontaneous) and the past (or "racket," as we discussed earlier). We all recognize the former easily, but the latter are often more subtle; although we register them accurately, we may not be consciously aware of them. Because "racket feelings" are active over a long period of time, they affect the voice, body musculature, and internal organs profoundly and are therefore diagnostically invaluable.

Fear is probably the most common racket feeling. As we'll recall from chapter 2, a racket feeling is a common feeling that emanates from unresolved childhood conflicts. The feeling may appear to come from the "here and now" but is really a revival of old emotions that are simply triggered by the immediate situation. A man who repeatedly assaults people for no apparent reason and whose father beat him as a child is probably still very angry from childhood. The anger is a leftover from that time. If people are depressed all the time, it's not because they have nothing to be positive about but because they're "racket sad." The sadness comes from their childhood. If they're angry all the time, it's because they're "racket angry," not because they've been singled out by fate to have bad luck. Some people are "racket happy." They go around with a smile on their faces while hurting inside.

"Racket fear" underlies most racket feelings. The large majority of people in Western society have a certain degree of this fear. It's the most basic of all the racket feelings, since it's really the fear of not surviving as a child. This fear results in various adaptations. If there were any doubts in the mind of either parent that they had the resources or the inclination to care for a child, or their mood reflected a general societal anxiety with the state of the world at the time (caused, for example, by the Cold War of the 1950s, the Vietnam War of the 1960s, or terrorism in the early twenty-first century), doubt may have entered the child's mind as to whether she could survive this danger. This doubt may have been negated by a greater preponderance of positive messages and simply be present in traces, or it may dominate a person's feeling, thinking, and behavior. Either way, it remains very obvious in a person's face and voice. Being scared is the most significant precursor to illness that I know.

The diagram on page 92 indicates a common arrangement of racket anger, sadness, and joy as an individual uses them to avoid confronting his basic racket feeling: the fear of not surviving. Between each racket feeling is a layer of fear: an emotion the individual uses to discourage his awareness of the structure of his defenses. All layers may be associated with their own physical signs and symptoms; these will account for changes in the nature of the client's complaints as therapy proceeds.

The opposite of a racket feeling is one that arises spontaneously and that we fully express so that none of it remains from that particular stimulus. If someone is clumsy and nearly runs you over in his car, you scream, "Hey, watch what you're doing!" You feel mad as hell for a minute or two, and then it's gone. If your lover leaves you for another, you cry every night for a month, and then you're over it. There's no residual sadness left; in this way, when your cat dies, you don't cry for weeks or get depressed. For most people this would be racket sadness caused by suppressing their sadness at their lover's defection, and not from the cat's death. Beyond the fear is joy. Happiness is not the opposite of fear, anger, or sadness. Happiness is an absence of racket (or leftover) feelings, and a preparedness to spontaneously feel joy, anger, sadness, and fear.

The voice of a person who's chronically afraid, which is a racket feeling, will be wavering, apparently struggling against great odds to even be heard, and the speech may begin and end abruptly. The breathing will be shallow and rapid, with little expansion of the chest wall. A feature of scared people is that they hunch their shoulders to hide their chest from view, as the heart is considered vulnerable. This further restricts the delivery of air to the vocal chords, whose movements already reflect the general indecision of the body musculature. These people don't trust life.

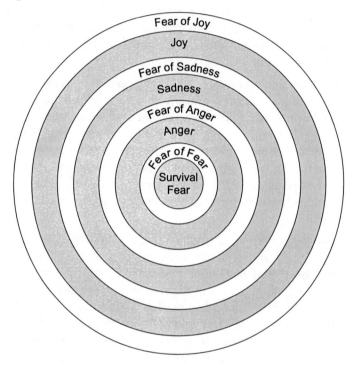

A common arrangement of the "racket feelings" (shaded area) as they have been used to protect an individual from confronting his or her fear of survival.

Both levels of feelings, the spontaneous and the racket, will be evident in the face, general body shape, and the voice. Racket feelings will be etched into the face by time.

Immediate or spontaneous emotion will overlie the general contour of the face, so that a generally happy person with a flexible and expressive face may show the grief caused by the recent loss of a loved one. Similarly, an individual who has generally cared for her appearance may appear slightly ruffled on the day I see her. The racket feelings are of great importance in diagnosing the basis of an individual's illness.

Because such feelings have been active for a long time, the external, visible changes will indicate alterations to the physiology and later the anatomy of the internal organs. As they may not yet have produced symptoms, a diagnosis of the psychological state can be predictive and therefore preventive.

Till now, there's been no need to take much notice of the content of the client's conversation. That will be important later, but right now the important thing is to observe her so that an independent impression of her problem may begin to take shape. I assume that if clients were so objective about themselves that they could see their way clearly, they would not have consulted me in the first place. Therefore it's of real value to allow an intuitive impression, based on subtle observation, to affect the practitioner. This is how fortune-tellers, tarot-card readers, palmists, and most astrologers work.

It's not what clients are saying but how they're saying it; not how they are trying to appear but how they look.

In addition, it's essential for the doctor to know something of herself. If she finds angry men attractive and she's feeling emotionally aroused, then she's probably dealing with an angry man. The practitioner needs to witness her own internal processes and seek confirmation of her observations at a later point. The fact that doctors and therapists have their own problems does not prevent them from being aware of what's happening with clients. In fact, they're usually interested in why others make themselves ill because they (the doctors) make themselves ill. Therapists who are motivated to resolve their own problems can be of help to clients wishing to help themselves.

After introducing myself to a client in the waiting room, some light conversation usually follows as I lead the way to the consultation room. I listen to what he's saying carefully during this time, because he's often off guard. He may notice paintings, or comment on the color of the walls, or look straight ahead in an effort to not notice anything. Everything he does is used to assemble a picture of who he is and why he's making himself ill. It's impossible for him not to react. Even not reacting is a reaction.

By the time the client and I sit down at the desk for the formal history, I can write a chapter of a book about him. Very often I can nominate the illness he'll complain of before he tells me. It's not some magic or some special power I possess; it's simple observation based on the premise that the disease the client suffers from is an integral part of his personality, and that personality is observable.

All of this has taken no more than one minute. I'm now ready for the next step, the history of the illness or, to my mind, the history of the client's physiological response to life thus far.

7

HISTORY AND EXAMINATION

WHAT IS THE PROBLEM?

It's now the client's turn. I listen to what the client is saying about his illness and, once again, observe how he's saying it. I give him the opportunity to tell me in his own words and at his own speed what he thinks is wrong with him, and where he feels that he's made mistakes in the management of his own health. I don't lead him in the early stages, since it's his opinion of his problem that's important here, not a medical label that I, through convenience, may need to tag him with. By resisting the temptation to categorize him as suffering from an orthodox disease that in reality bears little resemblance to his actual complaint, I'm rewarded by a fascinating insight into the relationship between his bodily dysfunction and the mind that spawned and nurtured it.

If nerve pain of the lower limbs in a woman with business problems is sciatica, then what's nerve pain in the lower limbs of a man who's just chosen to leave his family? Surely not sciatica! The two presenting symptoms are the same or similar, but the cause (pathogenesis) and therefore the treatment is entirely different. Standardized, inflexible treatments follow the expedient labeling of discomforts, needs, wants, frustrations, aspirations, fears, and destinies as being certain diseases. "Diseases" they are, but the same they are not.

I then ask the client a series of questions in order to elicit which systems of the body have elected to bear the burden of his unresolved childhood conflicts, and how dysfunctional he's made those systems. This is known as the "systems analysis," which I've outlined on pages 85–92.

By following a standardized format here, I'm able to provide examples of commonly suffered illnesses as they relate to the psychological profile (see chapter 11) of the sufferers. As you read this section, you'll come to understand your own role in conditions from which you've been suffering. You now have two equally valid general options: to continue with the illness or allow it to resolve itself.

After I've given the client the opportunity to include all the information that he thinks is necessary, I run through the following checklist in my mind, asking some of the questions and eliminating others. As you'll see in the interpretation of this data that immediately follows, I continually address myself to the client's motives for being ill or well, and my inquiry will reflect leads that I intuitively follow up and tangents that I think warrant further exploration. A physical examination follows.

■ ■ ■

PERSONAL DETAILS

Title: ....

Name: ....

Age: ....

Date of birth: ....

Address: ....

Telephone no: ....

Number of children: ....

■ ■ ■

PRESENTING COMPLAINTS

What is your major complaint?

What parts are affected?

How severe is it?

How long have you had it?

Describe a typical attack.

How frequent are the attacks?

Are they becoming more or less frequent?

Are they becoming more or less severe?

What other parts of the body are affected by this problem?

Do you have any pain?

If so, how severe is the pain?

Where is the pain?

When is the pain a problem for you?

Is the pain associated with any other malfunction?

Does the pain radiate to other areas?

What is the nature of the pain (sharp, dull, throbbing, intermittent, etc.)?

Do you feel nauseous?

Do you vomit often?

What investigations have you already had done?

Whom have you seen before about this complaint?

What was his or her diagnosis?

What laboratory tests have you had done?

Have you had surgery for this complaint?

Have you had any previous treatments for this condition?

Are you currently undergoing treatment?

If so, what, and by whom?

Have you had any previous drug treatments?

Current medications?

Drugs?

Herbal treatments?

Vitamins?

What connections do you make between this illness and your mental state, if any?

What do you think is your problem?

What do you want to do about it?

Do you have any general comments you'd like to make about the illness or yourself?

What's been happening in your life recently?

[Complaint no. 2, 3, 4, 5, etc. I ask the same questions about every complaint the client lists and encourage him or her to list everything. The more information I can gain about the body's reaction to the psychological state and vice versa, the more accurate the diagnosis.]

■ ■ ■

PAST HISTORY

What operations have you had?

What was the diagnosis on those occasions?

When were the operations performed?

By whom were they performed?

[In contemporary medical practice it's no longer a logical assumption that if an operation has been performed then it was for a good reason, a correct diagnosis was made, or it was necessarily in the patient's best interest.]

What serious illnesses have you had?

When and what were they?

What treatment did you undergo at the time?

Are you still undergoing treatment for these?

What is that treatment?

What childhood illnesses did you have?

Were you sickly as a child?

[This question checks the reality of the previous question against the body image of either being well or sickly.]

Have you ever had hepatitis, epilepsy, asthma, eczema, rheumatic fever, glandular fever?

> When, and how severely?

> How long did you take to recover?

■ ■ ■

FAMILY HISTORY

Do you have a family history of any illness?

Did any of your family members suffer from the same complaint as you?

Are your parents alive?

Are your children alive and well?

Is there any illness among the following family members that is significant to you?

> Mother / Father / Grandparents / Aunts / Uncles / Siblings / Children

> Is there any other person whom you consider has influenced the course of your disease?

Are your siblings well?

> If they're ill, what are their complaints?

Compare your body shape with that of your siblings.

Compare your body shape with that of your parents.

Compare your body shape with that of your children.

Compare your general state of health with that of your siblings, parents, children.

> List the names and ages of your siblings and your children.

> Who in your family as a child was "always ill?"

> Who in your family as a child was "always well?"

> Who in your family now is "always well?"

Can you recall what was said in your family as a child about you being ill and about you being well?

Did your family members often make any general comments when you were a child about illness, wellness, and people who were "always ill" or "always well?"

Do you often make comments about people being ill or well?

What are they, and about whom do you make them?

■ ■ ■

SYSTEMS ANALYSIS

[As noted above, I then conduct a systems analysis in which I ask clients a series of questions about various systems of the body in order to elicit which systems have elected to bear the burden of their unresolved childhood conflicts, and how dysfunctional they've made those systems.]

Gastro-intestinal System

Hop on the scales, and I'll weigh you.

Has your weight increased, decreased, or remained steady?

Over what period of time has it increased or decreased?

How do you rate your appetite?

How often do you eat, and at what times?

How much do you eat?

Tell me about your bowels.

How many times a day do you use them?

What is the consistency of your bowel motion?

Is it long and pointed, or firmer or softer than that?

Is it formed at all?

Is it loose?

Does it vary?

Is there any blood in your bowel movements?

If so, when?

How much? Bright or dark?

What is the color of your bowel movements?

Does the color ever change?

Does your feces float or sink in the toilet?

Is any undigested material present in your bowel movements?

Do you feel any pain when you use your bowels?

How does the variation in your bowels correspond to what's happening in your life at the time?

Do you know at what age you were toilet trained?

Are you willing to defecate in the presence of family, friends, or strangers?

Do you sit or squat on the toilet?

By what method do you clean yourself following defecation?

How is your bowel function related to your current complaints?

Do you have any abdominal pain?

[If yes, repeat the pain questions from the presenting complaint.]

Do you suffer from heartburn?

How is that related to meals?

How long after a meal do you feel the pain?

Put one finger on where the pain is.

How long does it last?

What do you take to relieve it?

Is it worse in certain positions (lying down or bending over)?

Do you often feel nauseous or feel like vomiting?

To what events in your life does this relate?

Do you suffer from hemorrhoids?

How long have you had them?

What makes them better?

What makes them worse?

Do you have them now?

■ ■ ■

Respiratory System

Do you smoke?

> What do you smoke? Cigarettes, a pipe, e-cigarettes, marijuana?
>
> How many do you smoke, and at what times?
>
> How long have you been smoking?
>
> Who in your family smoked when you were a child?
>
> Who in your family smokes now?
>
> Are you using nicotine patches or other anti-smoking drugs?

Does anyone in your family suffer from a serious chest condition?

> Has anyone in your family died from a chest condition?
>
> Do you know anyone who has died from, or has a serious chest condition?

Do you smoke at a level that you think could kill you?

What is your most common feeling when you reach for a cigarette?

> What might you be feeling if you didn't smoke?

How many times have you stopped smoking and restarted?

> Do you intend to quit smoking?
>
> When?

> *[I explore the reasons for smoking, and the benefits available from smoking to those who do smoke, in my book* Where There's Smoke...*]*

Do you have a cough?

> When?
>
> Do you bring up any mucus?

Do you suffer from hay fever?

Do you suffer from sinusitis?

How many colds a year do you get?

Has that changed recently?

Do you have any chest pain?

Do you exercise in a way that influences your breathing?

■ ■ ■

Cardiovascular System

Do your ankles ever swell?

Do you become short of breath without exercising?

Are you breathless when lying flat?

How much exercise do you do?

What is the nature of the exercises?

Do you have any chest pain?

Do you suffer from palpitations?

At what times?

Do you have varicose veins?

Have you ever had any heart problems?

Is your heart normal?

When you were a child, did anybody in your family suffer a heart attack or any other heart disease?

Did they survive?

Are your feet or hands often cold?

■ ■ ■

Musculoskeletal System

Do you have any aches or pains in any muscles, bones, or joints?

If so, describe the areas affected.

How long have you had the pain?

Is it worse in hot or cold weather?

Is the pain affected by the time of day or the amount you have exercised?

Have you had any x-rays taken related to this pain?

Do you have them with you?

Is the pain affected by your diet?

Do you have a family history of arthritis?

Do you have any arthritis now or in the past?

Have you ever broken a bone?

To what do you attribute any musculoskeletal pain?

■ ■ ■

The Genitourinary System

How frequently do you urinate during the day?

How frequently do you urinate at night?

How much urine do you pass at these times?

Does urination cause pain?

   Where is the pain?

   What is the nature of the pain (burning or scalding)?

What is the color of your urine?

   Does the color vary? In what circumstances?

Do you feel a slight tingling in the urethra when you urinate?

Is the urine cloudy?

Does the urine have a foul smell?

Do you have any pain in your loins? [*If so, the pain questions above follow.*]

Women

Have you ever suffered from cystitis?

   When, and how often?

Do you have a vaginal discharge?

   What is the nature of the discharge (color, consistency, odor)?

   How long have you had it?

   Do you have any symptoms with the discharge?

   Does intercourse affect those symptoms?

Have you had vaginal infections in the past?

>When did you have your last smear test?

>What was the result?

Do you suffer from herpes?

>If yes, to what degree, and for how long?

>Under what conditions?

>With which partners?

>What treatments have you tried?

>What do you feel when you have an attack of herpes?

Do you currently have menstrual periods?

>Are they regular?

>How frequently do you have them?

>How long do they last?

>Do you use internal tampons or external pads?

>>How many of these might you use during the first few days, and over the whole period?

Do you lose excessive quantities of blood (menorrhagia)?

Do you have menstrual pain?

>Describe the pain.

>Is the pain excessive (dysmenorrhea)?

>Is the pain a problem for you?

>Is the pain made worse by intercourse?

If your periods have finished, how old were you at the time they finished (menopause)?

How old were you when you had your first period (menarche)?

Have there been times when your periods were scanty (oligomenorrhea) or absent (amenorrhea)?

Do you have any children?

>What were the births like?

Have you ever miscarried?

[I take a more detailed obstetric history in the event of an obstetric problem: for example, failure to conceive.]

Are you currently having intercourse?

How often do you have intercourse?

How many sexual partners do you have?

Do you have orgasms with intercourse?

Do you masturbate?

How often?

Do you have orgasms from masturbation?

Are your sexual partners men, women, or both?

Which do you prefer?

Do you like men's genitals? Do you like women's genitals?

Describe what you like about them.

Describe what you don't like about them.

Describe your own genitals.

Are you married?

Do you practice any contraception?

What kind, and for how long have you used that method?

Is your current method of contraception satisfactory?

Are you aware of the time you ovulate?

Do you menstruate or ovulate during the full moon?

Do you menstruate at the same time as other women in your household?

Men

Do you have any discharge from your penis?

If so, describe the nature of the discharge.

How long have you had it?

Do you suffer from herpes? [*If yes, the same questions as for women.*]

Do you have any problems with your testicles?

Tell me about your urination

When you urinate, is there any dribbling once you've stopped?

Do you feel like urinating again soon after you've urinated?

Is your urinary stream as good as it used to be?

Do you have any trouble initiating urination?

Can you urinate in front of other men with no problem?

Are you currently having intercourse?

How frequently do you have intercourse?

Is your erection satisfactory?

Do you ejaculate satisfactorily?

Do you masturbate?

How frequently do you masturbate?

Do you have sex with men, women, or both?

Which do you prefer?

Is your anus a sexual area for you?

Do you like women's genitals? Do you like men's genitals?

Describe what you like about them.

Describe what you don't like about them.

Describe your own genitals.

How old were you when you started/stopped having intercourse?

Are you in a relationship at the moment?

With whom?

For how long?

Are you married?

■ ■ ■

Central Nervous System (CNS)

Headaches

Do you have headaches?

Describe them.

Where are they located?

How often do you get them?

When do you get them?

How severe are they?

What brings them on?

What eases them?

What medication do you take for your headaches?

What role does your emotional state play in the development of your headaches?

What events in your life regularly precede them?

Who in your family as a child had headaches?

Who in your family now has headaches?

When did either of your parents tend to get their headaches?

What can you remember hearing about headaches?

Have you ever had your headaches investigated? (x-rays, scans, blood tests, etc.)

Do your headaches incapacitate you for everything or for some things only?

Why do you think you get headaches?

How can you get rid of them, do you think?

Sleep

Do you sleep well or poorly?

If poorly, what's the problem?

Do you find yourself having difficulty getting to sleep at night?

Do you wake up earlier than you would like?

Do you wake up refreshed?

Do you usually sleep alone, or with someone?

When do you usually go to bed?

When do you usually get up?

General CNS Questions; Vision, Taste, and Hearing

Do you suffer from any disease of the central nervous system?

Do you have any unusual symptoms that you have been unable to explain?

Is your vision satisfactory?

Do you wear glasses?

> When did you first need glasses?

> How old were you at the time?

> What was happening in your immediate family at that time?

> Was that a problem for you?

Has your eyesight been improving/deteriorating lately?

Is your sense of taste normal? [*If no, I ask the same questions as for visual defects.*]

Is your hearing normal? [*If no, I ask the same questions as for visual defects.*]

Do you suffer from "pins and needles"?

> Where?

■ ■ ■

Medication

List everything you are currently taking that is not a foodstuff. This includes drugs prescribed by a medical practitioner, herbal medicines, homeopathic remedies, minerals and tissue salts, vitamins, flower remedies, naturopathic remedies, self-made medicines, folk remedies, over-the-counter medications, etc.

How often and in what doses have you been taking them?

How long have you been taking them?

How do they help you?

Social History

Do you live alone?

> With whom do you live?

> What is your relationship with the people you live with?

> Are they lovers, friends, acquaintances?

Are you in a relationship at the moment?

Are you happy in your current household?

What is the nature of your work?

>Are you employed in the workforce as a salary earner?

>Are you self-employed?

>Do you like your job?

Are you unemployed?

>How long have you been unemployed?

>Is that through choice or unavailability of work?

>Do you like being unemployed?

What skills do you have?

What qualifications do you have?

What's happening in your life at the moment?

What happened in your life a year ago?

Is there anything or anyone that you're missing?

Are you feeling generally happy, sad, angry, or afraid?

Do you have recurrent thoughts?

>Are you troubled by your own thoughts?

>What relationship do your thoughts and feelings have to your illness?

Are you financially secure?

Do you consider yourself a spiritual person?

>Do you belong to a religion?

>Do you meditate?

What are your hobbies?

Do you have enough friends?

Are you lonely?

What's happened in your family as a consequence of your illness?

What's happened to you as a consequence of your illness?

>*[This inquiry is expanded in chapter 21, "At Your Invitation Only".]*

■ ■ ■

Diet History

*[I now go through the client's diet, asking first what
he or she eats, then what he or she drinks; I ask for a
range of things, since each day may be different.]*

What do you have for breakfast?

   What time is that?

   How long do you take to eat it?

What do you have for lunch?

   What time is that?

   How long do you take to eat it?

What do you have for an afternoon snack?

   What time is that?

   How long do you take to eat it?

What do you have as snacks?

   When do you have them?

What do you drink?

   How much?

Do you eat the following?

   How much?

   Who prepares it?

   Is there anything else that you regularly eat that I haven't
   covered here?

*[The diet of one of my clients follows. I make no
comment on its suitability but use it to demonstrate
the level of detail necessary.]*

8:00 a.m. – Breakfast

Muesli, homemade, with nuts, almonds, cashews, sunflower
seeds, raisins, oats, millet, rye, wheat.

Milk with the muesli.

Honey from the supermarket on the muesli.

Toast, whole wheat, with butter, unsalted. The bread is from the local health-food store. Peanut butter or marmalade.

10:30 a.m. – Midmorning snack

Apple or banana.

1:00 p.m. – Lunch

Whole-wheat bread roll with cheese, lettuce, and beetroot, or whole-wheat sandwich with coleslaw, carrot, cabbage, and hummus

One whole-wheat cracker

An apple, or in season grapes, apricots, or peaches.

4:00 p.m. – Tea/afternoon snack

A dry cracker/biscuit with either cheese or tomato or both.

7:00 p.m. – Evening meal

Meat—steak three times a week, chicken three times a week, lamb occasionally, fish once a week.

Brown rice—once every two weeks.

Pulses (soy beans, lentils, etc.) occasionally.

Vegetables, cooked (boiled usually, sometimes in safflower oil, Chinese-style)—potato, pumpkin, beans, peas, cabbage, carrot, ginger, garlic.

Vegetables, raw—lettuce, tomato, carrot, cabbage, parsley, cucumber, radish, peppers, celery, green beans, mushrooms, endives, bean sprouts, garlic.

Desserts—the occasional apple crumble with ice cream; fresh fruit in season.

Drinks – in cups per day

Black tea (milk, no sugar): two

Coffee (milk, one sugar): four

Herbal tea (rosemary, peppermint, chamomile): one

Coffee substitutes: occasionally

Fruit juice: three

Cordials/liqueurs: none

Mineral water: occasionally

Tap water: two

Alcohol: one glass of white wine most nights, on weekends six glasses of beer and maybe some spirits. Two bourbons and three gins on both Friday and Saturday

Dairy Products and other items

[Rated between + and + + + according to the tone of voice. For example, "Do you drink much milk?" may be answered by, "Oh, a little." The inflection in the "oh" will give me an idea of the amount consumed. The reply to "How much butter do you eat?" could be "Oh, not much." This "oh" will sound quite different.]

Milk + +

Cheese + +

Yogurt + +

Cream +

Half and half +

Butter + +

Chocolate

Ice cream + + +

Eggs per week: three

Sweets: two muesli bars from the health-food store each week

Fruit (fresh per day): three to four pieces

Dried fruit + +

Nuts + +

Salt +

Pepper +

Curries, other spices +++

Herbs ++

Honey + +

Sugar +

■ ■ ■

PHYSICAL EXAMINATION

Those are all the questions I have at that point, although I tell clients to feel free to ask me any other questions or to mention anything that's not been covered. I then move on to the physical examination, in which I ask clients to remove their clothing completely and lie on their backs on the couch; I provide a sheet with which to cover themselves. I leave the room for a moment while the clients undress. If they've consulted me before and aren't bothered by undressing in front of me, I may stay and continue the conversation. Clients' reactions to taking off their clothes is obviously of importance in establishing their body image—that is, how they feel about their own bodies and about other people seeing their bodies. I do the orthodox examination first, followed by the acupuncture, naturopathic, and psychosomatically orientated examinations. I record the following:

- Blood pressure
- Pulse
- Heart rate
- Auscultation of (listening to) the heart
- General blood circulation
- Varicose veins
- Breathing pattern
- Auscultation of the chest
- Percussion (tapping), palpation (feeling) of the chest
- General shape of the chest wall
- General oxygenation of the tissues
- Mouth

- Tongue color, and the distribution of a pattern, if there is one
- Odor
- Tonsils
- Fauces (the cavity at the back of the mouth)
- Palate
- Gums
- Teeth

I look very carefully at each tooth and note if there are any fillings. I note the type of material the fillings are made from and if they extend below the gum margin. I ask about any root-canal procedures. I look for any uneven wearing of the teeth and note if the person is grinding away the tooth enamel or the filling, indicating anxiety or anger. I return to the desk and write down the findings before proceeding.

I then examine the lymphatic system by feeling for glands in the neck, beneath the arms, and in the groin.

In women, I next palpate the breasts, followed by the abdomen (for both sexes).

I feel for the major organs: liver, kidneys, spleen, bladder, womb.

I feel for the intestines, stomach, and colon and take notice of the epigastric area (looking for heartburn).

I examine the genitals in both men and women after I've indicated that I wish to do so and have provided an opportunity for clients to inform me that they would prefer I did not examine their genitals on this occasion. I will ask them why they may not wish to be examined—not by way of attempting to convince them otherwise but as further information about what may be contributing to their attitudes and their illness.

For men. I check if the penis is circumcised or not, the state of the foreskin, and the cleanliness of area; I feel the whole length of the urethra for pain and inflammation. I look for old or new herpes scars and note the shape and size of the penis. If I notice him getting an erection, which may occur with younger men, I may say something like, "You'll probably get an erection during this examination; that's normal, so don't be worried about it." If he does sustain an erection, I note the size of his erect penis. I palpate and examine the testicles.

For women: I'm more hesitant about the examination of women because of the risk of prosecution. This is unfortunate, but I make no apology for looking after myself first. In some jurisdictions, chaperones are required in the event of a practitioner needing to examine a patient, whatever the gender of both the practitioner and the patient.

In practice, I can usually tell if there will be a problem and omit part of the examination in those circumstances. If I need a specific examination of the internal organs, I will perform a vaginal examination with the woman's permission.

For either sex, if there's been an indication — either a symptom or a sexual practice that the client has mentioned — I will examine that area. I will perform other orthodox examinations, such as rectal examinations, when indicated.

I examine the eyes, ears, and nose when indicated, and on all occasions in children. Similarly, I examine the central nervous system when there is a problem in that area.

I will next ask the client to stand up and face the wall away from me. I look at the general dimensions of the body, the amount of fat, the spine, and the broadness and straightness of the shoulders. I look at the size and shape of the legs and buttocks and the general body posture. I then ask the client to turn to her side, since the protuberance of the abdomen, chest, breasts, buttocks, and spine are best viewed from that position.

I then stand about six meters from clients and examine them from the front. The general way clients feel about themselves is best seen from this angle. I note any stooped shoulders, one shoulder higher than the other, thrusting forward of the breasts or genitals, holding in of the waist, etc. Next the client returns to the face-down position on the couch and I examine the back, looking for spinal adjustments that may be possible or desirable in the future and feeling the musculature available to me in that position. I note the degree of muscular tension (or "armoring"). This can be seen in the muscles of the neck, shoulders, chest and buttocks, and can be very instructive. I've examined a man who was so relaxed that his muscles felt like the muscles of a cat, totally relaxed with no tension whatever. This is extremely uncommon. Most of us have muscle "tension" in many muscle groups.

I may return the client to the face-up position to check something I've noted elsewhere, such as tension in the chest muscles. I am looking for how much of this tension is chronic and how much acute, and what appears available for change. I may look at the muscle tension on the inside of the thigh, which, particularly in women, indicates sexual inhibitions. In men, external rotation of the feet indicates buttock contraction and sometimes fear of homosexuality. If some functional disturbance of the body musculature appears, the client is asked to adopt various positions so that this may be more fully assessed. For example, the client may bend backward to assess the flexibility of the spine. Very often he's asked to walk up and down the office.

If I suspect that the client is really very sad and struggling to conceal it, then I may press quite hard on the area that looks to be carrying the load of that particular suppressed emotion. This is very often the chest muscles in both men and women; firm massage of that area will usually result in the person bursting into tears. If I do that, I need time to handle the situation, so naturally I pick my time. Generally, I will not do body work during this first session.

Most doctors don't do any of the above, though individual specialists do examine in detail that part of the body that relates to their specialty. The fact that most doctors don't do such an examination doesn't diminish the value of this kind of examination, for the body tells you a story and is valuable in determining the forces that are acting on this person. Physical bodies cannot deceive, whereas people may contrive histories to mislead the practitioner.

By now, I have a pretty complete impression of the overall body shape of the person and can move on to more specific areas. Just as the face exactly represents the underlying personality, so does the body.

Next I take note of various proportions: for example, the head compared with the shoulders, the ears compared with the eyes, the relative size of the left and right breast, the upper-limb musculature compared with the lower limbs. The right and left side of the body are of considerable interest to me: Which side is hypertrophied, which side is thrust forward, which side is the more active or the more irritable? At the same time that I'm paying attention to this, I'm hearing in clients' speech and noting from their sphere of interests whether they are right-or left-dominant people. Functionally, it may be evident by one side of the face being more flexible than the other. Much has been made in acupuncture for thousands of years about left-or right-sidedness (and for a hundred or so years in homeopathy), but only relatively recently has Western psychology given the notion much credence. A person's sidedness is of importance in choosing the medium of communication and subsequent treatment of any individual. We're dealing here, in the broadest terms, with the symmetry of an individual's personality.

The degree to which the mind has instructed the body in its development over the years is the next area of interest. I pay particular attention to the nutrition of the various parts, since I believe that if the skin is shining, the muscles are powerful and flexible, the tendons are supple, and all parts enjoy a good blood supply, then the mind has an investment in those areas being strong. If the blood supply is poor, the skin dry and lifeless, the contour of the muscles indecisive, and their tone limp, I assume that the mind has not put much energy into developing that area and that the individual feels safer with that part being undeveloped. Such an imbalance of one area of the body guarantees an imbalance elsewhere. It's not a difficult task, using the techniques of yoga, autogenic training, or meditation, to increase the blood supply to particular areas of the body. I've found the feet to be very reliable in providing a general impression of whether or not the person wants to be upright and mobile. Beautiful, well-nourished feet inform me that this person is grounded and looking to move on with his or her life.

I continually monitor the client's reaction to this examination; any reluctance to undergo certain parts of the examination, as with reluctance toward any of the inquiry, is clearly significant. I may choose to investigate this reluctance by pressing on or by backing off and coming back to it later. In general terms, I strike a balance between taking the client's fears into account (and these are usually obvious) and confronting them. That requires an intuitive feel for the client's awareness. If the practitioner oversteps the mark, then she can expect to lose that client. Unless a sensitive practitioner does the inquiry, how do you know what's really going on? For example, a middle aged woman may have repressed her sexual desires and expression her whole life, which has resulted in multiple medical consequences. All she may need to begin healing is for someone to ask her about it.

■ ■ ■

That's the end of the physical examination for the first session; I then ask the client to get dressed. If some emotional catharsis has occurred and the client is indicating that he would like a hug, then I may hug him. This is unusual so early in our relationship, but people come to therapy in various stages of preparedness.

I've gathered information on two levels. First, I've written down the results of the orthodox examination in the case notes as well as some of the other information I've gathered. The majority of this information is stored in my conscious and subconscious, where I'll recall and reprocess it the next time I see the client, at which point the story will continue. I'll not even be aware of much of the subtle level information I've registered during the first session. It comes to mind later when supported by other information.

Occasionally I'll have time to suggest dietary recommendations on this first visit, but often this must wait until we meet again. By this time the client will generally feel safer with me. We agree to reconvene the meeting. This next meeting will either be for an hour or for half an hour. During that time, I will collate and summarize my findings. I'll then make a few recommendations at the level we've reached so far. During the next stage, I'll offer further inquiry into the underlying causes of the person's disease. This involves both establishing the advantages of the immediate illness and the psychological inquiry, or the so-called script questionnaire.

The first interview with the client has taken at least one hour. From the amount of data that I've been describing, it's clear that the pace of the interview is considerable. I would really like to take two hours for this initial contact, but the expense becomes prohibitive to a client relying on an often hostile insurance fund for reimbursement. There's no need to go into all the areas that I've mentioned with every client on the first visit. Indeed, with some of these areas, they never get investigated. Alternatively, the examinations that I've mentioned above represent a broad overview. For specific clients and specific conditions, more specific inquiry and examination is warranted. I may become sidetracked very early on in the interview and spend the whole hour dealing with the client's immediate domestic situation. Generally, I adopt the attitude that if the client — who is as aware of the restrictions of time as I am — chooses to remain on the one topic, she may do so. If I think she's using one topic of conversation to avoid more important and more sensitive areas, I'll confront her with that observation. Usually the client will focus her energy on her problem, so I usually go with her lead.

8

FAMILY NEEDS BECOME PHYSICAL DISEASES

GENERAL CONCLUSIONS FROM THE EXAMINATION DATA

The comments that follow are my own. I've arrived at them by observing myself and a group of people for whom they appeared to fit. In that sense they're both subjective (from observing myself) and empirical (from observing others). Because the observer is biased, they cannot be "true." In the future they cannot be relevant in exactly their current form, because times and people change. So, too, will my interpretation of the data.

Personal Details

Title

I don't ask women for a title directly; if they offer one, then I write it down. I'm not interested at this point in their marital status; in fact, often it may not be relevant at any point. If they are married and use the title Ms., then that may reflect either independence or adherence to convention. Men always call themselves Mr., which isn't much help in telling me what they think of themselves. I take note of the title that medical practitioners use.

Name

The name is always of great significance, although since I have no way of getting inside the head of the parent who chose it, I may not be able to use it fully. Eric Berne details the significance of names in his 1972 book *What Do You Say after You Say Hello?*. Here are a few simple examples. If a boy is called Robin or Pat, or if a girl is called Jo or Ronnie, then I look for gender identification: That is, in what proportions has the person adopted masculine or feminine traits?

Often clients with gender-ambiguous names will display characteristics of the opposite sex more obviously than people with unambiguous names like John or Jennifer. If you doubt this, think of the people you know and match their personalities with their names—or, more accurately, the names they go by. These characteristics may represent the individual's attempt to fulfill parental directives of "Don't be a boy" or "Don't be a girl," or the person has adopted them later for the purposes of social inclusion or rebellion. The ambivalence of the parent or parents toward having a boy or girl is embodied in the sexually ambivalent name. As such, it's usually of little consequence (heaven help us if we were all Johns or Jennifers), but it alerts me to the client's attitude to his own gender.

Women called Roberta who are the third child in an all-girl family and whose father longed for a boy may find themselves raised as a son and may be unwilling to be vulnerable with men. They may have scanty menstrual periods, imbalances of some kind in the genitourinary system, and general fatigue. In such cases, I question whether they've accepted being a female, and if their hormonal levels have been affected by that decision. I make the point that names are of some significance.

Age

The age of the client is of paramount importance in any sensible diagnosis and treatment. It's absolute nonsense to treat a fifty-year-old the same way you'd treat a fifteen-year-old. The aging process is relentless and cannot be stopped. To my mind, the treatment of a case of tonsillitis or appendicitis needs to take into account the age of clients and the life events that got them there. Teenagers who have not finished rebelling against their parents are different from twenty-year-olds who have as well as from five-year-olds who haven't started yet and are totally dependent on their parents.

From a knowledge of age, the ageing process may be assessed. Someone who enjoys being alive and celebrates his body will be less affected by age and be less ill than a person who isn't sure he was ever meant to be alive and has yet to decide he'll live. The decision to retain death as an option, or an ambivalence toward life, is often a major consideration of therapy. Why bother to decide to be well if you haven't yet decided to live?

Address

The address will sometimes inform me of the financial state of the client, or of her appreciation of trees, the seaside, the mountains, or the countryside. If she informs me later that she doesn't like living where she is or that she's about to move, then I ask why. Children can usually tell you their address by the time they are four or five.

Number of Children

People who have raised their own children or have been in close contact with others who have children have a different perspective on certain things. The difficulties involved in raising our own children often help us to appreciate the even more harrowing circumstances under which we were raised. We get a new perspective on all the "wrongs" we feel from childhood, which often proves invaluable when the time comes to forgive our own parents for the racket feelings we've held on to. As previously mentioned, the racket feelings are those feelings that do not come from immediate circumstances but from incidents in the past. They eat away at the mind and the body, are clearly visible in the face and physique of the person, and must be dropped if the person intends to be cured of the disease.

I repeat that the term "racket" is somewhat pejorative, since it implies some sort of wrongdoing, as in racketeering. People always do the best they can, including repressing their feelings. I'm of the view that it's not possible to do less than your best. That goes for both parents and children.

Children may comply or rebel. Often when they appear to be rebelling they're actually complying; and when they appear to be compliant, they may secretly be rebellious. Parents understand these things, since they see them every day. People who do not have children may take more convincing that children are responsive to the most subtle changes in the family and that illness is one of the ways they learn to manipulate their environments. Young children have no direct control over their lives, because they cannot keep themselves alive independently and in this situation are much more aware of other ways to get what they want. Being sick is a favorite, condoned as it often is by the parents themselves.

On the other hand, some parents will not admit the game their children are playing around illness, as it would be very frightening for them to admit either the same game themselves or their conspiring role which keeps it going, that is, encouraging the children to be ill so that the parent can fulfill a caring role. They may still be playing the game of: "I'm not in charge of my own life", and this may interfere with their acknowledgment of how they make themselves ill. Either reaction, the acceptance through observation of their own children, or the rejection through personal fear of the role of early childhood conditioning, is significant. Hence I like to know if clients have children of their own.

Presenting Complaints

By the time clients have talked about their condition in some detail, either volunteering information or answering questions, their general attitude to illness will be recognizable. Once again, both what they say and how they say it, are relevant. They aren't led when describing the presenting complaints. If they leave out relevant information, then clearly they don't consider it to be relevant (or don't want it to be) and this is often a clue where to look next. For example,

"Doctor, my eyesight has been failing me recently."

"How long has it been a problem, Mrs. White?"

"I'm not sure, doctor—a few months, maybe."

"What happened a few months ago? Anything significant?"

After a few moments, in which the client attempts to conceal the fact that she's crying, she tells me her husband died six months ago and she's finding the grieving difficult.

Now this demonstrates a few things. Give clients time and permission and in their own way they'll assess whether the doctor is receptive to the real story, and if so, will tell her. Secondly, the presenting complaint is very often a minor complaint, mentioned first for safety. If the doctor is uncomfortable with the emotional aspect of an illness, clients will often take care of the doctor by not mentioning it. In reality this is taking care of themselves by reaffirming their view of the medical profession as insensitive and unsympathetic: "Nobody can help me." My advice to clients is that if they have something they want to tell a helping professional then tell her. Any discomfort on the part of the professional is for her to deal with.

Those people who believe that their problem is the result of bungling on the part of the medical profession or others will usually have considerable energy available with which to discuss (i.e., condemn) previous doctors, diagnoses, and treatments. They're less eager to discuss the role that they've played in their illness. Some of course have a valid case against incompetent doctors, particularly when they were children and unable to pick a doctor for themselves.

I assess adults' needs to choose medical practitioners who are dangerous. We all have considerable intuition, and if we repeatedly consult a person on any matter and that person proves unworthy, then we aren't looking after ourselves. What do we say about ourselves when yet another medical practitioner proves to be useless, and how is being able to reaffirm that view an advantage? By such inquiry, awareness of the client's role in choosing an incompetent practitioner is established, and in most cases, anger toward the profession overlies anger toward one or both parents. This needs to be dealt with.

Forgiveness of both self and parents, or "dropping the past," cures more illness than antibiotics ever will.

We've spoken before about the tone of voice and how it may be deployed in establishing the psychological profile.

Nowhere is it more beneficial than here, when the client is describing an illness which is obviously of much distress to him. If he's in the habit of using his illness to manipulate others, the voice will often be powerless and pleading, wavering usually with the strains of life. Or it may be defiant, as in, "Yeah, well I'll bet you can't cure me!" And of course that's entirely accurate. Nobody can cure anybody else, especially if that person has declared himself incurable. It's the attitude to his illness that's initially important, not which particular physiological disturbance (disease) he's chosen with which to inconvenience himself.

A person's attitude is evident through observation of his body language, the tone of voice, and the way he expresses himself. When his attitude to his illness is established, a program can be devised to establish the needs being met by the illness and safer ways identified to satisfy those needs. The particular illness decided upon by the client will suit his purposes exactly and at a later time will provide much insight into his specific needs.

Medications

Current medications will provide much information about the degree of self-responsibility the client considers reasonable. If she's taking a large quantity of orthodox prescription drugs, that's tantamount to putting her faith in the orthodox medical profession. [In America, 70% of the population take a prescription drug, and over 50 million take prescription drugs for non-medical reasons. America consumes over 80% of the world's prescription narcotics, according to the Mayo clinic in 2014]. By taking a large number of drugs, our medicated client has absolved herself from most or all of her responsibility to be her own guardian. In this she's heavily encouraged by her advisers, who react with fear if she does something that's outside their immediate control. Some people who have no demonstrable pathology have been given over thirty medications a day, comprising some ten different drugs, by doctors unwilling to inquire about the client's psychological state. I frequently see such cases. On a more common level, the number of people who survive on uppers and downers of all descriptions is frightening. These people may find the need to criticize those people who take recreational, non-prescription drugs.

Seventy percent of Americans take mind altering prescription medications, and about 20 percent take prescription narcotics when they are not suffering from cancer induced pain, according to the Centers for Disease Control and Prevention in 2014. Claims of a drug's effectiveness, particularly concerning proprietary medications, is determined by whoever benefits from the information. The medical profession actively promoted narcotic use in the United States and in 2014, more Americans died of narcotic overdose than in car accidents, according to the US Surgeon General. There's no independence in any medical statistics concerning any medical matter. When a market becomes saturated with a particular drug, new medical criteria are introduced which increases the population to whom that drug can be marketed. For example, if the medical profession declare a lower blood pressure to now be the new normal, hundreds of millions of people can now be regarded as needing to be medicated. Medicine is the biggest industry on Earth.

Or the client may religiously avoid prescription drugs but take vitamin pills in large doses. Encouraged by those who dislike the orthodox profession and by the retailers of such pills, she believes that by taking doses of vitamins she's taking care of herself. She's not, at least not in my experience. While I accept that for brief periods of time some people benefit from vitamins, the general trend to take high doses of all kinds is both useless and expensive. I regard much vitamin selfadministration as no more than an individual clutching at straws intended to absolve him from becoming his own highest authority and, by keeping himself under the protective umbrella of the vitamin-pill manufacturer, guarantee the continuation of his dependence and his disease. Often these people are incredibly righteous. They don't take "nasty drugs" prescribed by the medical profession, they take homoeopathic pills prescribed by their naturopath. Commonly they declare:

"They can't do you harm, they can only do you good."

An elementary grasp of paradox will tell you that if something is capable of healing, it must also be capable of harming. It comes down to the dose, referred to as "posology." Without such a grasp of yin and yang, it becomes difficult to cure disease.

Disease itself is one of the great paradoxes. It both helps and harms.

Ignorance in these areas is widespread, and in this climate it becomes easy for the unscrupulous to prey on the fears of the public. "If you don't take a gram of vitamin C a day you're missing out on an essential ingredient of the diet!" is a common fallacy. The underlying message here is that by taking a gram of vitamin C a day, you'll be happy. A little of what you deem you need won't hurt you, but to place a great deal of importance on taking large doses of vitamins is bound to disappoint.

Some people will be taking remedies handed down through the family, which they're often reluctant to mention for fear of ridicule. I encourage them to tell me about these remedies, not only because this adds to my knowledge of the illness, but because I find the old remedies fascinating and use some of them myself. They're intervention to be sure but usually much more gentle.

It's interesting to note the ways in which the old 'flu remedies vary from one country to the next, often only slightly if the countries are adjacent like Poland and the Czech Republic. The remedies also vary between families. This is significant because illness begins within the family in the early days of the client's life, and old remedies usually reflect the parental attitude to illness. The early childhood folk remedies often provide insights into family dynamics and attitudes to health and disease. Warm honey and lemon, for example, may be conveying "I love you dear, this will make you feel better," while a mixture of ground ginger, pepper, lemon peel and garlic may mean: "If you get ill then you have to take this vile mixture." The recipient of honey and lemon may be more inclined to repeat the experience than the latter.

Diseases that are really a consequence of the collective family mentality are often thought to be genetically inherited. Eventually they may become inherited but in the first place they're probably behavioral. That's why I gather as much information about the family as possible, and old remedies that the client still uses are both informative about them, and interesting to me.

Herbal remedies are taken by people with such varying approaches to health that to conclude anything from the simple information that a client was taking them would be foolish. Further enquiry is required to establish whether they're being used as a panacea, which they certainly are not, or with the sophistication and the real value which results from them being used symptomatically with prudence. To take something every day of your life because someone has told you that you need it, without question, is an abrogation of personal responsibility. In today's litigious world, a doctor or health practitioner must look after himself before he looks after you. If a doctor's senior colleagues tell him he must prescribe a medication, even though he knows it to be useless or dangerous, he's bound to nonetheless prescribe it for fear of professional censure if he does not. To occasionally take an herb in order to abate a troublesome symptom while looking for the root of the problem can be valuable.

What Do You Think the Problem Is?

If the client doesn't volunteer this information then I request it. I'm interested in the weight she gives to her view of the illness, or if she has an opinion which she's concealed from all the practitioners she's previously attended, fearing their ridicule. It's not easy to maintain that your tinnitus is worse when your husband comes home drunk and violent, if the medical officer and the union representative are all pushing the line that it's an industrial injury and eligible for compensation. The evidence suggests some 60 percent of industrial injuries and illnesses have a psychosocial basis.

I believe clients know the origins of their illnesses. Deep inside will remain a vestige of awareness of what role the illness played when it was chosen, what it did for them then and what it's doing for them now. In giving clients the opportunity to express their views, I can assess how much they've been prepared to examine their lives in trying to heal themselves, and therefore how afraid they are. Such an assessment will be relevant in deciding at what level and at what time to pitch a remedy. Psychological training is unnecessary for a very sophisticated appraisal of the underlying psychodynamics, as the two following examples in which clients provide their own analyses demonstrate.

A man consulting me about his cancer started by telling me a family story surrounding his birth. This was unsolicited. The story was that his mother had tried to abort him by driving over rough roads. He figured he was an unwanted child, or at least ambivalence had surrounded his birth, and that was the reason for him deciding to give himself cancer and die. He reported that he'd never felt the unconditional right to be alive. Eventually that belief transformed itself into a physical disease capable of fulfilling the belief. People materialize both what they believe, and what they fear.

Another man who had cancer of the scrotum was very sexually repressed by his mother, and even though he felt too guilty to be openly angry with her, knew that the suppressed anger had converted itself into the cancer. He expressed this without prompting by whispering in exasperation, "Now I've caught this she ought to be happy!" Needless to say I heard that, mumbled as it was.

Other people refuse to admit any knowledge of what ails them.

"What do you think the problem is, Mr. Petersen?"

"You're the expert Doc. That's what I've come here to find out!"

Most people who come to see me have made a few preliminary excursions into their own subconscious before the appointment and are ready to let me help them take a few more steps, but if they haven't, then I respect the attendant fear and don't confront them initially. However, if they maintain a position of non-awareness and non-responsibility for too long, then I terminate the arrangement, or they do. Relief is the accompanying feeling for both of us. If they seek to dissuade others from attending me, that's also helpful.

What's been Happening in Your Life Recently?

What a question this turns out to be sometimes. Once again, clients are given ample time to mention this themselves but if they show no inclination to do so, I ask them. 0. C. and S. Simonton and J. Creighton, in their excellent book, *Getting Well Again*, published by Bantam Books, New York, in 1980, indicated that in the eighteen months preceding the onset of cancer, a significant life event often occurs. This event is traumatic in some way and initiated or promoted the cancer. The death of a loved one is a good example. My belief is that the basis of disease is earlier, and that precipitating events, such as those alluded to by the Simontons, are the immediate circumstances used in the service of the old childhood decision. In other words, the precipitating event is just one of a long string of events that have confirmed the decision taken in childhood about what sort of place the world is. Hence a man who decided as a child that death was always an option if he became too miserable or lonely, may, in the event of his wife leaving him, contract cancer and die. On an unconscious level, the man whose wife leaves him has chosen a wife whom he knows will do just that, and knows also that the event will precipitate a crisis for him. He knows that one way out of that crisis is death. When a life event confirms a view that we hold about ourselves, others or the world, we've often set that event up so that it becomes inevitable. Not everybody kills themselves with cancer when their wife leaves. For some that's not an option.

The personal circumstances mentioned by the client will be those he sees as the most significant. It's impossible for the practitioner to be a mind-reader. He can see the basic emotions, the body language, the underlying psychological state, but the histories responsible for those conditions will be extremely varied. Now in a way the immediate situation of the client's personal life is not significant, that is to say, isn't causative. We will see later how it's helpful. However, the details are usually of great concern to clients, as they look for rights and wrongs, and the best way to recover from a painful situation. Often they'll talk of relationships, but they could just as helpfully be talking about the collapse of the stock market and their ensuing fear and pain. The actual trauma is of importance only in that it provides a medium whereby the client's attitudes to life, himself, his relationships and his illness may be examined. The immediate situation will be remedied by addressing, exploring and identifying the underlying imbalance in his life, otherwise it, like illness, will recur.

In the case of personal relationships the situation may be beyond salvation and the parties must come to terms with losing someone they've cherished; then they need to grieve. Next time round they may choose someone different and consequently have no need for the migraine headaches that they chose to suffer from when their last lover came home late from work. In fact, if they feel safe enough after therapy they may not suffer much at all. Such is the range of available options. Illness and relationships are like motor cars: you choose the one you want. When one has served its purpose, you trade it in for another more suited to your current needs. Some people pick a suitable one first time.

In the most general terms, an individual who has a happy personal life, is happy with his finances and has achieved a level of spiritual grace is unlikely to be very ill, especially if she's about to take a vacation yachting about the Caribbean. On the other hand, someone who has come into a patch of "bad luck" — his business has gone bankrupt, his relationship is stormy and he's working too hard or not at all—is more likely to be seen looking and feeling ill. When a client tells me that everything in his life is wonderful and couldn't be better, and that the only thing bugging him is his recurrent bronchitis, I confess to not believing him. If he's convincing about being very happy, then I look at why he needs the pleasures of life to be interrupted by pain. There may be a family background of achievement but an atmosphere of anxiety. The child becomes less afraid when the situation is anxious (Mum and Dad fighting usually), because that's what he's used to and he knows the rules. When things go right for him, he becomes scared. He may have no information on which to fall back in the good times and that's anxiety-provoking. In order to make himself feel safer he makes himself ill, not seriously, and not something that will interrupt his work too much, but some irritating thing like an intermittent chest infection. Hence the bronchitis. Awareness of the game will often be enough to change the behavior, although this may not happen immediately and may be punctuated by remissions or return to the old pattern. On the other hand, someone who tells me that everything in his life is perfect I may distrust, seeing the agony on his face, and ask about his need to be seen to be functioning perfectly when he's not.

Medical practitioners have incidents in their lives as well as clients, and these may be accompanied by a change in the doctor's perspective. The perception of the illness by the doctor will be different as her life unfolds. Needless to say, her treatments will also be constantly changing.

Number and Nature of the Presenting Complaints

Some people have ten complaints that they list in chronological order because they find them equally irritating. Others have one major complaint, which they're not inclined to dilute with trivia. Others mention the worst complaint last, or they hope that if they pay it little attention, it'll go away. Those who hope that I'll be put off and declare them to be incurable if they mention dozens of ailments will often fail to draw breath during their history for fear of an embarrassing question from me. By so doing, they hope to return home and declare to their husband or wife that the doctor was unable to help, whereupon they both breathe a sigh of relief. They employ a form of verbal barrage as their first line of defense. In Freudian terms, that's what illness is—an ego defense mechanism. What

I'm observing is the life casualty—the stalwart or the fearful—and they're telling me, via a history of their illness, what their problem really is. I'm listening.

Past History

Some of this information is volunteered during the presenting complaint but much of it has little significance for the client, who therefore tends to omit facts which are essential in understanding how he's used illness in his life. The past history is a record of the early life decisions translated by the body into physical complaints. Usually the individual will have constructed life events which appear to correspond to the physical complaints, so that to the undiscerning the illness appears to have been triggered by external events beyond his control.

Now many events to my mind are beyond our control: famine, war, weather, earthquakes, epidemic diseases, and other people's actions (at times), to name a few—but most of the things that happen in our lives happen because we set them up. Often this is unconscious and reflects a childhood decision about what we and the world are like. Having decided, for example, that the world was a dangerous place in which one was likely to be physically assaulted, an individual will put himself in situations in which that's made more likely. He realizes that belief. He may loiter around places where aggressive people are known to congregate and where the odds of being assaulted are best. Or he may pick fights with people whom he suspects would react by giving him a beating. Why would anyone apart from a masochist get himself physically assaulted? He does it for excitement. This confirms he's alive. If a young boy is repeatedly hit by his father, and this constitutes the main interaction that the boy and his father have, in the mind of the boy this is regarded as the essence of the relationship between himself and this man he loves. Since the boy is well aware in those early years that it's on the whim of his parents that he's provided for, the act of being hit, staying alive and being loved become confused. When as an adult the man gets himself physically assaulted, as he was in childhood, he's reaffirming his existence. In childhood, physical pain meant both love and existence as far as he was concerned. If he's still very angry about his father's abuse of him, he may become an abuser himself. Most violent men have had violent childhoods.

As an adult, continuing to respond out of early childhood events keeps the adaptation going, irrespective of whether the person is complying with the parental directive or rebelling against it. The point is he's continuing to be run by it.

It takes a lot to stop children from loving parents but when they do, it takes even more for them to forgive. For those who manage it, nothing's impossible. In essence, therapy revolves about the willingness to forgive. Before that happens, techniques which establish awareness of personal behaviors, and encourage expression of suppressed emotions, are used by therapists to assist clients explore forgiveness.

What has all of this got to do with the past history of a medical inquiry? Those decisions that resulted in a man becoming a street fighter rather than an astronomer, or a boxer rather than a beauty consultant, also determined that he suffers from heart disease instead of headaches, rheumatics rather than ruptures, and venereal diseases rather than ethereal diseases. The frequency and severity of the diseases from which my client has suffered tell me whether the world has had its way with him, or if he's had his way with the world. If he's been brought up with the clear instruction that he can take care of himself, then the latter will be the case. If he has no belief in his own power and is too frightened to use it, then he'll be suffering. He believes that the world is more powerful than he is and it can have its way with him. What he fails to realize is that the world can only have its way with him with his permission. Usually he doesn't like to admit that permission has been given, however surreptitiously, and denies his power to even decide to be impotent.

Past Surgical History—An Example

Below is a typical surgical history of a fifty-year-old female who uses illness in her life as a way of manipulating her environment.

- Appendix removed: age 9
- Tonsils removed: age 12
- Adenoids removed: age 15

- ○ Submucosal resection for blocked nose: age 25
- ○ Sinus washout: age 27
- ○ Ovarian cyst: age 31
- ○ Gallbladder removed: age 40
- ○ Hysterectomy: age 45
- ○ Varicose-vein removal: age 47
- ○ Vaginal repair: age 50

This array of procedures is a high price to pay for something she could have achieved more healthily had she and her advisers taken the time and effort to point out her role in those illnesses.

If you think that the above list of operations is atypical, then ask a few women in that age-group and become enlightened about contemporary surgical practice. Each time an operation is performed there will be "very good medical reasons" for doing it. Any procedure can be justified if you choose a narrow enough frame of reference. Within the orthodox medical profession, despite magnificent achievements in both medical technology and surgical procedures, fear of the unknown is still very strong and keeps many doctors' frames of reference narrow. I believe their inflexibility stems from being regarded as omnipotent for so long; but today, total faith in authorities, professionals, technology, or anything else for that matter, has gone.

As I said previously, there's no guarantee that any operation performed these days is really necessary. I recommend that anybody who's been advised to have an operation gets a second opinion from someone with no investment in either the operation being performed or not being performed. Then listen to yourself.

In the case of the woman whose operations I've just listed, I suspect the notion that we create our own illness will meet with much anger. The anger will overlie the fear of change and of guilt at having used illness this way. It's essential (I'll continue to repeat this) that the woman is congratulated on having worked out a way to get her needs met in as safe a way as possible for her. I don't condemn her for having multiple operations, in fact, quite the opposite. She's congratulated.

There's also no condemnation of the surgeons for doing what they believed to be best. The majority of medical practice and the belief of the majority of the people about the nature of illness must be consistent. Most of what we believe in life is fiction, mutually agreed upon in order to belong.

The fact that the woman with multiple operations has come to see me will often indicate that she's reached the conclusion herself that alternatives are required. If she's angry at her doctors for all the surgery, she'll be quite different from a woman who defends her advisers. In the first case she may be racket angry, still harboring old grudges against her parents; and in the second, she may be compliant, denying her anger and being sad instead.

Where the body is supported in its efforts to heal itself (A), the level of disease returns to an acceptable level. At fifty years of age, the amount of disease within the body, as represented by the shaded area on the graph, is small. Where drugs have been used to suppress the symptoms of acute episodes (B), the body never returns to its pre-existing state but accumulates disease until symptoms are continually present. This is chronic disease. The shaded area in this case is far greater, making cure of the illness much more difficult.

A client may give a history of little surgery but a large number of medical conditions over the years. Sometimes when a person is asked if she's had any operations, she becomes very indignant and righteously announces that "I've never had an operation in my life!" Meanwhile she may have a long history of swollen ankles, period pain, cystitis, backache, sinusitis, winter colds and sciatica to her credit. Obviously there's been some powerful parental injunction against having surgery but any number of medical complaints have been condoned. That, remember, is the child's interpretation of what she sees and hears from her parents about illness and wellness. It will also be reflective of the modeling that the child observes in her parents and others. If mother has a headache when she doesn't want sexual intercourse, then the daughter may either comply with that use of illness and behave similarly, or reject that as an option and "never have headaches." In both cases the client is still in script, that is, still following those decisions that she took as a child which were her best options then but could be bettered now that she can keep herself alive without her parents' help.

It's interesting to note whether the client accumulates treatments or if she moves onto the next condition when the old one is no longer useful. It's long been recognized in naturopathy that if a condition is suppressed, which is nearly always the case in orthodox symptomatic treatment, a new disease will eventually take its place. The changing needs of the client as well as her changing body physiology account for giving up one disease and adopting another. The suppression of acute diseases using drugs guarantees the later development of chronic diseases, as body physiology is interfered with in its attempt to complete an unfettered course of recovery. (See diagram on page 92)

The role of illness in the life of any particular individual may not change dramatically, and yet we all know of people who have suffered many illnesses in their lifetime, some of which appear to be quite different from those that preceded them. I can think of some clients who are no sooner over one illness than they give themselves another. A person may decide to have asthma because he's afraid to live his life without his mother, and his asthma attracts women to him who love looking after asthmatics (as did his mother). It may be that he needs some time off work, and as a child the only time his father would allow him to stay home from school was when his asthma was severe. It may be that he has an important performance coming up at the auditorium and is scared of failing. He may be exceptionally angry with his wife for smoking inside the house, and rather than tell her directly that he's angry, he swallows the rage and gets asthma instead. He may be a teenage homosexual who has come to the city from a small town in the country in the hope of escaping persecution, only to end up with asthma every time he sees someone from his past. Or he may be a well-adjusted boy of nine with a family history of asthma so severe that he feels pressured into having it for a few years, but he's already made up his mind that in a short while he'll remove it forever.

The same external physical symptom, in this case asthma (constriction of the bronchial tubes), represents a myriad underlying psychological profiles. The advantages in having asthma will be as numerous and as different as the individuals who suffer from it. When a person's situation changes in any way, either by external factors beyond his control, such as a car accident in which a drunken driver caused a sudden and totally unavoidable collision, or by internal processes such as his reaction to the death of a parent, the need for the frequency, severity and the nature of illness may similarly change. Under such conditions, he may give up the usual illness, escalate it, trade it in for something more effective in the new circumstances, or give up the illness option altogether. And since we all grow older every day, our situation changes every day. The progression of illnesses that people who exercise the illness option choose to have is not surprising. A young man who needs hepatitis to keep him away from a sport he thinks he "should" play but that terrifies him, doesn't need to justify inactivity as he gets older. He may, however, need to justify a lack of promotion in his work. For this, chronic back pain is better suited.

Childhood Diseases

This is a revealing section of the past history. Generally those people who have been accustomed to illness as a child will continue to use it as an adult, that is, if you were sick as a child you'll probably be sick as an adult. Before the reader applies that rank generalization to his own case and finds it wanting, let me hasten to add that in human beings real change and maturity is no more spectacular than in the area of illness and wellness. Being ill or well is the mirror of the soul. Some people blossom from humble beginnings, others decay when they appear to have been given a head start. And so it is with disease. The sick child with a history of scarlet fever, polio, earache, encephalitis, glandular fever, mumps, chicken pox, rubella and epilepsy may reject all major diseases in adulthood and become an Olympic athlete. If he does this for himself, he can expect to remain well for ever. If he's rebelling against his parents' use of illness (a system he adopted under duress as a child) and still harbors a grudge, then he can expect to become ill again once the energy for being well to spite his parents has worn off and has been replaced by depression. In this case, he's not made a decision within a new frame of reference but has maintained the old belief system, that is, whatever happens to you as a child affects you for the rest of your life. Within the belief that nothing really changes, any number of options are available, none of which proves satisfactory. Sick children will become sick adults unless, from a position of self-love, they decide otherwise.

Some nurses are very well when they're working and become sick when they retire. They've clearly been given the message in childhood to look after others, usually mother herself, or a younger sibling, and in fear of not getting love may continue to follow the messages as adults and become nurses. If this is the case, that is, they're looking after others because they think it's the only way they're lovable, they'll be afraid to become sick them-selves. They're supposed to be taking care of patients. Although they are themselves well during their working life, their belief system is unchanged from childhood. They still believe as adults that to be loved requires selflessness and if you're unlucky enough to be ill, you get cared for. When they're older and haven't felt the closeness and caring that years of nursing were meant to provide, they become disillusioned, particularly if they have no family and are lonely. They may become angry at years of what they now regard as lost time. In this mood they become unwell, often seriously, and this means that someone has to care for them as they cared for others all those years. They may make terrible patients, demanding, aggressive, never satisfied and often alcoholic.

Although they've been given "be well" messages, they have no permission to be well for their own sakes, only for the purpose of taking care of others. When they become ill themselves, they do so within the same old framework.

I make the point that if illness is to be cured, some or all of the following need to happen: awareness ("So that's how I make myself ill!"); emotional expression ("Damn it, Mom!"); forgiveness ("Raising six kids during the Depression must have been impossible"); and acceptance ("I love me, and I love others"). This means dropping the old belief system we adopted as children and taking full responsibility, without fear, for who we are.

Take the case of another woman who was a senior nurse. Having found that this occupation that her mother had recommended was at times taxing, she decided that while at work she would care for the patients as their conditions warranted and get the caring she needed for herself at other times. She found herself a lover, another nurse as it turned out, with whom she was mutually supportive. The two children of her lover's previous marriage were a source of joy to her. She allowed patients on the ward to do small things for her in return for the effort she put into their recovery. That effort was often directed toward showing them how they could reduce their dependence on their medical caretakers. This woman had no need to become ill, neither to confirm her right to caring nor to relate to her partner. She and her partner both believed in self-responsibility and mutual care within that responsibility. Both women in the first place had been encouraged to take up a caring occupation but both had subsequently decided that they could both care, and be cared for.

The frequency and severity of illness in childhood will reflect parental attitude to illness as well as genetic predispositions, birth trauma, environment and family diet, and a whole lot besides. If the individual continues to suffer multiple illnesses or at least continues with illness as an active part of his life, he's still adhering to the old decisions be made under external pressure as a child. If a man has been remarkably well following a sick childhood, then he may be rebelling against his parents, still hoping to get something from them that he didn't get as a child. "I'm going to be so damn well they'll realize their mistake and give me what I want." In this case he may end up sick, unhappy or both. Alternatively, he may decide that his earlier position no longer suits him and that in future he'll do things for his own sake. He can then expect to be generally well and occasionally suffer the minor irritations of a hostile environment until he has successfully satisfied his will to live. When he has satisfied his will to live, presumably, he'll die.

THE FAMILY HISTORY

Now that we've studied the prevalence of illness in the client as a child, we now turn our attention to the general family history. This reveals the parents' attitudes to their own state of health and provides more information on the sorts of messages the child would most likely have received. We can then compare these messages with the client's recall of what they were directly told about illness as a child; if we find any discrepancies, we can assess the reasons for those discrepancies and their effect on the client. This area is often of considerable importance in determining why people make themselves ill.

The ostensible or social message may vary substantially from the ulterior message. Take the following example: Joanne's mother was always ill. She was city-born and "just knew" she'd hate the country property where she and her country-born husband re-located. Her daughter was born a few years later, and from the outset mother had decided that this further imposition in life (the country was bad enough), was more than she could handle. She resolved to be unwell. This she did with a certain flair, for she had more than a touch of theatrics about her, and to the young Joanne such a display of infirmity had more than the desired effect. Her mother made it quite plain that Joanne was at least one reason for her unhappiness and that for this, the girl would pay by attending to her mother assiduously.

At the same time she was commanding attention and caring from Joanne, mother would declare: "It's terrible being ill dear, and the worst part is being a burden on you and your poor father. If there was one thing I could wish for you it would be good health, so that you wouldn't need others to take care of you." Any untoward thoughts that Joanne may have had about her mother's illness were easily engulfed by the wave of guilt she experienced at hearing her mother's words. How could she be so callous when the poor, sick woman only wished that she could stop being a burden on her family? What a trick to pull on a child or, more accurately, what an act of great hostility. When Joanne came into therapy she was very angry at her mother, needless to say. She had developed herpes at the age of twenty and feared death from cancer of the womb. It had become almost an obsession. During the past history, I elicited that as a child she'd been very well (in order to look after mother as it turned out), and without the family history which she had omitted, a very incomplete picture of her situation had emerged.

The past history suggests messages about illness which would prohibit the child from being ill—"Don't be ill and be a burden on others"—but the modeling, or the ulterior psychological message from the mother, was quite clearly, "Life's a burden. You can ease it by getting ill and being looked after!" A combination of both the past and family history had made the situation very clear. The conflict had been, in Joanne, between the parent (grown-up) and the child (little kid) in her own head. While the parent said "Be well," the child sabotaged this with a "Be ill." She resolved this problem and developed into a self-caring woman once she learned to use her power to be well.

The family medical history is a record of the physiological responses of that family to the pressure of living. No doubt the reasons for the family as a whole being well or ill go back a long way, but for the purposes of investigating any particular client, the grandparents are as far into the past as we need to go. Also, the general influence of the media is much stronger now than in the past; this is having a significant effect on people's attitudes to wellness and is probably reducing the significance of the family. Still, the Internet, social media, and TV cannot keep babies alive.

During the family history I compare the state of health of the client with that of his siblings, his parents and his children. This further differentiates the overt from the ulterior messages. If I'm dealing with an obese client then I want to know who else in the family is overweight. Have his brothers and sisters similarly afflicted themselves, or was he singled out in some way? Was mother obese from over-eating, under-exercise, sexual repression, a need for power or none of the above? As a child was he sickly, and did his mother become scared and over-feed him? In the latter case, the older siblings will probably be of normal weight, while the younger ones may have decided, like him, that it's dangerous to be thin.

I may ask to see a sibling, a parent, or a child so that I can get a different perspective on the client's illness. In addition, this enables me to see and demonstrate to the client the mechanisms that have resulted in illness in the parents; therefore, if he's willing, we can use this information to steer him clear of the same dangers.

That's preventive medicine. It's very edifying to see the healthy son of the grossly obese forty-five-year-old lawyer come into my practice. It's both exciting and sad to see how the client himself must have looked as a youth of nineteen. Eliciting the scripting is made so much easier by such experiences. In this case, it's unlikely that there's a genetic component to his obesity. Instead, he made a decision years ago that "When I get older and lose the bloom of youth, I'll grow fat." There's a good chance the son will do the same thing.

Statements made in the family about people who were "always ill" or less often "always well" is of much value in determining the scripting and the racket feelings the client may have about his illness. If the client himself uses metaphors or cliches such as "Ah well, mustn't grumble," or recalls that a parent used them, his resignation toward life and illness is made so much clearer. I'm reminded in this of my grandmother, who would religiously inform me, "Your health is the most valuable thing you have, dear."

Listening to every metaphor, family saying, social platitude, and frivolous comment, usually passed off with a laugh, is invaluable in eliciting the reality of what I'm dealing with. Every nuance and every inflection of the voice is of great importance. It's the subconscious of your client telling you what she really believes and what she'd like you to know despite the at times well-constructed diversions.

Ask yourself if there are some stories or sayings that you recall from relatives about health, and if there are, look at them literally. They may help you to understand your own need for illness, as illustrated in the following example of the woman who remained happy and well as long as her husband remained alcoholic. When he dried out, she went to hospital with pleurisy. "Mum always said that if Dad came home from the pub sober just once, she'd die from the shock!"

9

SYSTEM SPECIFICITY—
WHICH DISEASE BEST
FULFILLS MY NEEDS?

GASTROINTESTINAL SYSTEM

Women, and to a lesser degree men, in Western society, have been brainwashed in the area of weight and sexuality. There are very few women of any age who do not regard the process of weighing themselves as either a moment of some trial, or triumph. For obese people, it's the moment of both shame and relief. They're ashamed of their "weakness," subconsciously needing to affirm that they're not OK, and simultaneously relieved to find that they still have their "complaint." People are the exact weight they need to be at any particular time in their life. The weight "problem" avoids even less desirable thoughts, feelings and actions than their self criticism for being overweight.

When people consult me complaining of obesity, I won't see them unless they agree to psychotherapy, in conjunction with diet, lifestyle, exercise and meditation counselling. People choose a weight which is safe for them. Why should being a "perfect" weight be unsafe for anyone? This is a reasonable question, given the social acclaim which accompanies such a state. The following case demonstrates why it wasn't safe for one woman to be of normal weight.

When Jessica was two days old, she had a seizure. Thirty-five years ago, country hospitals were less sophisticated than they are today, and in the frustration of not knowing what caused it (and then what to do about it), the matron of the hospital informed Jessica's mother that the child had nearly died through lack of sufficient nourishment. (Babies hardly eat anything in the first two days of life anyway.) The accuracy of this information was less relevant (as was the ill-considered timing) than Jessica's mother's own internal needs to have a fragile child. What made her mother take such a drastic option I don't know, but she took it, with the result that young Jessica was overfed and grossly overweight from an early age.

At the slightest hint of an ailment, however minor, Jessica's mom would overfeed her. In turn, the child had few options in the situation. She could refuse to overeat and perhaps withstand the threat from her mother to "eat or be ill," in case her mother had little investment in the situation and was merely repeating what her mother had told her. But that wasn't the case. Young Jessica didn't have the maturity to handle the tension in the household if her mother was afraid. And her mother was terrified if Jessica didn't eat, since she believed that a disaster of some kind was imminent. As a consequence of Jessica taking care of her mother's fears and subsequently overeating, she was quite overweight by the age of twenty. I saw her when she was thirty-five. She came into my office accompanied by an older woman with whom I had no contact; I guessed she was her mother. Her mother's weight was normal, and after a short conversation with her daughter, it was mutually decided that the mother would remain in the waiting room and not accompany Jessica during the interview.

By this stage, before a word has been spoken, the astute observer has diagnosed gross obesity (no prizes for that), with a considerable maternal investment. Now, there aren't too many cases of obesity without a large maternal investment, but you don't often get to see it played out before you. Asking how Mom and Dad individually feel about having a fat daughter will indicate which of the parents has been most significant in the client's decision to be overweight.

So great were her mother's fears that when Jessica married in her early twenties and moved from Australia to England to live, her mother followed her and moved in with her daughter and son-in-law and proceeded to do all the cooking—in excess quantities, of course. Eventually the husband, who clearly liked grossly obese women but not, apparently, their mothers, could no longer tolerate the intrusion and moved out. Jessica and her mother moved back to Australia and took an apartment together, and once again the old routine of the mother overfeeding her daughter began. Of course, all this happened with Jessica's consent. Jessica wasn't prepared to confront her own fears, which were made more acute no doubt by the presence of her real mother. If her mother hadn't been there, the situation would probably have been little different. Jessica would simply have maintained the fear of dying if she didn't eat from her own "internal-parent" and "child-ego" states. Her own internal parent would say, "You should eat or you'll get sick!" while her own internal child would regard the situation from a survival point of view. Thus the leftover thoughts and feelings we adopt in childhood maintain the power of those early-childhood messages to continue dictating our behavior as adults. Life's circumstances provide the opportunity to revisit these thoughts and feelings and, with the maturity of the grown-up, explore and expiate them.

Jessica had clearly decided that she couldn't stay alive without being overfed by her mother. She still believed that unless she was obese, she would die. She'd been told that the way to stay well was to be fat, and therefore believed that if she lost weight she was risking becoming ill. This is an example of keeping unwell in order to stay well. Such paradoxes need to be understood if a cure is to be attempted. The alternative (and this will be familiar to many readers), is to spend a fortune and often a lifetime on the merry-go-round of dieting and weight loss, frustration, over-eating, more weight gain and more dieting. After a while the dieting makes little or no difference to body weight anyhow. The physiology of this has been discussed in The Childhood Basis of Disease on page 34.

Therapy centered on Jessica addressing her early childhood decision to be fat in order to help Mother feel comfortable, and taking responsibility for keeping herself alive. The decision to be both healthy and of normal weight was augmented by a program of healthy living and eating. We'll look at treatment programs more specifically in a later section.

This case is a good example of psychological medicine working in an area that is very poorly catered for by the orthodox methods that are used in general practice. Very few cases of obesity are referred to psychotherapists for treatment. The majority are given a diet that doesn't work in the long term or, worse still, an appetite suppressant, or, in extreme cases, "lap-band" surgery (short for laparoscopic adjustable *gastric* banding surgery). Little more than such poor treatment is possible in the time that is spent with the average general practitioner. This is a shame, because the average general practitioner is in the field because of both her interest and skills in the area of family and psychological medicine.

THE BOWELS

Within the systems inquiry, two specific areas are available for scrutiny of the internal functions: the bowels and the kidneys. In these areas we are able to assess the internal processes by observing and testing the excreta. By matching our findings with the psychological state, a direct method for assessing the body-mind axis is available. This is invaluable, so I spend much time inquiring about the exact nature of these functions. Most people find being asked ten questions about the nature of their feces amusing, while some are offended by the inquiry. Of course, their reaction is informative, as the following conversation shows.

"How many times a day do you use your bowels, Peter?"

"Normal."

"Well, for you, how many times each day is that, on average?"

"Oh, you know—normal!"

He's becoming agitated. I press on.

"Some people go to the bathroom once a week, and for them that's normal, while others go three times a day. I'm wondering where you fit into that range?" By this time I'm pretty sure that the answer will be "Once a week."

"Well, if it's important, I suppose I go about once every few days, yes, about two or three times a week." Well, I was wrong about the frequency, but the quite severe constipation of his bowel reflects his mental constipation, not to put too delicate a point on it.

The bowel is an eight meter long, hollow, smooth, muscular tube. It's very susceptible to emotional changes, as anybody suffering from a stomach ulcer, heartburn, or Irritable Bowel Syndrome (IBS) will tell you. The bowel is often affected in people who conceal their emotions, particularly anger and fear. The fact that they're reluctant to express their emotions may already be evident in other areas such as voice, dress, body shape, physiognomy and their use of language.

The client's attitude to being questioned about his bowel function is an important indicator of the emotional climate which surrounded his early toilet training. Freud says the "anal stage" overlaps the "oral stage" (between birth and about eighteen months) and lasts until about three years. Children are usually toilet trained in this period, often quite aggressively, and issues stemming from that sort of treatment may result in individuals who are narrow in outlook, punctual in attendance, and fastidious. They may suffer from lower-bowel problems, especially those closer to the anus, such as IBS, hemorrhoids, or cancer of the rectum. They aren't going to recover from those diseases until they're prepared to free themselves up and adopt a more laissez-faire attitude to life. This is often really scary for them, but it's my experience that if they take the plunge, they become very rewarding clients indeed. The change in their faces is beautiful to see: more relaxed, more open, more accepting. If a person has a tight, defended anus, then the same may be assumed of the psyche: impenetrable, with much protection or "ego defense."

The nature of the feces informs me of the diameter of the anus during defecation, and the degree of spasm. The consistency is indicative of the diet and the degree of digestion: a person who does not want to be nourished for fear of surviving may have "intestinal hurry": loose, frequent bowel movements with visible undigested material. If the bowel movement floats in the toilet, then its specific gravity is lower than that of water, and the fat content will be higher than normal, which indicates that for some reason the liver is not removing the usual amount of fat from the ingested food. This often indicates a state of suppressed anger—a condition that I've found, and that Traditional Chinese Medicine also claims, causes dysfunction of the liver. Thus the nature of the excrement may tell me why the client has arthritis (in this case a consequence of suppressed anger): a condition with apparently no connection to the bowel at all.

The bowel is the main organ with which we directly relate to our environment; the skin and the sense organs also relate to the outside world but in a more passive way. If we don't want to see or to hear something, then we can interfere with the reception of these organs by decreasing their sensitivity. This way we become more dependent on our own internal processes, since we've reduced the external stimuli. If we need a very narrow view of the world to survive its rigors (or perhaps if we are a Buddha...), then this may suit us. In order to survive, however, we're unable to stop using the bowel altogether, although we can reduce or interfere with its function, as in anorexia nervosa.

Each day we commit something of this earth to our bodies. In this way we become of the earth, or its many products, be they organically grown kale or a synthetic soft drink. By the great variety of foodstuffs we select, the frequency with which we ingest them, and the process by which we choose to digest them, we indicate our love of both this planet and our body. The bowel is the organ that must continue its relationship with those things about us if we're to survive. Its place in the psychological profile of an individual is unique, and it's because of these reasons that dysfunction occurs readily in some people and why the bowel occupies such a diverse place in our body image.

The location of a bowel complaint will often indicate the area of psychological concern. Already I've indicated that lower-bowel problems are prevalent in areas of traumatic toilet training, or where an interruption of the child coming to friendly and social terms with his own excrement has occurred. Upper-bowel problems—such as gastritis, heartburn, stomach or duodenal ulcer, gallbladder problems, pancreatitis, and diabetes—begin in the oral-gratification stage. In this case, the areas affected are those that are involved in the assimilation of food, rather than its excretion. People with little investment in nurturing their physical bodies will therefore be prone to upper-intestinal complaints. The personalities of people who suffer from upper-intestinal complaints, or complaints of digestion, will be quite different from those who suffer from complaints of excretion.

Food occupies such an important place in our society that I don't intend to undertake an analysis of it just yet. I'll do that in the section on diet. The need for instant gratification, which in Western society is breeding generations of sugar junkies, is responsible for an enormous increase in the incidence of problems of upper-bowel assimilation, such as diabetes and hypoglycemia. Once again, the physical problem (diabetes), the early-childhood emotional circumstances (anxiety), and the solution to that problem (eating ice cream) have all shown themselves to be interdependent. It's missing the point to put clients on insulin, stop them from eating ice cream, or treat their anxiety. All three, and usually much more, need to be considered. This takes time.

Whether for instant gratification, as in a child addicted to fruit juice, or the denial of gratification, as in an anorectic, the upper gastro-intestinal tract reflects the personality of the client. This information can be made use of by a practitioner who observes the signs, listens to the symptoms and then constructs a personality profile from this data. The early childhood decisions that the client took which resulted in both her personality and subsequently her physical symptoms, are made available to the client to change using individual and group therapy techniques.

A cure is effected when the client escapes the early childhood dependence on parents and subsequent parent figures, including the therapist, and takes full responsibility for herself. Within self-responsibility, I include the preparedness to make a decision to be well or unwell from a position of personal power.

THE RESPIRATORY SYSTEM

People don't get lung cancer because they smoked too many cigarettes. No, people who want to risk dying select one of the many methods available to them that are socially acceptable at the time. Lung cancer is one of these. The cause of a popular disease must be something that will remove the responsibility from the sufferer and "blame" an outside agent, in this case cigarettes.

If people can no longer blame cigarettes for their lung cancer, the cigarettes become redundant to that group. There never will be any hard data on the matter because there's no such thing as hard data in the case of human beings. Statistics become meaningless. They'll always show what they're required by at least one invested party to show. If one person dies of lung cancer who has not been a smoker, and of course thousands have, then smoking is not the only cause of lung cancer. Smoking may certainly be used to facilitate its development by those people needing to hand over their personal power to an addiction. Common sense tells us that smoking isn't "good for you," but that doesn't assist us in defining the common "good." What's good for one person isn't good for another.

Those people who don't want to die of lung cancer and who want to smoke can have their cake and eat it, too. If their constitution is such that they can smoke twenty cigarettes a day and withstand an obvious (self-inflicted) environmental hazard, then so be it. Smoking in this instance is clearly part of their internal balance. If I smoke more than occasionally, I have a sore throat. I'm scared of certain things in life, and smoking is one of them. When I'm really sad, scared, or lonely but am unprepared to feel those emotions, I may reach for a cigarette. When I'm less afraid, I'm prepared to feel emotions and not truncate them. Similarly, when I'm not scared, I can smoke and enjoy a cigarette and not suffer any ill effects. There's a dynamic balance in these things. In the East it's called yin and yang; in the West it's called paradox.

If a father or mother was responsible for telling the child about the dangers of smoking, and if a member of the family or a close friend died from lung cancer and that death was attributed to cigarette smoking, then heavy smoking in such an individual as a teenager or an adult will alert me to his existence issues—that is, his will to live. I assume that a heavy smoker with such a background has decided to not look after himself (and maybe kill himself) using a method in which he was instructed in childhood. If the client smokes and genuinely does not believe it will do him any harm, then I agree with him. If he has terrible bronchitis and smokes like a chimney, then I assume that he likes having severe bronchitis. There's no point in removing the bronchitis until we discover what advantages he extracts from it and how he can replace those benefits. By the time many people come to see me, they've decided that they want to change, although they may be unclear about both the old and the new system. Very few people who smoke more than a few cigarettes a day are looking after themselves.

Sinusitis is a fascinating condition, because it's so debilitating, so widespread, and treated so universally badly. I have mentioned previously that it's linked with poor bowel function in most cases. The constipation of the bowel reflects mental constipation, mostly in inflexible people, while the sinusitis (in men particularly) often indicates a reluctance to cry. The mucous membranes are chronically inflamed and swollen: a consequence of poor bowel function; environmental irritants such as pollens, exhaust fumes, and cigarette smoke; or a failure to be exercised and then rested appropriately. Let's examine this. If we're reading a book in good light, we can read easily and clearly for a time until our eyes get tired. If we then stop reading and rest our eyes, we can resume reading with no problems. If we continue to read beyond our capacity in poor light, however, we may get a headache from the strain. Instead of working properly and then resting, we have caused our eyes chronic fatigue. Mucous membranes react similarly.

If we cry when we're sad, the physiological response is tears from the eyes and nose. When we've finished being sad, the mucous membranes in the nose and sinuses settle back to the normal uninflamed state. If the sadness isn't ever directly expressed by crying (racket sadness), the mucous membranes remain chronically, perhaps sub-clinically inflamed, never really producing mucus and never really resting. Low-grade inflammation results in swollen membranes that eventually block the openings to the sinuses, causing pain and further discharge. This is chronic sinusitis.

Apart from not crying effectively, the other factors contributing to the development of sinusitis are the consumption of dairy products in excess, and inadequate fibre in the diet. Also a decrease in the biodiversity of the intestinal flora, such as from taking multiple courses of antibiotics, affects the capacity of the intestine to both absorb, and excrete. There are no standards. Requirements vary between individuals. Multiple allergy testing confirms what the client already knew. For this the client pays handsomely both financially and, if he ends up on the merry-go-round of desensitization treatments, physically. Usually external agents are not of much consequence in sinusitis. They can be more prominent in the causes of hay fever. When a profession has little real knowledge of an area commonly held to be within its field of expertise, spurious methods will be developed which may be useless, but which are defended aggressively by the profession for purposes of saving face. Modern medicine abounds with such spurious treatments, and might benefit from withdrawing from those areas to which doctors make little contribution and concentrating upon those in which it excels.

Upper respiratory tract infection, the commonly designated URTI, appears on sickness certificates all over the world with a frequency probably exceeding any other illness. An URTI is a socially condoned method of taking a day or two off work. In most cases the certificate of sickness should read, "suffering from overwork, anxiety, or pique" or, more accurately, "suffering from nothing at all, but wants a rest day." To my mind it's silly for people to make themselves sick in order to take a day off work. If people were allowed to take a certain number of days without a doctor's certificate, then they could decide for themselves whether they wanted to spend the day sick in bed or whether they wanted to enjoy their day off. Much socially condoned behavior rewards illness and penalizes health.

For many people the common cold is like an old friend. For some it's their best friend or even their only friend. Rhinitis, hay fever, sore throat, tonsillitis, earache and conjunctivitis have never received recognition for the enormous amount of work that they perform in giving people days off work, getting people cared for by others, getting sympathy from lovers, avoiding unwanted appointments, confirming the world as lousy and generally providing proof of our misery for all to see. For all of these great and selfless deeds the common cold is maligned, abused, attacked with countless chemicals and even forced to undergo operations. This latter act is one of great hostility indeed and only undertaken by someone determined to appear very needy. I can imagine how this is very hurtful to the common cold, working overtime as it does with absolutely no thanks from anyone, only to be superseded in promoting non self-responsibility by an operation. It really must be frustrating.

The common cold is not a disease so much as an institution. Those who don't want to be particularly ill but want a period of incapacity employ it skillfully and effectively. Having achieved that incapacity they can then address whatever's troubling them. Most of this is subconscious. In this way the common cold or any minor respiratory complaint is used to rebalance the psyche and the internal organs. For most people it does little long-term harm to their body but may be regarded as an unnecessary or at best inefficient way to get what they want. In addition, it's damned unpleasant! There's no point throwing it away until something equally effective and less distressing has been found to take its place. Perhaps low blood sugar (hypoglycaemia) with its general incapacitation, or repetitive strain injury will fulfil their early promise. Sleep apnea is also proving effective in creating general disability.

THE CARDIOVASCULAR SYSTEM

The client is a twenty-eight-year-old female. "How can I help you?" I ask.

"Well, my father died of a heart attack when he was forty, my uncle died of the same thing at the age of forty-three, and my grandfather also died of a coronary when he was quite young. I'm worried that I might also die early of—"

"Do you have any brothers?" I interrupt.

"My brother died last year, of a coronary. He was thirty-two."

My face reflects the sadness I feel when anybody dies young, and my spine shivers at parental messages so dutifully and so needlessly fulfilled. The predictability, the inevitability of it all. If only I could have seen him before he died, I could have guided him in deciding to live. All this is racing through my mind. I have temporarily forgotten the client's real concern with her own prognosis, but already I can tell by looking at her that the same fate won't befall her, since the family modeling was that only the men of the family die of heart attacks. I'll return to her later. "What did the postmortem show?" I inquire gently, struggling a little to conceal my interest.

"There was apparently absolutely nothing to see," she replies.

"What, nothing? No obvious damage to the heart muscle; no blockage of the coronary artery?"

"Nothing."

I find this even more interesting, even though clients rarely provide accurate pathological reports, since they themselves are rarely given accurate information. "What sort of man was he? Did he enjoy life? Did he seem happy?"

"He was a very easygoing—apparently contented—fit and healthy young man. He was an active sportsman and always had been. His diet was nothing unusual, as far as I could see. His body was slim and muscular, and he was obviously attractive to women."

"Have any women in your family died from heart attacks?"

"There's a rumor, which my mother can't substantiate, that an old aunt of Dad's died of a heart attack, but she was quite old at the time."

"Do you know that your father's, uncle's, grandfather's, and brother's deaths are totally unrelated to you, since you weren't subject to the same indoctrination in childhood that 'All the Halisham men die young of heart attacks'?"

"Yes, that's my strong feeling and belief. I can recall talk in the family of how all the men in the family were subject to heart attacks, and I can recall my brother being quite scared about it as a young boy; then he seemed to adjust to it, and it no longer bothered him."

The interview proceeded with an explanation of the fundamentals of scripting and how diseases are passed down within families. Diet was also used as a method of reinforcing her belief that she could prevent any heart disease in herself and in her male offspring. She departed with both of us feeling very confident of her good prognosis and a little sobered by the relentlessness of family dynamics. Had she been less convinced I would have ordered the usual tests, but really, they weren't required.

Heart disease is interesting. Society has given it a certain significance, not unlike the niche reserved for upper respiratory infections in community thinking. In fact, all diseases are either socially condoned or discriminated against, for very complex reasons. Popular disease is determined on anthropological criteria. I find this fascinating, because if our quest is for more pleasure and less pain, we'll need to pay some attention to our need for illness as a society.

I've previously discussed how a heart attack may be precipitated when an individual is under excessive strain, often at work, and has no permission from parents to slow down. Alternatively, part of his childhood belief system may be that in the event of overwork a heart attack is an acceptable way of confirming to himself, and demonstrating to others, that he's had enough and wants to slow down or quit. And usually, it's very effective, reserved by society as it is for just such a purpose. A man who was struggling for promotion and not enjoying it may through the good offices of a heart attack be transferred to lighter duties. The heart attack is often as effective in achieving desired changes within the family as it is at work.

Many business people enjoy the fight for financial security and that's not the climate within which heart attacks are welcome. Usually they occur in dissatisfied individuals found in the more soul-destroying jobs such as production-line work than in occupations in which a person has more control over his destiny. A component of work frustration is an unwillingness to try anything different and usually parental messages on that score were clear—either parents risked or didn't risk. Heart attacks are the result in many cases of people who have decided to work hard in order to be loved by parents, and who have no parental permission to slow down or change direction if the job no longer suits. The heart attack is condoned by the parents, and as an adult, it's the parent in our head we're dealing with. Venereal disease wouldn't serve the same purpose.

Much like the ancients, I regard the heart as the seat of the emotions. In the past one hundred years, it's been fashionable to ridicule the primitive concepts and the elementary anatomy that resulted in such an easily disproved statement. Everybody knows that the emotions reside in the brain. Well, the neurons may be firing in the brain but the physiological consequences of those emotions are reflected elsewhere, and I've already mentioned the anger which may be stored in the liver and the fear which affects the kidneys.

As of now, the year 2017, the science used in medicine is nearly a hundred years out of date. Throughout science, quantum states have superseded mechanistic Newtonian physics for the purpose of understanding the natural world, but not in medicine. A contemporary view of human biology suggests that there's no separation between mind and body, between soma and psyche, between one person and another, between organisms and us, nor between us and the Universe. Mechanical views of disease are significantly out of date. Many treatments rely upon medieval concepts that have little applicability to humans.

In the case of the liver, chronic anger decreases the excretion of lipases, which are responsible for the absorption of fat from the diet; in severe cases this may result in chronic hepatitis. Fear may diminish the blood supply to the kidneys, which will result in loin pain, kidney stones, or chronic inflammation from autoimmune disease of the kidneys. In these conditions, the body is attacking itself.

Where the heart is strong and stable, so is the personality. A person who has a heart strongly pumping blood to all corners of the body will have visibly healthy extremities, with beautifully sculptured warm hands and feet, a lively color to the skin, clear eyes, shining hair, large blood flow to the ears, and responsive genitals. I suppose I see one such person each week, and it's both refreshing and sobering to see a fully functioning human being. Their parents have given them the unqualified right to exist: the unhindered, uncluttered, unmodified message that they're a delight and that their existence is a joy to all. That's how they end up as adults: a delight. It's possible to teach children that they can't always have their own way, and that they have an obligation to society, without modifying their right to exist. By so doing, a strong heart develops, which in turn pumps health promoting blood throughout the body. Vivacity is the result, and it's there for all to see.

Apart from the positive aspects of a strong heart, other emotions are readily reflected by heart function. We all know that part of the "fight or flight" reaction is a rapid heart rate. When we're either scared or angry the heart rate increases and in some instances becomes irregular. Palpitations may result. Chronic sadness may result in a slow heart rate with a small output. If any of these emotions are prevented from being expressed and discharged, a chronic state of fear (anxiety), sadness (depression) or anger (aggression) may result. The long-term effect on the heart is disease.

In the case of fear, the chronic tension may result in irregularities and eventual conduction defects. Anger results in a chronically elevated cardiac output with an increase in the size of the heart muscle required to cope with the extra load. If this muscle hypertrophies (grows excessively large) beyond the capacity of its blood vessels to keep it supplied with oxygen and nutrients, or the blood vessels themselves become diseased, a heart attack results. A heart attack is simply a piece of the heart muscle dying through lack of blood. This is called an infarct. Prior to an actual heart attack, the whole cardio-vascular system may respond to an increase in muscular tension in the peripheral blood vessels, with an increase in blood pressure. An angry person will often have an elevated blood pressure (hypertension) prior to suffering a heart attack. Sadness slows the heart and decreases the volume of blood (cardiac output) which it pumps to the tissues. If this continues for long enough, the tissues become undernourished and don't grow as well as they might. To see this may require close inspection. The body shape is mean, not full, the feet are cold and narrow, and the skin is dry. The person looks weak. All this may be the consequence of a mind that never believed in its right to be alive and as a consequence the heart under-functions. Because of the poor blood supply, all organs of the body are less protected against organisms and other hostilities and hence the individual is more susceptible to infections. People who are severely depressed are therefore physically at risk, and may die.

The cardio-vascular system, and the heart in particular, is therefore very important in the physical well-being of the individual, reflecting both his past psychological profile and his current emotional state. Games which centre about illness may be played using heart disease as the vehicle for a pay-off. With an organ as crucial to survival as the heart, these games are often played for keeps.

THE MUSCULOSKELETAL SYSTEM

When I was a medical student and was interviewing patients in hospitals, the inquiry into the musculo-skeletal system was the one I disliked most. It struck me as mundane; arthritis, sciatica, old fractures—hardly exciting stuff. Now that I'm older (and more mature), I still dislike it. However, the musculo-skeletal system is like a mirror. Other observations are often confirmed or thrown into question after the inquiry into this system.

Someone who reports disease or injury of the muscles, bones or joints is invariably reporting a decrease in mobility. This may be for a short time, as in the case of a fracture, or a much longer time, as in the increasing debilitation suffered with rheumatoid arthritis. As in all illness, if we look at the end result, the role of the illness becomes apparent. In the case of diseases of the skeleton, we look for the reasons the person may benefit from a period of immobility, either brief or protracted. Very often the immobility is related to physical, emotional or social withdrawal in some form.

It's been my experience that the two elements of diseases of locomotion most often present are fear and martyrdom. People who decrease their ability to get around for any reason are usually afraid to be fully mobile because of the demands, either real or imagined, that full mobility implies. I've noticed that a high proportion of women who haven't taken partners suffer arthritis as a way of alleviating the fear of socializing and perhaps finding a partner. I've also had cases in which middle-aged women who behaved as second-class citizens in their marriages to aggressive men contracted arthritis in an effort to moderate the bullying. Others have developed the disease to get some caring from otherwise insensitive husbands, or have used it to keep husbands in positions of devotion. Arthritis appears to be more common in women than in men, or at least more debilitating, and I wonder whether that's because in our society men prize their mobility to a greater degree, and for them to trade immobility for the benefits of disease would be too great an imposition on their masculine self-image. Women are often socially less mobile anyway.

By continuing to explore arthritis in middle-aged women, I run the risk of being labelled sexist, but most societies are sexist and sexism is one of the causes of disease. Where a woman has spent many years child-rearing, that strenuous, unpaid and often un-thanked job, and where the personal rewards from seeing the children grow didn't compensate for a lack of care from her husband, she may use arthritis to confirm life as unfair, a drudge, unrewarded and long suffering. Her opinion about life is established in childhood, and for safety, she chooses a non-caring man to marry. He simply confirms what she already knows. A caring husband would terrify her.

Martyrdom is the end result of this process, unless it's depression. I see many middle-aged women basking in the benefits of their infirmity: people, usually men, rushing to open doors; bus drivers taking longer to stop and accelerating more slowly; the hushed tones of commiseration from passersby. The effect on others is so powerful that they would not trade their arthritis for the world. The pain, severe as it is, constitutes part of the martyrdom.

Men with arthritis, on the other hand, are generally angry. Frustrated by life, dissatisfied with work or promotion, often unloved at home, they give themselves a physical component to be angry about. This reconfirms their anger and effectively prevents them confronting other unfelt emotions, often sadness. It may be unacceptable for a man to show his sadness in our society, and as a consequence anger may take its place.

In women, sadness is acceptable and anger is not. These now-obsolete societal requirements have created much despair and illness.

In my thirties I ruptured my Achilles tendon, which is a serious injury, and may herald the end of a sporting career or significantly affect recreational sport. In discussing the advantages of illness with particular reference to immobility, I believe it would be of value to look at my own case, something I was more than reluctant to do at the time. I'd been back from a six-month study tour of the United States only two weeks when my old squash club called, asking me to fill in for somebody who was injured. I recall a feeling of exhilaration at being asked, as I was rather uptight at the time, and my usual method of reducing anxiety was to play competitive sport. I was fit and had been playing regularly, so there was no increased physical risk of injury. I'd been scaling down my level of aggression in sport for some years, consciously and subconsciously needing it less. This match was a return to my most aggressive style. I knew at the end of the match, waiting for me as usual would be a certain hollowness at expending all this energy and aggression, and not really getting what I wanted from it. What I wanted was love and caring but for various reasons, was at the time reluctant to secure these. My tendon snapped after I'd been playing for about an hour, a very close match. I recall a feeling of enormous anger, followed by sadness, which I didn't show in front of the onlookers, and then the peace of "Why me?" It was a familiar question I recall from my youth, used to maintain my anger at parents who didn't give me what I wanted. Instead of asking directly, I justified my fear and anger by claiming fate, not I, was responsible for any adverse events in my life.

The injury required surgical repair, I was in a cast for several months, and I was inactive for a whole year: a considerable imposition. I fully recovered. Next time when I want some caring, I'll ask for it, or, if I'm afraid to do that, I'll do something that takes care of me and is safe.

One of the reasons I fully recovered is that the surgeon who repaired my ruptured Achilles tendon did a great job. It was a Saturday night, when emergency departments at major hospitals are full of sports injuries and the violent consequences of alcohol. My surgeon was the most junior surgeon on duty.

"I'll call in the professor of orthopedics," he said. "You know that as a doctor at this teaching hospital, you have that right." Now I figured that if I called in the top brass on a Saturday night—in which he was probably enjoying some precious time off and perhaps drinking alcohol—he'd be none too well disposed toward me, his patient.

"Have you performed any of these repairs?" I inquired of my junior surgeon.

"Funny you should ask," he replied. "In fact, as luck would have it, I've done a number of them, and what's more, I've got a real feel for them. They've all done well."

"Great," I said, "You've just scored yourself another one!"

A history of repeated fractures indicates either a constitution lacking in essential minerals or a person who "likes" being injured. The latter is commonly the case, and if an individual reports frequent vehicular accidents, always recalled with great excitement, then I consider that she's trying to harm herself, and I look for a "Don't exist" injunction from one or both of her parents. In the case of youths riding motorbikes, there's often little willingness among them to acknowledge the fact that death is final, since group prestige is gauged by a willingness to defy death.

I believe that nearly all "accidents" are engineered by the subconscious. I hesitate to say that "there's no such thing as an 'accident,'" preferring instead to believe that there's no such thing as *certainty*. The distinction, as we'll see later, is significant.

Back pain is one of the most frequent complaints to confront a general practitioner. Back pain is also the most common disability found in insurance claims. It may well be of an acute nature and be the presenting complaint, but in a detailed history that invites listing all problems it is more often squeezed in at the end. As such, it represents one of life's obstacles, one of those irritations about which the English have been heard to mumble with resignation, "Mustn't grumble." Unlike my early days, when I followed my teaching—which was that you basically ignored back pain and it went away, or the patient at least stopped complaining to you about it—I now take careful note of back pain, since it's a very helpful indicator of the progress a client's making in therapy. If a client decides to resolve those issues that have been contributing to her illness, then back pain usually disappears without fanfare.

"By the way Mrs Bonkowski, how's your back pain you told me about when you first came to see me two months ago?"

"To tell you the truth doctor, I'd completely forgotten about it. Yes, isn't that amazing, it'd been there for years!"

I gave her no active treatment for an extremely irritating complaint and it nevertheless disappeared. She subconsciously decided to drop it. She began to "back herself."

The causes of back pain and the reasons they respond to psychotherapy are too numerous to list. Back pain is a good indicator of progress in therapy. When a client remakes some decisions about her life and changes direction, those decisions are often accompanied by some dramatic changes to her physical appearance. The individual may stand up so much straighter than before that she grows an inch in height, or walk with a new spring in her step, which alters the back tensions and posture. The stoop of depression may be lost, or excessive weight may be shed. All of these things dramatically alter back pain. I've found this previously chronically frustrating area of practice to be very rewarding using the principles of mind-body medicine.

I've briefly discussed using the shape of the body to alert me to those areas of the psychological profile contributing to the illness.

We'll await the physical examination to evaluate it further.

THE GENITOURINARY SYSTEM

Sex plays a large part in the life of human beings and has often been exploited by those desperate to maintain power over others using guilt. The church, the law, the institutions of society all come to mind as organizations that have no hesitation in playing the sexual guilt card. It's no surprise that these same organizations come to mind in respect of the sexual assault of minors. "Holier than Thou" is a fundamental fallback position to those who've elected to replace reason with cant, and have little to offer but condemnation and guilt. Diseases of the genitourinary system reflect the complex attitudes of individuals and society toward sex and sexuality.

Sex may be flirtatious, esoteric, intimate, aggressive, casual, wild and passionate, passive, fast, noisy, tantalizing, dominant, rhythmical, elusive, slow, quiet, fulfilling or disappointing. It may be regular, frequent or rare. It may be a way of life, a way to deny closeness and caring, the icing on a wholesome cake, a reason to adopt a radical political or religious viewpoint, an effective method of maintaining guilt, or a self pleasuring activity. It may occupy an individual totally or not at all. It may be an act of love of both self and others, or an act of hostility, intended to hurt both parties.

A. According to the law of yin and yang or the law of eternal change, anything capable of such great pleasure and love must be capable of the antitheses of those things. Night and day, heat and cold, fast and slow, all move imperceptibly from one into the other. There's no single point where one stops and the other starts. They're all part of a continuum. The sexually permissive person is often similar to the sexually outraged one who sees sex as the scourge of the earth and would have all offenders punished. Despite apparently diametrically opposed behaviors, their psychological positions may be similar (see diagram on page 168). For the child, sex and punishment are often linked. Use and abuse, excess and denial are all part of the cyclical nature of our sexualities, both individually and collectively as a society. We use sex to sell things and as a consequence are assailed by it relentlessly. It's one of the last free pleasures and is a part of us that we can deny but not ignore. Only a person with no eyes and ears may escape people and things being advertised using sex, and then such an individual would be so refreshingly naive that to some they would anyway be considered a prized sexual object. Innocence would rapidly be lost. Sex is everything.

B. Sex is sinful.

C. Sex is what you make it.

Using the circular concept, it's evident that the two strident positions are actually the closest, despite protesting themselves to be polar opposites. The please-yourself option remains neutral in both models.

In this climate of active sexuality, it's no wonder that sex is generally considered to be a large part of the personality and equally no wonder that our body image is dominated by our sexuality. Because of these things, diseases of the genito-urinary system constitute a significant proportion of current medical practice and, like all diseases, indicate the relevant area of the client's psyche.

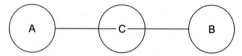

The linear notion of the spectrum of opinions

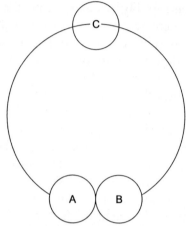

The continuum of opinions

A = Sex is everything; B = Sex is sinful; C = Sex is what you make it

As a therapist, I have to be aware of my own sexuality. I'm readily able to identify a sexual nuance, either expressed or denied, which is very effective in establishing why a man should be suffering from herpes or a woman is unable to conceive. I give clients permission to have their own sexual feelings. I'm at ease discussing orgasm with a middle aged woman. I'm equally at ease with the concern a middle-aged man shows for his future sex life following a diagnosis of prostatism and am happy to acknowledge an erection a youth has sustained during examination, rather than pretending it didn't happen.

I may be the first person with whom a middle-aged woman has ever discussed masturbation and orgasm. These women may have spent years overcoming negative social attitudes to speaking of their sexual needs. The therapist needs to be a willing listener and respectful of disclosure.

Any personal bias of mine is capable of distorting my therapy, if I'm unaware of it. When given the chance, people who haven't spoken of their sexuality for years, or at all, usually have a few questions stored up. They express relief at the chance to discuss things that have long bothered them.

This is all possible if the practitioner allows people the time and provides the environment in which it's safe to express feelings. Of course, some people react adversely if questioned about sexual function and that's equally as informative as the answers they might have given.

One of the more insidious aspects of current orthodox medical practice is the way in which doctors make a lot of money and a lot of mistakes in the area of women's problems. Problems of contraception, menarche, menopause, menstruation, conception, urinary tract infections, vaginal infections and sexual disinterest constitute a significant portion of the average doctor's practice. There's no evidence that female doctors counsel women any more effectively than their male colleagues in these areas, though to be sure their experience is first hand and women often feel more comfortable during the physical examination if the doctor is female. Whereas male practitioners may dismiss female complaints with a disbelief that is a consequence of their own unresolved grudges toward their own mothers, a female doctor may, by joining in a game of "Ain't it awful" with the client, contribute to her misconception of the disease as not of her own making—and therefore beyond her power to influence. The refusal of doctors of both sexes to make themselves aware of the sexual games they're playing in their own lives prevents accurate diagnoses and effective treatments of their clients' problems. Because there's considerable polarization of the sexes, there's also considerable distrust.

In general terms, people who enjoy their own sexuality will not suffer from diseases of the sexual organs. Alternatively, someone who comes to rely on his sexuality for intimacy, to the exclusion of friendship, can expect that if he's unhappy, a disturbance of his genitals will be made more likely. The source of comfort becomes a source of frustration; if a man translates this frustration into self-hate, then a disease of the genitals confirms to him that he's unworthy. In the case of a man who's become sexually promiscuous from rebelling against a puritanical parent, developing a cancer within the genito-urinary system merely highlights his failure to discard the old belief system. The following case is such an example.

Jeff Peters was a thirty-three-year-old man who came to see me with a diagnosis of cancer of the testicle. The right testicle had been removed at operation and his prognosis was good. He wanted to learn how to avoid the chain of events contributing to his disease, and thereby prevent a recurrence.

He was the only son of parents who'd fought a protracted divorce, an event he recalled as being extremely traumatic. His mother, with whom he'd lived following the departure of his father, had often said that her only reason for living was to be with him. Without him, life wasn't worth living. She exhorted him to never leave her and would sabotage the romantic affairs he began as a teenager and young man by becoming distraught with the idea that one day he'd get married and abandon her. As a consequence, he related poorly to women and had never established a satisfactory relationship.

When he was twenty-nine, he and his mother took a brief excursion to a neighbouring town, a distance of some fifty kilometres. On the return journey, he rolled their car and his mother was killed. He blamed himself for the accident and, having been very angry at his mother for the ruthless way in which she attempted to dictate his life, felt very guilty that subconsciously he'd wanted to kill her. This was no doubt the case, and such thoughts constitute a common response of a child to parents who aren't providing what he wants by way of love and protection. Two years after the accident, when he'd been in a promising relationship with a woman for a year, he developed cancer of the testis. He reported that he still dwelt on both the accident and his mother's plea to "never marry a woman and leave me." He knew he was giving himself a serious illness in order to atone for both these sins. The one he'd chosen, threatening both his sexuality and his life, was quite specific. No other would have done.

For a number of reasons I sent him to another therapist. He became sufficiently aware of the dynamics of his illness to decide to both live and feel good about his sexuality. For him, that is wellness. Wellness includes both awareness and the willingness to take responsibility for decisions we make in our best interests. It does not necessarily mean the absence of disease but rather taking responsibility for those diseases we elect, mostly beyond our awareness, to suffer.

Many women have suffered from painful periods at some stage in their lives. If the pain is severe, then analgesia is required. Occasional disturbances will be a reaction to stress, pollutants, not wanting to have sex, fluid retention or many other factors. Provided pain is not a regular event, then beyond the inconvenience the disturbance is of little consequence. If painful periods (dysmenorrhoea), excessive blood loss (menorrhagia), decreased blood flow (oligomenorrhoea), absent periods (amenorrhoea) or any other disturbance of menstruation is regular, answers to how these problems have arisen will be found with great regularity in the area of the woman's sexuality and attitudes to reproductivity.

For an organ or a body system to be healthy, it requires a certain amount of exercise. If it's under-exercised, then it runs the risk of deterioration, through diminished blood supply. If overused, it may hypertrophy and run out of blood supply, become exhausted, or create imbalances elsewhere. In both cases, malfunction of that organ or system results, and is followed by compromising other organs which are then forced to compensate for the increased or decreased function of the aberrant system. The lungs, for example, may be required to handle a greater acid load as a consequence of temporary shut down of the kidneys. The kidneys, in turn, may be forced to handle a greater solid load as a consequence of the failure of an enzyme system. This may result in gout. Many systems, the liver, pancreas, thyroid and adrenals, may be overworking in order to compensate for a great overuse of the gut during an eating binge. Let's apply these principles to the genito-urinary system.

A woman who enjoys her sexuality, loves her body, admires her breasts, and finds looking at her genitals a pleasurable experience will generally be guaranteeing their well-being. If, in addition, she enjoys having her naked body admired by others and enjoys having regular intercourse with one or more partners (during which she frequently experiences orgasm or fulfillment without guilt), she'll have healthy sexual organs. The frequency of sexual contact will, of course, vary, and one is no more desirable than the other. For health, the requirements are simply that enough regular blood flow be established to keep the part active and that the woman regard her body and sexuality as things of great beauty. By so doing, the clitoris will be sensitive, the vagina will be well lubricated and relaxed, the cervix will have a healthy blood flow capable of being buffeted by the penis during intercourse, and the womb will contract, build up, and empty with efficiency and minimal discomfort. The woman's self-image as a fertile, sexually responsive person will guarantee a regular, effective ovulation, often synchronized to either the cycle of the moon or the cycle of another woman with whom she has an intimate relationship or with whom she shares a house. Regular, trouble-free menstruation, with an absence of ovarian problems, is the result. The woman effortlessly achieves conception when she decides she's ready to have a baby. That decision will need to be both subconscious and conscious; otherwise pregnancy may not result.

Conditioning with regard to childbirth and child-rearing is usually powerful, and at the time the woman considers having a baby all these early childhood stories resurface. If they're mainly frightening, they may well upset ovulation and render the woman temporarily infertile. The period of infertility may last from between a few months to the whole of her child-rearing years. It depends on how soon she resolves the fears, and that usually depends on how great those fears are.

If a mother repeatedly tells her daughter that she nearly died giving birth (either to her or to her siblings), then the girl is likely to decide at an early age that childbirth is dangerous and to be avoided. There are, of course, other causes of infertility that are less directly related to the mind, such as diet, drug addiction, congenital deformities of the genital tract, past infections of the ovarian tubes, and hormonal irregularities. It's my belief that the large percentage of infertile women who have been investigated and who demonstrate no obvious physiological or anatomical pathology have decided to remain infertile. Once again, the "decision" is taken out of their awareness.

If you ask someone "What's frightening about being pregnant?" and she snaps the answer "Nothing!" back at you, then you have confirmed the presence of underlying fear. Psychotherapy helps the woman resolve the fear of pregnancy, and a child may result. Men, of course, are often responsible for the failure of a couple to produce offspring, and I believe their case histories will reveal similar injunctions or early life decisions that affect fertility. If we look at a couple of examples of women who prevent themselves from conceiving, the psychological mechanisms involved will become clearer.

Melissa came to see me when she was thirty, complaining of a failure to conceive. She'd been married for about eight years and her husband had always wanted children. She was more wary. The gynecologists and obstetricians had given her a clean bill of health. Her problem in orthodox terms was a failure to ovulate, something that had been difficult to remedy with the drugs available for that purpose. Her husband had a normal sperm count. She believed that for one or more reasons she was preventing herself from becoming pregnant.

She was an exceptionally attractive woman with beautiful big eyes, a very handsome face and a slim figure which she dressed to perfection. She was flirtatious. She'd obviously learned early in life that she was attractive to men, and in fact reported that her father loved her so dearly that her mother was jealous. Mother and father had expended their relationship by the time Melissa was born and had lapsed into an uneasy truce. Melissa became the number one girl in her father's life and he would say so quite unashamedly. She enjoyed this favored position, even though her mother reacted with anger at being rejected by her husband in favor of her daughter and took out her frustrations by being sarcastic to Melissa. Melissa believed fathers had daughters and loved them more than their wives. This made their wives very unhappy.

Melissa was now the wife. If she had a daughter by her childadoring husband, chances were that he would become so enamored with the baby that he would abandon her. This is what she'd experienced in childhood, and there was no reason to suspect that things were any different now. She wasn't prepared to risk her marriage for a child. In addition, her mother had blamed the arrival of the children for her own miserable existence and had stated frequently that "Children tie you down and force you into intolerable situations." This was hardly an encouraging reflection. No, having children was definitely not in Melissa's best interests.

Therapy involved her deciding that she hadn't married her father and receiving assurances from her husband that he wouldn't abandon her when the baby was born. In addition, she realized that if things didn't work out between them, she could always leave. Her body changed significantly over a period of six months. Her somewhat girlish figure was replaced by a fuller sensuality, reflective of women who enjoy their own sexuality. She decided to postpone having a baby until she felt safer about it and, as a final twist to the story, began to practice contraception after "trying" all those years to become pregnant.

When a woman has not become pregnant and over the years has not used contraception, believing herself from experience to be infertile, then the commencement of contraception is a clear indication that she's now approaching fertility. If she reports that "I've never bothered with contraception and I've never been pregnant, but I thought I'd better stop taking risks," I assume that she's decided that she'll start ovulating. Melissa has now conceived.

Men with low sperm counts often result in a couple failing to conceive. Male fertility is as responsive to psychological factors as a woman's failure to ovulate. I'm unable to prove this, as I don't have any experience with men with low sperm counts over a long period of time, but sperm motility, prostatic fluids and sperm morphology change with a man's circumstances.

It's been reported for example that when a man is away from home for a week or so, the chemical composition of his sperm changes so that it acquires a spermicidal element. The purpose of this is to destroy the sperm of another man who may have had intercourse with his wife whilst he's away.

If women or girls complain of small breasts, or if men or boys complain of a small penis, I'm interested in how that's a problem for them. I don't accept the opinion of the client as it may not be borne out by the physical examination. What we are dealing with here is a problem of body image. If a woman has small breasts then I presume she needed small breasts for some reason and I wonder, now that she has them, why she should give herself a hard time over them. If I can establish why she needs to criticize herself, and why she's chosen the size of her breasts to effect this, it may be unnecessary to change the breasts themselves. She may end up delighted with her small breasts. If she decides she no longer needs the small breasts, she'll allow her hormonal systems to enlarge them. As breasts are involved in both sexual attraction and in feeding babies, it may be safely assumed that the poor body image revolves about issues to do with either or both of these things.

A fifteen-year-old boy came to see me a year ago complaining about his small penis. At his insistence, his mother waited in the waiting room during the interview. It was clear that there was some sexual injunction from the mother toward her son's sexuality, and much to her credit she'd realized this. Not wanting her issues to influence her son's happiness, she brought him to me. He was grossly obese for a fifteen-year-old, a time when boys are often letting their manhood flower in the form of fine muscles and a proud posture. His penis wasn't visible from beneath the pad of fat sitting just above the pubic bone, and I thought at first that he wasn't exaggerating his problem. Closer inspection revealed a normal penis and I suggested he go away and masturbate, which he was doing already, and not feel guilty about it. When I saw him six months later, he was much slimmer and no longer had a problem with the size of his penis. I believe that men who have a genuinely small penis can alter the size to some degree by psychotherapy. I have no experience of this but am led to conclude it from the other physical changes I've seen people make, such as significantly increasing their height.

Herpes is one of the curses of our time. Unfortunately, I don't have a cure for it. I've tried just about everything that has appeared to be remotely encouraging in both the medical and lay literature, all with little success. I haven't been able to attribute those few successes I've had to the particular remedy in question. Homeopathic remedies for a time seemed valuable in herpes of the lip, but not in genital herpes. The condition is incredibly widespread and probably increasing. The literature is full of the suffering that clients experience as a consequence of such a serious disturbance of their sexual functioning, but my perspective is that their chances of contracting herpes, or having multiple recurrences of it, are made greater if they don't like something about their genitals or their sexuality.

At the time of contracting the disease they may have needed to modify their sexuality or have a "need" to be miserable or appear to be the victim of fate. None of us, it seems, likes to see ourselves as totally responsible for ourselves, and for the purpose of proving that we're the victims of circumstance to some degree, are prepared to give ourselves illnesses. This reaffirms our vulnerability. Under pressure we tend to revert to the relative safety of childhood beliefs and practices.

A condition like herpes which has such a disturbing effect on a person's sexuality, uncovers his attitude to his own sexuality in general, and his genitals in particular. What's the role of parents in this? Children, like adults, love being cuddled. Human touch is one of the most profound of all human experiences, mentioned over one hundred times in the Christian Bible.

It's impossible to overstate the beneficial physiological effects on the mind and body of being lovingly and respectfully held and cuddled. Parents have the opportunity of allowing their children to believe that their bodies are beautiful, and that pleasurable feelings come from being held. Child sexual molestation by fathers, uncles, loved ones, and sometimes women has such devastating consequences for the child that I'm loathe to even mention the natural contact between parents and children for fear of being attacked by those who seek to deny their own sexual insecurities. They do this by assigning wrongdoing to parents who have close physical contact with their children, which is the most natural thing in the world. I'm of the view that no balanced parent could possibly deny the value of cuddling and holding children.

Commenting favorably on children's bodies, and not implying that the sexual areas of their bodies are bad or wrong, makes contracting herpes and other diseases of the sex organs less likely. If people's distorted sexuality demands that they put their own needs for safety and "being right" ahead of the need to create healthy children, then they may attack physical closeness with children as inappropriate. The reality is that the great majority of parents do this naturally, without needing to think about it, without needing to justify it, and as part of the most beautiful and wholesome relationship they will ever have—that of the relationship between themselves and their children. Boys who don't experience parental discomfort with the boy's genitals have a better chance of growing up to have healthy genitals and a healthy reproductive physiology. That way, a boy comes to believe that it's a wonderful and respected part of his body, and the feelings he gets from it are both welcome and healthy. I believe he's less likely to suffer from genital herpes than someone who's been fed the mantra that you must not touch yourself in those areas and that masturbation will make you go blind. He's less likely to suffer from erectile dysfunction or premature ejaculation as he gets older.

The prevalence of genital herpes reflects the prevalence in our society of some very bigoted and powerful sexual conditioning. Some religious and self-declared moral organizations propagate their own sexual pathology, which is that sexual diseases are caused by too much sex in the community. It won't surprise anyone that when these organizations cajole teens into abstaining from sex until they're married, the consequence is that these teens then become pregnant more frequently than teenagers who were allowed to be more natural in their sexual development. If parents encouraged their children to find their own style of sexual fulfillment, then the matter would defuse. People would be uninterested in the sexual habits of their neighbors. In such a climate, sexual disturbances that are the end result of parental and societal bigotry would disappear, as would opportunistic infections of the sex organs. These manifest because of a disturbance of the natural protective physiology that is present when the human organism is not having to waste precious resources combating leftover childhood injunctions against sex. In the years to come, I'm hoping the above paragraph will be archaic and will become irrelevant.

I've treated a few cases of genital herpes in great depth via group psychotherapy over a period of a year, and while I can report a decrease in the frequency and severity of attacks, I cannot report a cure. The fringe benefits are worth the exercise alone, however, or so my clients report. If a pill or vaccination is developed to cure genital herpes, at this stage I would recommend taking the pill and addressing the sexual injunctions over the following course of one's life.

Before we leave the topic of sexuality, there's a final point that should be made. As a society, we're more concerned with sex and money than with many other things. Both of these things can be and are used to create divisions within the society. I don't think that this is wittingly orchestrated by any particular political lobby, although it's certainly in the interests of big business to keep people to some degree separate, and in small and numerous buying units, that is, couples or families. Additionally, it's probably in the best interests of politicians generally, as they're clearly of the belief that they know what's best for all, to discourage any closeness between people that might generate independence. My point is that factors are operating in the community to keep people away from each other, scared of each other, distrusting and skeptical of each other, and that these attitudes are promoted by interested parties. What's this got to do with the diseases of the genito-urinary tract?

Sex and closeness are two of many variables which in any relationship constantly change. On one end of the sexual spectrum may be the classic "Wham, bam, thank you Maam," and on the other, long-term, non-sexual friendship. There's not a thing wrong with either contact. If either is practiced in the denial of the other however, imbalance may result, and disease follows imbalance.

Many people practice a combination of the above types of personal interactions and are perfectly satisfied by the arrangement. If they have monogamy contracts with their spouses, they may allow their casual sexual drives to be satisfied by flirting. Given the emphasis on sexuality in the community and the lack of closeness, however, many people in fact use their sexuality to avoid getting close to other people. Some churches and others who preach that sex is bad actively promote this attitude, thereby encouraging those who do indulge to feel bad about it and to withdraw for their crimes. With the media at every opportunity encouraging people to have sex, and the prevailing moral overtone that it's a sin (and thus hidden from parents, teachers, and others), the climate for casual sex becomes established. People often end up with frequent sexual contact and no real caring, and that's imbalance. Those who actively campaign against sex are of course achieving the opposite result of what they intended.

An alternative attitude would be to allow children to develop naturally, without excessive parental injunctions, and teach them ways to assess the caring available to them to both receive and to give in any relationship. They could also be taught to look for signs that indicate danger. Very soon people would be establishing intimate contacts with people who cared as well. By doing these things, sexuality would disappear as a contentious issue, making many people's lives so much more fulfilling and guilt free, and the major predisposition toward sexual diseases would be removed. Sowing the seeds of health in children is real preventative medicine.

THE CENTRAL NERVOUS SYSTEM: AWARENESS VS. ASPIRIN

Orthodox medicine affords considerable status to diseases of the brain and spinal cord. These diseases are generally considered somewhat exotic, and the practitioners who deal with them—neurologists and neurosurgeons—occupy an exalted position in the medical hierarchy. Diseases of these systems therefore appeal to a certain type of patient, particularly medical practitioners. You can almost hear the little kid doctor in them saying, "Nah, nah, my disease beats your disease!" Many of the diseases of the nervous system are commonly considered incurable, such as multiple sclerosis, motor-neuron disease, neurofibromatosis, Huntington's chorea, and trigeminal neuralgia, so people don't have to give them up after they've spent time and effort in establishing them. If they decide on a tumor of the brain, then the neurosurgical team may operate for fifteen hours (sometimes successfully), and the follow-up treatment is usually the best the hospital can provide. Diseases of the CNS are truly the doyens of diseases.

Because these diseases are generally considered incurable, it might be worthwhile to shake the psyche and the soma by reframing them. Rather than approach them with breathless resignation, it may be beneficial to pepper our discussion of them with a few lighter aspects of the human condition that we can all relate with. This in no way diminishes the often tragic and massive suffering that these diseases cause.

This might be a good time to reiterate that people always do the best they can at any time. Arguably, it's not possible to do worse than your best.

I don't know whether the common headache is the most commonly experienced temporary discomfort or "dis-ease" in humans, but it must be close. It's also important because I think that it represents the area where most people will allow themselves to look a little more closely at the circumstances that have contributed to them feeling unwell. Whereas few people will admit to having any role in the development of their arthritis, and no one will admit to contributing to their multiple sclerosis, most people will admit to tension or aggravations at work or home as features of recurrent headaches. That's a start, and you have to start somewhere.

People often ask, "How can I get off these pain killers?" or "What must I do to learn to relax?" People use headaches to avoid so many things that if you suffer headaches and want to find out why, look at the end result of having them. For example, if having a headache at home means that your wife stops talking about the neighbor's problems, ask yourself whether you aren't sick of hearing about others' problems. If you take time off work because of headaches, ask yourself if you really want that job. If you suffer from headaches after intercourse, ask yourself what you're feeling and what you're saying about yourself having had intercourse, and you may be able to identify a benefit from the headache.

Of course, some people turn head pain into life-threatening illnesses such as brain cancer, and occasionally some of these people decide that they don't want to die after all and survive, often with the help of the neurosurgeons. Each person suffering headaches must decide for himself how much he wants the condition investigated because he's the only person who really knows how much self-harm he's capable of. Therein resides the great flexibility of the headache. It can be used to manipulate a marriage for years (with the approval of both parties of course), or can be an occasional thing, reserved perhaps for avoiding weddings.

The frequency, severity and the area of the headache are often taught quite specifically in childhood, since the very real hard work of caring for children is one of the tasks capable of being moderated by a headache. By protesting that she has a headache, a mother may entice a reluctant husband to wash the dishes, for example. Children therefore learn about these things early. Boys may learn that if they come home late from the pub and claim a headache, then they feel better about the severe admonishing they have courted and consequent expiation of their guilt, whereas girls may learn that instead of being angry at your husband, you give yourself a headache, seduce him and then claim insensitivity on his part. Both parties have predictably (and in these examples stereotypically) given up their own power and self-responsibility in favor of having a headache. It seems almost a silly thing to do, given an outcome where both partners remain secretly angry at each other and neither is satisfied, but that simply demonstrates the power of the early conditioning. A child who has experienced the manipulation possible with skilful use of the headache is going to believe that illness is an acceptable way of relating to loved ones. The likelihood is that she'll use similar tactics, or be so outraged at the dishonesty that she'll rebel and never suffer from headaches at all. If she's rebelling as an adult and still angry at her parents, she'll most likely choose another form of incapacitation, perhaps recurrent laryngitis. You'll hear her protest that, "At least I never suffered from headaches!" If she gets mad as hell at her parents for what she didn't get, acknowledges that they were doing what was safest for them in threatening circumstances, and drops the anger, she's unlikely to need anything of significance to be wrong with her.

I repeat the basis of this thesis: If you have no need of major illness, you will have no major illness.

Everything we become aware of as children or adults must register through one or more of the five sensory channels: sight, sound, touch, smell, and taste. (There's more than five ways of connecting with our universe and other people, but this book is already too radical for many people, so we'll leave the discussion of subtle interconnectedness to others.) We experience things through these channels, and when we recall the events of childhood, it's likely that the recollection will favor one or more senses above the others. In such a way, the smell of a tanker truck passing by may be a more vivid memory than its sound. It is for me. Some people will regularly favor one system of registering events over others, which means that someone may be predominantly a visual person, an auditory person, a kinesthetic person (one who registers movement), or an olfactory person. The system that a person primarily uses is known as his or her "primary representational system." (See Stephen Lankton's *Practical Magic* from 1980.)

The particular system favored by the individual will be evident in his language, for example, "I can see you don't believe me," is the way in which a visual person may speak. An auditory person may say, "I hear that you don't believe me!" while an olfactory person may say, "Well, the whole thing smells of insincerity!" To communicate effectively with people, it's helpful to be in the same representational system as they are. Hypnosis makes use of the sensory preference of the subject in just this way.

In considering diseases of the central nervous system, we're obliged to consider diseases of the sense organs, such as blindness, deafness, loss of taste and various sensory defects. Some sensory aberrations are in fact diseases of the peripheral nervous system, and some diseases such as tertiary syphilis affect both the central and peripheral nervous systems. The defect in the ability of the sense organ to register events taking place about it varies from minor to complete, for example, from a minor visual defect to a total loss of sight. Many of these defects, particularly the severe ones, are present at birth and are a consequence of genetics, poor diet or lifestyle of the parents, environmental pollutants such as small particles from car exhausts, or infections such as rubella. Many are avoidable, some are not. Those that develop later, often in childhood or as a young adult, may be the consequence of making a decision to shut down the function of that organ. That decision is nearly always subconscious. Someone with no obvious physical trauma can suddenly, or over a period of time, no longer see. Another individual may slowly lose hearing until he's partially or completely deaf. The hearing loss may be a nerve conduction defect and in some cases be accompanied by tinnitus (ringing in the ear). There may be no logical explanation for the onset or the continuation of the disease. Under those circumstances I ask myself (and then the client) what's too frightening for the client to either see or hear. What's so terrifying for him that the safest way out is to simply not register events around them?

It may be an acute thing, like not wanting to hear what the boss says at work, and then claiming compensation for industrial hearing loss. Or it may be chronic, deep-seated anxiety, as in the case of the orphan who was told by her stepmother that she was only given a home because of her poor sight. Recovering sight to this girl may well have meant a loss of support. Until she feels safe enough to take care of herself, which may be never, she'll keep the visual defect. She may marry a man who feels that he needs to atone for his unworthiness by looking after someone full-time. Such men will often choose partners who want to remain in need of care and who, in order to justify this arrangement continuing, cite their partner's disability.

Now if I were suffering from a major hearing or sight loss of inexplicable origin and I were reading this, I might have one of two reactions. First, I might be absolutely outraged and shout something like, "What the hell would he know, anyway!" and then retreat into my private but not very helpful explanation of the disease. Or I could say, "Well, I don't know, but neither does anybody else; it may help. I'll ask myself a few questions about it and see if I can't establish my own investment, if any, in this disability."

The first approach won't yield results right now, because the person is still protecting himself. That's the best thing for him to do at this point: enjoy his outrage. In the future, he may feel safe enough to think about it. The second option establishes the benefits (if any) of the disease and may or may not be helpful at this time. The pathology may be so long-standing as to be irreversible; on the other hand, real gains may be made.

The power exercised in the creation of the problem is harnessed to remove it. This will be both frightening and exciting. The prize and the risk will always be balanced.

10
DRUGS, DIET, AND PERSONALITY— WHO'S TAKING WHAT

MEDICATION

In America, 70% of the population regularly take a prescription drug, and over 50 million take prescription drugs for non-medical reasons. America consumes over 80% of the world's prescription narcotics [according to the Mayo clinic in 2014]. Data from most developed nations is similar, except perhaps for the narcotic intake of Americans, which is significantly higher than other countries. More Americans now take opioids than smoke cigarettes. The cost to the US economy is in the order of US$ 200 billion per year.

In Australia, as noted earlier approximately 55 percent of people take regular medications of some description in any given two-week period. Of those drugs that are taken, about 50 percent are prescribed by medical practitioners; the rest are prescribed by naturopaths or are bought in supermarkets, health-food stores, or over the counter at pharmacies. These figures demonstrate that a majority Americans and Australians have incorporated drug taking into their way of life. Similar drug use occurs in most countries. When we include drugs of social intercourse—alcohol, nicotine from tobacco, caffeine from tea and coffee—and other recreational drugs, it becomes clear that many people are under the influence of drugs most of their lives. Think about it for a moment and ask yourself about your own drug intake. What would life be like for you if you couldn't take drugs?

Why do so many people take so much medication? It may be from not wishing to experience the thoughts and feelings that would arise in a drug-free world. We can avoid taking full responsibility for our lives by taking drugs.

Several drugs have been developed which have dramatically altered the course of disease for some people, if not saved their lives. Penicillin, insulin and cortisone come to mind, and if we add aspirin, morphine, digoxin and the contraceptive pill, drugs which have affected the quality of life, we have almost assembled the significant advances in medicine over the past fifty years. Following the Second World War, people were led to believe that along with the great social reconstructions and burgeoning affluence, health and longevity were problems capable of being solved by technology. The enormous quantity of drugs consumed by the community is a legacy of that belief. Psychologically, the consumption of drugs is synonymous with administering happiness.

"If you take this pill you'll feel better" (and by implication, all your troubles will go away).

Becoming materialistic and affluent has bred its own share of new social and emotional problems, and so has the belief in the theory of instantaneous drug cure. We hoped, quite reasonably, that it would work. We hoped that while the politicians and the capitalists or the totalitarian regimes would make us happy and prosperous, the doctors would make us well. I'm sorry to inform you that the experiment has failed. I'm sorry to inform you that for the large majority of people, drugs, in the long-term, make things worse. I'm sorry to inform you that you must, if you wish to be well, look after yourself. When I say I'm sorry, I mean that I'm sorry for me: sorry that a parent won't look after me for the rest of my life, sorry they didn't do it perfectly when they had the chance and sorry that they won't do it now. By taking pills we're assuming the inventor, discoverer, manufacturer, prescriber and dispenser all know more about us than we do, and that in their collective wisdom, they'll take care of us. Taking drugs, I've suggested, is like taking happiness. It represents the parent that we hoped would make us secure, loved and happy. I'm not admonishing you in this, I'm commiserating with you. This crisis consists of both danger and opportunity. The danger is of deciding to remain loveless, helpless, hopeless and ill, and the opportunity is to take full responsibility for ourselves and to harness the power within. That way we become our own parent, our own physician, and have little need for drugs.

Knowing the frequency and the nature of the remedies that clients take helps me understand how much they've relied on orthodox or unorthodox remedies (folk remedies, family remedies, or self-administration) to keep themselves well. Conversely, taking people off medication is like prying a bone from the jaws of a hungry dog—not to be undertaken lightly. The medication is often an integral part of clients' belief systems, and any rapid changes may be too frightening for them (as well as being counterproductive). I found that out through being bitten a few times. My usual practice was to insist that the client immediately stop taking all medications. Now I wean people off medications only after they've established new ways of caring for themselves.

If they're a "pack of nerves," they'll be taking a pack of tranquillisers (presumably one for each nerve), or if they're too scared to be diagnosed as ill but feel lousy, they may be on twenty vitamins a day. Usually this makes them feel nauseous but at least they figure that they're looking after themselves. If they're a bit trendy, and enjoy the game of "My doctor out-diagnoses your doctor," then homoeopathy, with its appreciation of idiosyncrasy and personal prescription, will probably be the choice. Doctors' daughters who were abandoned by their fathers at the first signs of puberty and who subsequently never forgave their fathers for not continuing to be physically close to them, may be rebelliously taking no medication at all. They'll boom it out at you, the anger scarcely concealed, "I never take drugs of any description!" I may get them taking some drug as a way of energizing their impasse. Random controlled double blind drug trials have established for a long time that at least one third of reported drug effects are placebo, which further suggests that the effect of many drugs is mainly psychological.

The role of drugs in contemporary society is complex, concerned not only with people's needs but also with big business, power, money, and technology. Drug companies are among the most powerful institutions on earth and as a group one of the most wealthy. Drug trials conducted by researchers who receive any benefits at all from the outcomes of their research can be totally dismissed. The researchers don't have to be frauds, but they cannot know and counter the impacts of their own interests, which nullifies the trial outcomes. The declarations of interest that prestigious medical journals require of their contributors are completely insufficient to negate researcher bias. Nearly all drug trials are conducted by researchers who receive tangible benefits from the outcomes of the trial, whether that interest is financial, professional advancement, or, the most powerful of all doctor drivers, being more knowledgeable than their peers, or being "right."

SOCIAL HISTORY

This section is perhaps the most significant in the client's history, because it's where I confirm previous observations (or make adjustments where I've been incomplete or wrong). I believe that the psychological profile of any person and her body must be consistent: that is, they must mutually reflect each other. The same can be said of a client's personal circumstances. Events in a person's life that are normally considered to be totally unrelated to his medical state are in fact reflective of his physical state, and vice versa. Personal circumstances reflect both the psychological and physical state. Life events that are never the subject of medical inquiry are in fact just as informative as an orthodox history and far more informative than the vast majority of laboratory tests. Because of this, PROMs (Patient Reported Outcome Measures) offer much promise for improving health. People who are generally happy are generally well. I don't believe that illness "causes" unhappiness any more than I believe that unhappiness "causes" illness. Unhappiness and illness are states of mind, reactions to events, and they are at once mutually supportive, mutually antagonistic, and constantly changing. This paradigm will emerge as the cornerstone of both the understanding of illness and, more particularly, its treatment.

Let's consider an example. I had acne myself, so this example, like the rest of this theory, is close to my heart. If a boy has acne, and he uses this to remind himself of how unsightly he is, the acne "causes" him to be unhappy. But the acne developed because he was unhappy about something, perhaps even the way he looked. He increased the secretions of his sebaceous glands, using hormonal control, and the muscular tension in his face closed off the pores, resulting in acne. Therefore, the unhappiness "causes" the acne. This example demonstrates mutual support between unhappiness and acne.

The boy, however, feels safer having his opinion about his looks confirmed by his acne (since illness "causes" happiness) and, in turn, is content to be unhappy (since unhappiness "causes" wellness), because at the moment that's safest for him. In this context, being well means taking care of greater fears. The same example has now demonstrated mutual antagonism. When this boy matures and drops some of his fears about being attractive and wants to attract admirers, we can expect him to gradually remove his acne. The relationship between his illness and his happiness will then be different and will continue to fluctuate over the years; that is, the relationship will be constantly changing.

Perhaps the concept of illness and emotions being mutually dependent can be more economically expressed by saying that we're attracted to circumstances, including illness, that cause us to suffer (which we don't like), but which also provide safety from the unknown (which we do like). Ordinary life circumstances possess the capacity to confirm our attitudes, beliefs, and illnesses, but they also provide the opportunity to address those things and allow them to change. Without suffering, perhaps we wouldn't evolve much.

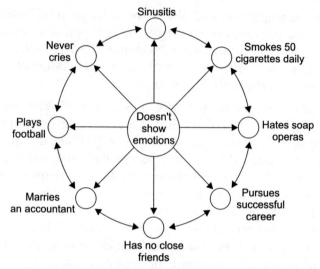

The childhood decision not to show emotion results in the above. The personal circumstances do not cause each other, for example, smoking doesn't cause sinusitis, but are interrelated as shown. Exploring the original decision will remove the disease and alter those circumstances which were in the service of the original decision and which are now disadvantageous.

I've yet to see an unattractive person who didn't benefit in some way from appearing unattractive. The psyche has, over a period of time, faithfully sculptured the bones, muscles and skin to suit the individual. Additionally, self-caring and self-respect always transcend those asymmetrical facial features caused by genetics or old misadventure. Social circumstances may be used both to determine causes and plan treatment programs for illness. Self-love, the fabric of both love for others and wellness, is evident in the everyday life of an individual. I suggest that it's not possible to have self-love or the love of others in isolation. You have both or you have neither. The separation of self from others is spurious.

Happy people are healthier than unhappy people. That's a bold statement, which you may confirm by thinking of yourself or others that you know who were ill, and remembering the events in your lives at the time. The personal circumstances of individuals will reflect their medical history, and vice versa.

As I've said earlier, one does not "cause" the other. The social environment at any time, like the physical state, is a reflection of the early life decisions that were taken as a child. The current circumstances "represent" the old decisions. "Represent," broken down into "Re" and "present" reveals that the current circumstances bring into the "present" something from the past. (Pronounce "present" as in "present time" to fully understand this point.) The past events continue to contain psychic energy, and have yet to be expiated. So they keep recurring until they're done with.

That's why the social history is of such value. It will often verify that clients are not getting what they want for themselves in their lives and, in these circumstances, it's unlikely the client is protecting himself from physical disease. We all know people who appeared to be very happy in their personal life, perhaps happily married with lovely kids, a good income, a nice home, were well respected, good looking and in the prime of their life who've been stricken by a serious illness and perhaps died. How does that fit into the theory of personal circumstances correlating with illness? We all know as well of people who appeared to have all those advantages and who turn out to be "less" than we thought. I say "less," because it's a feature of all of us, in our quest for someone, somewhere, to look after us, or to be a higher authority than we are, that we readily hoist others onto pedestals and are then shocked when they don't turn out as we fantasized, for our own needs, they would. Once again, we're angry at having been betrayed, or at least not looked after properly, by our parents. No-one is a higher authority on you than you are. (You can still pick the brains of whoever makes himself available to help you.) The downside of being our own highest authority is that it's a bit hard to keep blaming others for our own misfortunes if we take responsibility for ourselves. We'll usually avoid taking responsibility if there's anyone remaining at all who we might be able to cajole into looking after us. This tendency is manna for at-fault lawyers.

First, our impression of the "beautiful people" who have "got it all together" (and who, as a consequence, should have no illness) is often a figment of our needy imaginations. Second, it's often far more important for some people to be seen to "have it together" than to be seen as needy. This is part of their scripting. Underneath the coping exterior is a scared child who learned very early that if he wanted approval, then he'd better not demand too much. Even more, that if he wanted approval (and to the child this meant being allowed to stay alive), then he'd better take care of either Mom or Dad. These people are afraid (unless they decide to change) of expressing their own needs, so they take care of others instead. Often the only legitimate way to get the caring they need is to be ill. Usually one of their parents would have modeled that behavior. And I repeat, these are often the people whom we think are coping very well, because we want them to be coping very well. "If they can't survive this rat race," we might say, "then how the hell can I?" They, in turn, need to be seen to be in control.

It's important to note the difference between correlating the social circumstances with the illness and saying that the social circumstances "caused" the illness. Many authors who write on the psychological factors involved in physical disease adopt the latter position. They can see that illness and personal dissatisfaction are related, and therefore they believe one causes the other. In this they are not unlike their mechanistic fellows who are still at the point of believing that streptococci cause tonsillitis, or excessive alcohol causes gastritis, or lack of exercise combined with excessive, eating causes obesity. Rather, to take the last example, the lack of exercise is a consequence of depression that has arisen in someone who as a child adopted a loveless script. The excess sugar from overeating suppresses the sadness and anger at being unloved, while the obesity renders them unattractive to others and to themselves. None of these three features — lack of exercise, overeating, and obesity — caused the other; instead, they were all the result of, and were maintained in the service of, the early childhood decision that "I'm unworthy."

I've abandoned the linear notion of cause and effect in illness in favor of the cyclical interdependence of mind and body. This is most cogently expressed in the well-known yinyang symbol. Illness, wellness; hot, cold; happiness, unhappiness; light, dark; sanity, insanity; are all a continuum. None is definable without the other.

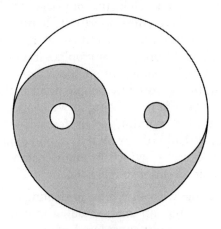

DIET HISTORY

We often hear phrases such as "You are what you eat."

Then again, perhaps "You eat what you eat because of who you are."

Diet has always interested me as a treatment modality, at least since I decided about ten years ago to do something about my own state of health, suffering as I was from a rebellious, immature overdose of junk foods. Since then, I've been intrigued with how powerful and effective a tool diet can be when used skillfully. You'll get little sympathy from orthodox medical practitioners for this view, mainly because they regard it as against their interests to have the public self-administer an effective remedy which obviates the need for the practitioner; and secondly, historically, they know little about diet. It's been said that the average American medical receptionist knows slightly less about diet than the average American doctor, unless the receptionist has a weight problem, in which case the average receptionist knows marginally more than the average doctor.

Contributing to this abysmal lack of knowledge about an essential component of human well-being are the drug companies, (which provide most of the money for medical research and don't fund advances in any discipline bar their own) and the conservatism of medical teaching authorities. I once heard the well-known British physician Dr. Denis Burkitt say that if he were given the opportunity to improve the health of the people of the Western industrial nations, he would remove white bread from sale and replace it with whole-wheat bread. Such a small change for such a major benefit! As I've said, however, the reason why people don't make this change is because they benefit from being unwell, since illness can be an effective tool for avoiding certain fears. Those fears center on taking stewardship of our own lives and confronting what we think we "know" — which in many instances are fictions that we maintain in order to feel safe.

When dealing with diet, one is dealing with the whole personality, not just an intellectual appreciation of those things that are generally considered edible and nutritious. A careful diet history will reveal an enormous amount about the psychological and personal circumstances of the client. Certain personalities eat certain diets, and changing the diet can alter the mood of a client substantially.

Someone who is flighty and inconsistent will often be eating fruit in excess and, if he wants to calm down, would do better eating brown rice and boiled vegetables. Eating excess quantities of red meat may facilitate aggression and bad temper—a decided advantage if you're a professional football player. Vegetarians, on the other hand, may be so placid that the world treads all over them. The lack of adrenal stimulation from eating only vegetables results in a low level of aggression in an often already-placid person.

Most people, I think, will have some image of the eating and drinking habits of different members of the community. These images are no doubt stereotypical but are sufficient for my purpose here, which is to show that diet, like clothes and cars, is indicative of the personality. A bar owner is expected to drink large quantities of alcohol. A writer is expected to be slaving over a computer with a coffee in one hand and a cigarette in the other, while businesspeople are expected to be seen emerging, bloated from food and alcohol, from fancy restaurants. Eating habits reflect people's social movements, such as how often they eat at home or out and how much money they spend on ingredients. Garbage collectors have always claimed that it's possible to tell the personalities of the inhabitants of a household from their garbage. I'm considering asking clients to bring in their trash so I can rummage through it and save them an hour of interrogation!

Eating is one of the last free choices people have. While the foodstuffs themselves are far from free, and finances are clearly limiting, within a range we can choose the food we want to eat without interference. This means that those choices will accurately reflect an individual's wants at that time. In the case of children, compliance and rebellion, acquiescence and anger, are all expressed through food acceptance or refusal. These patterns have a habit of lasting into adulthood and when people eat a certain way, they may still be rebelling or complying with parents' wishes. It makes things interesting when the doctor attempts to change the diet. Immediately the client is confronted once again by someone telling her what to do; more often than not, this will precipitate emotional catharsis. Diet is therefore an exceptionally effective diagnostic tool, used for revealing the personality when the diet is changed, as well as being able to observe the physiological effects from a change in diet. Orthodox dietetics may lack this psychological perspective, depending as it does on a simple balance of the constituents of foodstuffs – the fats, carbohydrates, proteins, vitamins and minerals.

Diet is of such importance to our health that I will engage in fuller discussions on both diets for acute problems and for long-term prudent diets in chapter 14, "Remedial Dietetics and Prudent Diet."

11

THE PSYCHOLOGICAL PROFILE

BEYOND STRESS

If I believed all illness to be a consequence of stress, and that an investigation of the client's social circumstances would reveal the source of that stress, then my history taking would be complete. I believe instead, however, that people construct circumstances for themselves that they then react to with stress — that is, they're not being stressed by external events but are stressing themselves using the "external" circumstances to do it. They're attracted to stressful circumstances in order to place the locus of the stress and the locus of power outside of themselves and by imputation, beyond their influence. We all do this. Therefore, I need to expand my inquiry to include the first times in our lives we made decisions which resulted in stress. That time is childhood.

The child, forced by parental pressure to make a decision he's ill equipped to make, responds with stress and makes an adaptation. As an adult he no longer needs parents to keep him alive, so he no longer needs to continue with the adaptation or script decision. Stress as an adult is a consequence of the grown-up failing to relieve his own internal little kid from the burden of the early decision. With no protection from the parent and adult parts, the little kid is as stressed in the grown-up as he ever was in the child. As a child his options were limited, but as an adult he can expand these and get the grown-up parts to assume responsibility for his decisions. With the pressure off the little kid, he need no longer be worried and can decide to do things differently. This process represents the protection part of successful psychotherapy, that is, the client's grown-up part protecting his own little kid.

All illness is a consequence of stress; not stress arising from an individual's immediate environment but left over from a time in childhood when survival made an adaptation necessary. The current stressful circumstances are acting in the service of the unresolved early childhood conflicts. Until people decide to explore those matters in their lives which trouble them, they'll continue to set up stressful events in their lives. This reconfirms their childhood decision and helps them feel safe, painful and full of suffering though it may be. Illness may result from this stress and may also provide the discomfort which initiates the individual changing, that is, the physical discomfort eventually exceeds the psychological discomfort which spawned it.

Stress, like illness, is assumed to be beyond the control of the individual. It may be beyond "control," but it's not beyond influence. In reality it's self-created, and a synonym for fear. The fear can take many forms, such as fear of not making a deadline, fear of failure at sport, fear of losing the love of a spouse, or fear of not earning enough money to support children. These are all considered to be unavoidably stressful, but are really personal reactions to situations, rather than stressful situations of themselves. The stress is old fear.

An example of how a stressful early childhood decision may repeat itself later in life, and lead to disease through fear, can be seen from the following: The first born child in a family of eight, particularly if she's only a year or so older than the next child, will often be required to help her mother look after her brothers and sisters. If she were under no pressure to do so she would have no more than a passing interest in the welfare of young infants, and would be too concerned with her own life and needs to respond to theirs. Being too young to take responsibility for herself, she can hardly be expected to care for anyone else. That she does so, and does so very well, reflects the active encouragement of her parents. When she cares for her younger brothers and sisters she's told by her mother, "Mummy couldn't do without you." The message to the young girl is interpreted as being, "We love you and will attend to your needs because you're selfless."

Our young girl really wants to play, eat, sleep and be cuddled by her parents but finds she gets less approval from them if she does what she wants, than when she cares for her younger siblings. She's stressed by this. She decides to get her parents' attention and love by forgoing her own needs and looks after the others. This stresses her as well but less than having to contend with a mother who's covertly hostile toward her for not helping. Children will make whatever adaptations they feel are necessary to attract the love, support and approval of their parents. This is the innate survival mechanism of human beings.

For the next fifteen years the girl grows up taking care of her brothers' and sisters' needs, her mother's fatigue and her own fears. The caretaking becomes a significant part of her personality. She'll often be attracted to a man whom she can take care of. Provided she doesn't change and doesn't get exhausted herself, she'll probably be content and healthy. If she does change or becomes exhausted then she's likely to become ill.

The following format establishes the early child decisions and how they result in certain personalities suffering from certain diseases. It's variously called a personality profile, psychological profile, psyche profile or script questionnaire.

The idea is to uncover the forces dictating the adaptations the client made as a child, and in all probability, continues to make as an adult. I say in all probability because the person has attended a practitioner complaining of a problem.

REGRESSION

Worst Scene

Describe the worst event in your childhood. If you're able to recall several that you'd put in that category, then describe the earliest one.

What happens?

Who's there? Your mother, father, grandparents, siblings, friends?

What are you thinking?

Make up a short sentence to summarize your position.

What are you feeling (happy, sad, scared, angry, or combinations)?

What are you deciding to do in the future as a consequence of what's happened?

What's your mother thinking, saying, feeling about you?

What's your father thinking, saying, feeling about you?

If either parent was not present, then put that parent into your fantasy and make up what you think he or she may have said, thought, or felt.

Best Scene

Repeat the steps used for the worst scene.

Favorite Fantasy Character

[Storybook, television, comic book, cartoon, etc.]

Who is it?

What's special about him/her for you?

What was his/her motto in life?

Assign one to the character if he/she didn't use it as a mantra.

Life Fantasy

The next step in our inquiry is for you to imagine that you've been born, that you've lived your life, and that there's a point at which you die.

How old are you when you die in this fantasy?

How do you die?

Where do you die?

Who's at your funeral? List them.

What are they saying, feeling, and thinking about you?

Now imagine that on your gravestone is one short sentence that summarizes your life.

What is that sentence?

Present-Day Heroes/Heroines

Who are they?

What do you like about them?

How are you like the heroes/heroines, and how do you differ from them?

Birth Inquiry

Tell me what you know about your own birth.

Have you heard any family stories or jokes about your birth?

How long was the labor?

What type of delivery was it (natural, induced, cesarean section)?

Was the birth early, late, on time?

Who was there?

Were you a planned pregnancy?

Did your parents want a boy or a girl?

Who chose your name?

Were you named after someone?

Who was it, and what do you know about that person?

What's your exact name on your birth certificate? (If unsure, obtain a copy.)

Parents

What's your mother like?

What's your father like?

Imagine you've just won a race. What does Mom say? What does Dad say?

Imagine you've been caught shoplifting. What does Mom say? What does Dad say?

Name

"Nhoj." That's a word in the Martian language. You've never heard it before.

Pronounce it. What does it mean?

Following are the first letters of the four words in a sentence.

Complete the sentence; it doesn't need to be grammatically correct: N...H...O...J....

INTERPRETATION OF THE PERSONALITY PROFILE

Regression—Worst Scene

From his language, it's possible to tell which sensory system the client prefers; auditory, visual or kinesthetic; is he *hearing* what was said, *seeing* how his father looked, *feeling* as if he was ignored or re-experiencing the movement that took place. This information can be used at a later date to access the client's subconscious, and help in both diagnosis and treatment.

The racket feelings, those frequently expressed feelings that remain from childhood, in fact from the very scenes that the client is now describing, will usually be the first expressed. In other words, the worst scene of childhood will contain elements of a person's life that were traumatic to him at the time and continue to cause him anguish as an adult. Racket feelings will often be used to deny underlying feelings that the client finds more difficult to express. Men, for example, may be angry in order to avoid feeling sad and to avoid crying. Women may cry rather than show that they're angry. The men may develop sinus congestion from not crying and the women may develop high blood pressure from suppressing anger. The worst scene usually brings out the racket feelings. When a client tells you about the bad past, he's really telling you how bad it is for him now. He keeps the scene alive in his memory by recreating it in his life as an adult. The energy for doing exactly the same thing in his life now comes from the fear of changing. Those events in childhood which "spring to mind" in both the good and bad scenes do so because the factors which generated them are still operational. By inviting clients to talk about past events, they'll tell you what's happening in their lives now. When they stop operating out of the past they'll drop the memory, or have no energy for recalling it.

Often a decision that the client made which continues to affect his life will be obvious here. The pressure he was under can be assessed from the danger to himself during the worst scene. If he was being physically abused by his drunken father, a decision about his safety would have been more prudent than it might have been in the event of a threat by his mother to suspend his pocket money. In the former case the child decision will be longer lasting and produce greater pathology than in the latter, although the number of times such situations occurred is equally important. Clients often express veiled anger at one parent for not protecting them against the other.

And arguably, after providing love, food, warmth and comfort for the child, the role of a parent is to protect the child from the excesses of the parenting coming from their partner.

Healthy parenting means not delegating your own parent role to a partner, something very frequently seen in Western families, and generally from the father to the mother.

The parents' comments in the worst scene will often be the injunctions and the drivers. (See chapter 2, "The Childhood Basis of Disease.")

If the client is asked what he'd now demand for himself if he found himself in that situation again, an assessment of his current awareness and his will to evolve, is possible. The woman who was sexually molested by her father and is not prepared to acknowledge her feelings about it is likely to continue suffering from herpes until she admits to herself that she was angry about it, goes through a process of self-conciliation at a minimum, and moves beyond it. Whatever she decides to do about it legally and politically might have less bearing on her own long-term personal well-being than coming to terms with the left over feelings of anger and betrayal. This might mean fully and explosively expressing them.

Regression—Best Scene

If the best scene that a client describes takes place away from the family, the likelihood is that there wasn't much joy within the family for that child. Some clients have trouble remembering a good scene at all, in which case they led a very somber childhood and will probably be having little fun in their lives now (or at least will be nervous about it). As soon as they begin to feel happier than they "should," they may give themselves a minor complaint to take the edge off their happiness. Recurrent headaches, colds, and ringing in the ears are favorites.

The thoughts of the parents in the best scene will often give clues about the drivers. The support or condemnation of children by their parents when the children are enjoying themselves is at the heart of people deciding whether life is to be enjoyed or to be suffered. It's not difficult to see the role illness has in the latter case. Very often the good scene has some distinctly unpleasant (to my mind) ending to it, for example, "I was down the creek playing doctors and nurses with the boy next door, and it was really exciting. Then my elder sister found us and told Dad." In this person's mind pleasure is quickly followed by reprisal of some kind. Guilt and sexual dysfunction are likely.

The best and worst scenes will indicate the sorrows and aspirations, the fears and resentments, the wants and the dreams of the client. They'll give an indication of how far the client intends going in therapy.

If either the best or the worst scenes involve illness of the client or of others in his family, that's very significant. You'll recall that in the history I specifically asked for reactions of clients and their families to illness, both in the client and in the other members of the family, that is, the reaction of the family, particularly the mother and father, to illness in the client, and the reaction of the client to illness in either parent. In addition, the reaction of parents to other family members who are ill will often shape the attitude of the children to illness in themselves. If not directly causing the illness, these factors will have a bearing on the sufferer deciding to maintain or remove his discomfort.

Favorite Fantasy Character

The appreciation of characteristics in others indicates those things we like and don't like about ourselves. If Peter Pan is the favorite character, then the client may regard not growing up as a good thing to do, since Peter Pan himself didn't grow up. This is known as a "Don't grow up" injunction and, as mentioned previously, is a common reaction of the child to a mother who's had several children, the last of whom she encourages to remain at home. The response of these people to illness is usually childlike, in which they want intense caring and no responsibility. This means that when they themselves are needy, they're likely to make themselves ill. The youngest child in a large family often continues to enroll the family in his or her life as an adult.

A "knight in shining armor" may indicate a rescuer, whereas a "damsel in distress" may represent a victim. (A discussion of the Game Triangle is to be found in Chapter 15 –Individual Psychotherapy, on pages 242–43.) Rescuers usually look after others until they realise they're unhappy themselves. The good health which they've enjoyed for years, and which has enabled them to be caretakers; is replaced by a significant illness intended to attract love for themselves. However, it rarely works, and resentment is generally the outcome. Family dynamics can take a lifetime to overcome. The roles assigned to family members as children, and adopted by the child for approval, may keep haunting them forever. Victims are nearly always suffering from some complaint, however minor.

Superman was my favourite character as a child. I was very unwilling to see the Superman movies when they came out for fear of spoiling the illusion. I saw myself doing great and selfless deeds that brought me accolades from my fellows and love from my parents. There was little acclaim of the ordinary in my house. It's not surprising that I'm involved in client-led health while my colleagues are dispensing drugs and driving Porsches.

Self-denial was part of the fantasy. A test for me will be whether or not I'm able to enjoy the success of this book.

The favorite childhood character will give an indication of the script that the person has chosen for himself. The script, like the character, may be a winner, loser, banal or tragic. Illness, being part of the script, will usually have a significant role to play in its fulfillment. People with "winner's" scripts usually don't die young of a fatal disease.

Life Fantasy

An adult who fantasizes that he's died at ten when he's already forty has a "Don't grow up" injunction. Similarly, one who claims that she lived for two hundred years will not want to grow up, either.

Death imagined by violence or suicide suggests a "Don't exist" injunction. These people are in danger of having fatal "accidents" or contracting fatal diseases, particularly if they've fantasized an early death. In therapy, making a contract to stay alive is warranted.

The comments that family members make at the funeral will elicit the failures of the individual as she sees them.

"What does your father say?" I often ask clients.

"He doesn't bother to come."

"Put him there, and see what he says."

"OK. He'd say, 'I knew this car accident would happen; he never could get anything together. I'm just thankful no one else was killed.'"

Or, in the event of a case of pneumonia gone wrong, the client might say his father said at his funeral, "He always was the sickly one. Thank goodness the rest of us have strong lungs."

Notice that in both of these common fantasies, the client is fulfilling both a family fear and a family prophesy. His death is condoned by the family. Grieving for him rebalances them.

Imagine a single sentence that would fit your own gravestone. Does it show the love of you by yourself and others? Is it angry and disillusioned? Perhaps you play the joker to the last, as in the comedian Spike Milligan's wonderful epitaph, "I told you I was ill!"

Correlate your answer with your health.

Present-Day Heroes/Heroines

These choices generally indicate the personal characteristics that the client believes his parents wanted for him. (Wanted him to have for their own needs is more accurate.) In a person with a "be perfect" driver, they're never achieved and this serves the purpose of constantly reminding him that he falls well short of the standards required of him. Someone who wishes to remain angry at his parents rather than assume full responsibility for himself will make himself as unattractive as possible and then idolise a glamorous personality. Someone who's decided to be as physically incompetent as possible may make a hero of a famous sportsman. This reminds him of how clumsy his father told him he was.

On the other hand, people may achieve the goals they set themselves as embodied in their heroes. If they do this for themselves, and not in the hope of parents loving them better, they'll be able to enjoy their success and will most likely be healthy. The gradual dissipation of early childhood influences is the work of a lifetime, with many ups and downs along the way.

The difference between the client's achievements and those of his hero will give an indication of whether the client views himself as a winner or a loser, the severity of his medical condition, and how much therapy may be required.

In general terms, the difference between what the client is and what the client says he wants will indicate the drivers and the injunctions. (See Chapter 2 – The Childhood Basis of Disease.)

Birth Questions

Here are a few responses I commonly hear. "When I was born, Mom figured she would try to give me away, but nobody would have me." Laughter follows. Or "My father said I looked like a skinned rabbit. He figured I'd run like a rabbit when I was older." A third says, "Aunt May said it was the happiest day of her life. All those girls' clothes she'd knitted would finally be used. After four boys, she was beginning to despair." A fourth client says, "Dad said Mom would drive over rough roads and hope nature would take its course."

The first and last subjects of these examples may have decided that they were not wanted, may have decided not to live, and may have had an "accident" or become seriously ill. It depends on whether the parents adapted to the new baby and came to love him or her or not. Very often the parents' resentment will remain below the surface even though the child's needs are met. The second client may fulfill his father's wish for him to be a runner or, if it's more advantageous for him to do so, rebel and become fat and slow. Client number three rejoices in being female, she has regular, trouble-free menstruation, and she has no vaginal infections. She can admire her own body in the mirror.

Anxiety surrounding the birth of an infant often predates similar anxiety about raising the child. We've seen before how parental fears will usually be taken up by the child who then becomes unsure himself. Fear of not being able to survive is perhaps the greatest cause of illness, resulting in multiple adaptations both psychologically and physically.

We've spoken before of the needs of parents to have boys or girls. If Mother wanted a girl, Shaunine, and a boy came along, then he may have been called Shaun. If he was expected to take care of Mother's hope for a girl, and was stroked for "feminine traits" and not masculine ones, he's likely to be feminine. This is a "don't be a boy" injunction. Mother is unlikely in these circumstances to encourage him to appreciate his maleness, and he in turn is likely to adopt her attitude that there's something unacceptable about his gender and his male characteristics. His penis may be smaller, his testicles smaller, his sperm count lower and his sexual encounters less enjoyable in this event, and his predisposition to sexual diseases, such as nonspecific urethritis, gonorrhea, dermatitis, and herpes, will be greater.

Many people have learned that they were adopted when they applied for a passport and saw their birth certificate for the first time. This may put a new light on their medical history.

Parents

The modeling available to the child will be apparent from his description of his parents. It doesn't matter that his opinion of them is biased, it's his reality we're dealing with. From his description of his parents will come an impression of whether he's fulfilled their aspirations, or whether he's failed them. Constructing imaginary situations and noting parents' reactions to them will confirm the scripting. For example, imagine you've just won a race and your mother is there. What does she say? Or imagine you've failed to graduate from High School. What does your father say?

Name

The word I've used is my own name, John, spelled backward. The client's own name is written backward and he's invited to pronounce it and then to give it a meaning. He's not told that it's his name, although often he'll notice that it is. The object is for him to freely associate with his own name.

When he writes a sentence using the letters of his name spelt backward to form the first letters of the words in the sentence, the last word will often be his name, for example, when John becomes Nhoj:

Now Here OK John.

This is often revealing, as in the name Percy: "You / Can / Reveals / End / Percy." Or Janet: "Together / Ever / Now / Attains / Janet." Percy is likely to have more of a problem than Janet. Some people don't insert their own names as the last word in the sentence. What do you make of that?

You may recall that when I take the history I'm listening on one level and observing on another. I've expressed this previously by saying that the content is often less important than the way in which it's said. This is certainly true of the psychological profile.

A young man with digestive problems was telling me that he was better at sports than his two older brothers. He then added that he was also better than they were at his studies. As he was declaring this apparently bald and quantifiable statement, he smiled nervously. The little kid in him was looking up at me and asking, "Will you love me Daddy now that I've been so good?" and, "Please don't make me prove myself again." His tentativeness was because he knew that however well he performed his father was unlikely to give him the unconditional love he'd craved all these years. He was both proud and unfulfilled by his own success. It hadn't been effective in getting him what he wanted, and his gut problems both reaffirmed his incompetence and gave him a suitable excuse to stop performing. Even his father knew a sick man when he saw one. All this information was available from a combination of the text and the emotional content of that simple statement.

This completes the psychological history. Much more detail will be offered by the client during therapy, at a rate that is safe for him. I now have a good idea of the factors which initiated the illness, and the unresolved conflicts that are maintaining it. Whether or not a client makes use of his new awareness (I keep him informed of my responses as we proceed) will depend on how much he wishes to risk at this time. I respect his need for safety and am careful to distinguish between what he wants for himself and what I want. This is often difficult for me, as Superman tends to hurry things along.

Allowing, rather than urging the client to evolve, and providing a safe, caring environment for this process to take root, are the essential prerequisites to the next step, the healing process.

12
THE ILLNESS OPTION

The first car Ted ever owned was a Morris Minor. He'd bought it nearly ten years before, and it wasn't great then. Now the engine had just about given up, and the mechanic who'd serviced the car over the years had declared that death was at the most three months away. Ted needed a new car. He drove the Morris down to the local dump, figuring that this way he could save the cost of towing the car when it finally broke down, and, with the ceremony due an old friend, pushed the car over the edge of the dump. He went back home to look for a new car online.

Being a student, he found that most cars for sale were well above what he wanted to pay; he even noticed a few Morris Minors like his old one for sale. Not having a car made it very difficult to get around and look for a new vehicle. He began to wonder what had possessed him to throw away something that was still of value to him before he was sure he had something better to replace it with.

Five years later when the gearbox was failing on his Pontiac and the brakes needed renewing, Ted remembered the old Morris. This time he drove the old car around until he secured a replacement, thanked the Pontiac for its reliable service over the years, and even kept it for old times' sake until he could no longer afford the registration. Then he sold it.

Illness looks after us well, though the pain, like a leaking radiator, may inconvenience us at times and make us downright miserable at others. When we decide to get the advantages of illness for ourselves in new ways, we can retain the old way of behaving until we've practiced the new way and are totally familiar with its operation. There's no advantage in throwing it away before an alternative is established. An appreciation of the role it's played is a good place to begin looking for a replacement. By so doing, we learn what we did last time and decide what we can do next time. Gratitude is a great start to the healing process.

Illness is an option. It may not be perfect, like the old car, but if it enables us to avoid doing things we find more scary or unpleasant, like asking our wife if she loves us, fulfilling our potential in business, or even walking to and from work, then we're benefiting from it. It may be the direct physiological consequence of years of unresolved fear, sadness or anger left over from childhood. It may be the way we choose to stop taking responsibility for ourselves and keep ourselves beneath the umbrella of parental care. The old parent may of course be replaced by a surrogate parent such as a doctor, lover, spouse or our own children. It may be a behavior learned directly from a parent, the media or relatives. "If you feel overworked, it's OK to have asthma." Illness is a way to obtain love, to get out of work. It confirms the world as slightly unhappy or perhaps downright miserable, confirms our belief in fate, justifies us being less successful than we hoped, or provides a drive for success. There are many other uses of illness. All of them were chosen by us as children without realizing it, in order to make ourselves feel safe in the world. They were all valid options, actually, perfect options—that we selected at a time when we had few or no alternatives.

Therapy involves simply maintaining the old option or illness while new ones are discovered and practised. In such a manner, Ted from our story retained his old car until he no longer needed it. Eventually, at a rate which is different for everybody, the old choice of disease is "put out to pasture," returned to only under extreme duress and finally removed when the person is confident he or she no longer need retain it as an option. This describes the architecture of the recovery process.

Let's look at an example of a young child choosing illness. Baby Peter was only six months old when his mother became pregnant again. By the time he was a-year-old, he knew that an exciting event was about to take place in the family and that things would be different, but the exact implications for him were unclear. Up to now, he'd enjoyed the complete devotion of his mother to the exclusion of almost everything else in her life. It was a position of security he enjoyed immensely.

Soon after the new baby arrived, and despite his father taking time off work to take care of him, Peter realized that the days of his mother's undivided attention were well and truly over. Needless to say, he was distraught at this, being only fifteen months old himself and needing his mother as much as before. To his infant mind, the new baby took mother's valuable caring away from himself and this was a serious, even life threatening, event.

About this time, he was pushing through a new tooth; this, coupled with the fact that he and his father got caught in a freak rainstorm, resulted in his developing a fever. Much to his astonishment and delight, his mother, whom he feared had almost abandoned him for his baby sister, became suddenly very attentive to him and patted him to sleep. The next time he became unwell a similar thing happened, and the next. Eventually it became obvious to his parents that these fevers were attention-seeking. Before they could take remedial action, however, Peter had developed another fever so serious that he had a fit. His mother was distraught, blamed herself for not caring enough for the older child, and, on this and subsequent occasions, called in her own mother to look after the new baby while she cared for Peter.

The fits were so effective in getting his mother to drop her other commitments and concentrate on him that Peter incorporated them into his pattern of behavior. Tests in the hospital revealed the usual pattern for epilepsy, and the whole family put a tremendous amount of energy into his illness.

Peter, while not causing the initial fever, used this mechanism to be cared for. He learned the behavior and, because of its effectiveness, maintained it. Meditation practices can enable some people to directly control body functions (such as temperature), and I noticed working in hospitals that some schizophrenics appear to have the ability to exert direct control over body processes. Most of us are not in touch with our autonomic functions to such a degree and therefore control our bodies indirectly.

Diagrammatically, Peter's case looks like this:

Original decision made under parental influence by a child with little power:

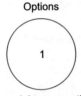

Options

1

Age eighteen months

That is, to get Mother's attention away from the new baby, the child decides to suffer from epilepsy.

Let's examine this word "decide," because it doesn't fit with our experience of life that a new baby would "decide" to do anything against its interests. But if you allow for the "decision" to be out of awareness, then perhaps a child suffering from epilepsy is attempting to avoid an even more undesirable outcome, such as a loss of parental love, approval and caring. Then the "decision" is very much in his interests. These losses are far worse than epilepsy, as loss of parental caring is life threatening to a child unable to keep himself alive. Seen like this, "deciding" to have epilepsy is more like "deciding" to remove your hand from boiling water. No "decision" is recognized. It just happens. You just do it. It was pro-survival to remove your hand and it's pro-survival for the child to adapt in ways which keeps the baby alive.

As an adult, the client is able to take care of himself. He marries a nurse from the neurological clinic, who supplies his drugs and is up on the latest information on the disease. When their first child is born, neither can understand why this joyous time should be marred by his suffering almost continuous severe epileptic attacks, necessitating increased medication and eventual hospitalization.

The fear of not receiving adequate attention precipitates an attack of epilepsy, exactly as it did in childhood. At this stage of his life, he's using the option he learned in childhood, and as a person who wants to stay alive, this is his best option. He may or may not be aware of what's happening, but he's afraid to use any of the other options available to him as an adult who no longer needs his parents' approval. That solution worked then, it was incorporated into his personality, and he became Peter the epileptic.

Diagrammatically, this looks like this:

Age twenty-seven years

The epilepsy option is still operational. The other circles represent those alternatives available to him as an adult but which he's chosen to ignore, is unaware of or has considered and rejected. They're all capable of easing his epilepsy but their choice is accompanied by fear. Some of these alternatives might be:

1. Get a guarantee from his wife that despite the new baby, she'll still have time for him.
2. Ask his wife to reaffirm her love for him.
3. Get a friend who has no child-minding commitments to come over two nights a week and rub his shoulders.
4. Put the child up for adoption.
5. Address his fear about not getting looked after as a child, and explore how he can best get taken care of while he's in the process of deciding to care for himself as well as whom to enroll to assist him.
6. Escalate the epilepsy into the early signs of multiple sclerosis.

7. Drop the epilepsy as being a lousy way to get cared for.
8. Do none of the above.

There are softer and harder options, and their choice will depend on how life-threatening the child perceives the arrival of the new baby to be. If the mother was very sure that she wanted to have another baby, and the child perceived her obvious pleasure, then he may not be seriously threatened by the new arrival. If she were unsure about her ability to take care of yet another child, then the child would rightly fear that his needs might not be met. As we've said, this starts him worrying about whether he'll be able to survive this new event, and he will repeat any behavior that he stumbles upon at this time that results in his mother putting more energy into him. In this way, the parent or parents condone the child's choice. This, we've seen, is called a script decision.

The fever which accompanies an earache may be escalated by the child into a fit if he finds this is effective. The benefit comes from the parents' increased caring for the child, who've unwittingly validated illness as an option and guaranteed its repetition.

Science is increasingly discovering how physiological reactions, previously considered out of our control, are actually a consequence of the autonomic nervous system reacting to our mental state. Hence those psychological responses to our environment which are subconscious are continually modifying our physiology and our anatomy. By such a mechanism, the child develops epilepsy. Previously, doctors would have explained the onset of the disease as fate, chance or, more popularly, a virus. Quite specifically the child decides to have the disease and the body accepts the decision, taken as it is in the interest of the survival of both body and mind. Neither can survive without the other.

If our epileptic is very dependent upon his disease for caring, it's unlikely he'll feel safe enough to simply drop the disease overnight. He may decide, however, that he's had enough pills, and he may want to begin taking a more active part in the management of his own illness. In such a mood, he may seek a practitioner who elaborates on his options and uses techniques to help him experience the feelings he's blocked or suppressed.

He's now at the following stage:

Age thirty years

The illness option is still active. Peter is aware of options two and three, and beginning to practise them. These will be the options that he finds least threatening. The remaining options, although perhaps leading to a quicker resolution of the illness, are still too alarming for him. For example, he may be willing, in the early stages of therapy, to ask his wife for a back rub, but be afraid to directly discuss the symbiotic nature of their relationship for fear of losing her support. Even later, the couple may want to discuss whether their relationship can survive without the illness. His fear that his wife will feel threatened if she doesn't have a sick husband will often be well grounded. After all, her scripting was that she wasn't a good wife or mother unless she was caring for sick people. If she wasn't a good wife and mother, she was unlovable, and if one's parents didn't love her, they wouldn't keep her alive. Hence the wife's role in her husband's disease is active and powerful, and of course this is one of the reasons they were attracted to each other and married.

The lightest-shaded option, the one representing total cure of this disease, may never be exercised. It symbolizes what Eric Berne in his 1964 book *Games People Play* called "autonomy" and what others know as "enlightenment." Not only will it mean that this disease is removed but also that no other serious ones will take its place. This option means dropping all the old damaging childhood conditioning, retaining the helpful parental messages, accepting yourself, forgiving those against whom you have maintained anger, and rejoicing in taking total responsibility for yourself. Gratitude for just being alive accompanies the exploration required for a fulfilling life.

If a person has given herself a life-threatening disease and for her own reasons decides to revoke the original decision and survive, she'll for urgency choose a more drastic option than she might otherwise have done. When the fear of dying or suffering becomes more painful than revoking the original decision, then the lesser of two evils may be making a decision to live. Some people who die from an illness do so in a state of calm because they're actually fulfilling what they believe their parents required of them. This may or may not be the case, but remember we're speaking of adults who have failed to free themselves of childhood decisions. The person who chooses to die young has obviously been under some real or imaginary pressure as a child to choose that option and is now too afraid to revoke it as an adult. The force of the original decision and the secret harboring of death as an active option mean that most people will not choose the hard survival option if they're suffering from cancer. They may be surrounded by relatives and caretakers who have an active investment in the patient fulfilling the early decision and dying. Most if not all spouses intuitively recognize that their partner is suicidal in one area or another, and this is a major factor in their choice to spend their life with that person. Similarly, the victim's family, having been an integral part of the original decision, will be expecting the patient to die. In certain ways, this restores the balance of their own lives.

In considering the validity of this, caste your mind back to some powerful dynamics in your own family when you were a child and ask yourself if those dynamics continue to be maintained within the family now, even though your parents may be old and your siblings all grown up with their own families.

When the general consensus is that the patient should die, it takes a lot of courage to choose the hard option of survival. The alternative is to follow the original script decision and die. The lack of fear is seen as serenity and bravery by those around the person; I recall as a medical student the aura of excitement when a younger patient died on the ward. Despite the natural sadness we all felt, it was as if that person had done us all a favor by choosing to die and, as a consequence, improving our chances of surviving. It reminded us of the practice of some Inuit, where the old people walk out into the blizzard to die, thereby guarantee the survival of those who remain. We're not so sophisticated that we don't jostle for survival.

This rather strident and brutal interpretation of cancer might be just what a person suffering from cancer needs to interrupt his current "Why me?" and shake his physiology into surviving. It may also be used to direct his rage at dying toward someone other than those people who might actually have had something to do with it in an earlier life.

But back to our man with the epilepsy. He's tentatively begun practicing options two and three. This is seen in the diagram as a darkening of the circles as those options are practiced. There are many options which he may have considered and already rejected, such as having the baby adopted. Whether he continues to remove his disease or not depends on what level of discomfort, or what sort of discomfort, he's prepared to trade off against his fear of becoming completely well. Epilepsy, for example, is an intermittent disease. It is very convenient for short bursts of total disability which require complete care. Between attacks the client is usually completely fine and can get on with following a successful career. Epilepsy will therefore be chosen by someone who needs temporary, rather than permanent, incapacity, as might be provided by severe arthritis. It's also frightening to watch and difficult to ignore, but is easily concealed when there's no benefit in showing it.

If the arrival of the children in the family means that having epilepsy is no longer convenient, or if his wife refuses to continue to regard his illness as her responsibility, then Peter the epileptic may decide to continue to expand his options and considerably reduce the frequency or the severity of the disease, or even cure himself. Some people come to realize the way they've been using their illness through self-discovery and decide to remove it. I believe most people who make significant changes to their lives do so without the intervention of professionals. Others make changes by finding strength in

God or by surrendering to a guru. Most religions work by using a figurehead to give the devotee parental permission to drop both their pain and their illness.

Once Peter discovers that he has some influence over his epilepsy, he tentatively decides to remove it. He's now at this stage:

His epilepsy continues to improve, and he's well advanced in the practice of the two early options (two and three). These, you'll recall, were to examine, in conjunction with his wife, the role the epilepsy played in their relationship. As a consequence of them both deciding that Peter had to take responsibility for his condition, they've been less angry with each other these past few months. The bonuses for their relationship will continue as the symbiosis involved in this disease lessens. In other areas they may well decide to maintain their symbiotic relationship, since they both enjoy it. Most importantly, from the illness's point of view, as the other options are exercised and practiced, so the epilepsy option is phased out.

The decision to have the epilepsy is old in Peter's memory (since he made it all those years ago as a child) but very strong in practice, since he's practiced it all these years. The newer options, on the other hand, are weak in practice but strong in memory. The object is to make the new options automatic in practice so that eventually being well becomes the usual and expected state of the body. To this end, Peter the epileptic may decide to look at his remaining options.

To be totally free of this disease, he may need to become aware of the decision he made to have it in the first place and be prepared to explore and release the feelings that he's associated with that decision. For example, he may still be resentful that he was forced to buy his mother's attention by making himself ill. Although he hasn't realized it, his wife has noticed that he becomes very agitated when his mother begins to fuss over some minor complaint in their children. On one occasion she can even recall her husband saying to his mother, "You know, you can cuddle them when they're well, too, Mom!"

Aware of it or not, this deep-seated resentment toward his mother about his illness will stand in the way of a cure. Once again, some people deal with this alone, others require professional help. In the case of Peter's epilepsy he may need to make a conscious decision that he's lovable without his epilepsy, that he no longer needs it to get close to the people he loves, that he can ask for the caring he wants without having to prove he's ill and therefore deserving. He may need to understand the reasons behind his mother's attitude to illness and, having understood the pressures on her, forgive her. Or he may be prepared to do that without any conscious awareness of the factors involved in his parents' psychology. Each individual is entirely different, as is their therapy.

Compare this with the treatment of epilepsy by uniform chemical means; which treats a statistic, or clinical trial, but not anybody who actually suffers from the disease.

At any point of awareness about his condition, Peter practices the options that are safe for him at that time. As the years go on, his subconscious mind will allow into his awareness new and interesting angles on the disease. Diagrammatically, he's at this stage now:

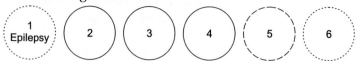

The epilepsy hasn't been entirely removed from his range of options, and with many people it never will be. It's no longer a problem, however. Under duress, Peter may choose to return to his disease. In fact, the night his mother died he suffered his first attack of epilepsy in fifteen years. His wife comforted him and was very glad to do it, since by this point both really understood his epilepsy completely for the first time.

Illness is an option. It's a perfectly sensible option arising from the perceived danger of withdrawal of parental support.

It enables us to continue to function without the continual fear that our existence is in jeopardy, which is intolerable. It's something we create to allay our greatest fears. It reveals that we're prepared to undergo physical discomfort in exchange for psychological security. Simplistic removal of physical symptoms (as in much surgery) may unmask the psychological component too suddenly, and precipitate dysfunction. The individual may develop a new disease to take the place of the one so suddenly removed without reference to the multiple factors accompanying it.

An appreciation of the disease – "Thank you, disease, for the way you've looked after me" – is indicative of the selflove necessary for cure. To continue to berate something which is part of you, has developed at your request, and has been in some ways an advantage for you is to hang on to the old insecurities and guarantee continued illness. When the advantages of the illness are established, options can be worked out to cater for the needs previously catered for by the disease. When we no longer need the disease we de-commission it and may put it out to pasture.

Jane was eight and had been suffering from epilepsy for four years. She had a sister, Penelope, who was only a year older than herself. There was another girl who was eighteen months old.

The usual investigations had been performed, and an electroencephalograph (EEG) confirmed the diagnosis. Jane was taking the drugs that doctors commonly prescribe to lessen the frequency of the seizures. When the patient came in to see me, she was accompanied by the two other sisters as well as by her mother. I was soon to find out why. My first question was, "How old are you, Jane?"

"Eight," her sister Penelope answered.

"And where do you live?" I asked.

"At 48 Station Way, Pinefield," came Penelope's reply, and for good measure she gave me her phone number.

"I see; and how much of a problem is the epilepsy for you, Jane?"

"Well," Penelope answered, "sometimes she has fits, and then I watch more carefully when I take her to school in case she has a fit in the middle of the road and gets run over by a car."

Noting all this time their mother's nods of approval at the answers the elder daughter was supplying, I was beginning to see the family dynamics. "Now we're going to play a little game," I proposed. Penelope took up this suggestion with some gusto, and seeing her sister so enthused, Jane smiled eagerly. "I'm going to ask some questions now, and I want Jane to answer them. During this part of the game, Penelope is going to see if she can be very silent, even though she knows the answers to all of the questions."

I'm immediately thwarted in this strategy by the mother, who simply takes over where the brooding Penelope left off, so I eliminate her answering the questions by simply asking her to desist. This leaves Jane squirming at the end of the simplest questions like "What games do you like playing?" and "Have you ever been hit by a car?"

The method this family has worked out to give its members a feeling of being needed and therefore loved is to clearly demarcate the roles. Penelope, only one-year-old at the birth of her sister, and furious at this very dangerous intrusion into her life, learns that to get the care she needs, she must appear to love the new baby. Mother encourages her in this, as she fears Penelope's anger, and wonders if she'll do the baby some harm. Mother's anxiety about sibling rivalry forces Penelope to take care of Jane to such an extent that the younger girl couldn't even answer for herself. Her epilepsy served the obvious purpose of providing a visible handicap that justified this state of affairs continuing. Jane would play ill and incompetent, Penelope would take care of her, and the mother would feel safe and support them both in their respective roles.

Therapy in this case was family therapy. There was no point in treating Jane in isolation, because the pressure on her to continue having the illness was so strong. The whole family needed a new range of options whereby they could all feel safe and loved without needing one member to be ill.

We did this over a period of three months, with me frequently congratulating all concerned at a very clever and effective way of sorting out the way in which they related to one another. Given any set of circumstances, I believe people work out the very best solutions for themselves and, at a time when it's safe for them, search for new and more effective options.

The second case of epilepsy that I describe illustrates how orthodox medicine might benefit from taking more time with the history and less time on the routine investigations and then the routine prescription of drugs.

Lisa was sixteen and recently arrived from Canada. She was staying with friends of her family who were worried by her obvious epilepsy, suddenly acquired and at the time of consultation occurring nightly. The woman with whom she was staying was a trained nurse at a local hospital, and on cue, Lisa had a fit in the office of the neurologist she was taken to see, confirming the diagnosis. She was given the usual barrage of investigations which showed a common result in these cases, that is, nothing abnormal. Nevertheless, to make the case completely typical, she was given a large dose of drugs; I gather that this was because of the frequency of the attacks but, in my view, quite indiscriminately and without proper inquiry at any stage.

Apart from the attack in the neurologist's office, which I put down to sheer anxiety and certainly wouldn't blame her for, the other attacks had all occurred at night. My line of inquiry therefore centered on her thoughts and feelings as she went to bed. She had no recall of any dreams.

She wasn't easy to coax, being somewhat shy, but eventually volunteered that she was given the responsibility at home of rocking to sleep her younger brain damaged sister. This was no easy task, but there were six children in the family, and Mother certainly didn't have the time. As long as she could remember, Lisa had rocked the girl to sleep, and if the task was not completed successfully, then the brain damaged girl would keep the whole family awake, resulting in a major upheaval for which Lisa was held primarily responsible. As a result of the commotion, the brain damaged sister would often have fits.

As she was drifting off to sleep, Lisa would think of these things and feel guilty that she wasn't at home looking after her sister. In the absence of her family's condemnations, she took to punishing herself; the epilepsy, induced as it was by fear, proved helpful in this regard. Therapy took only one session and involved the girl fantasizing that her younger sister was being well cared for (which was actually the case) and understanding that she was not her sister's keeper.

I didn't see her again, but I did receive a letter from the hospital saying that quite miraculously the attacks had stopped some months previously and hadn't recurred. I looked up my notes and found that the time corresponded to our treatment session. Much to the neurologist's credit, he took her off the medication.

These cases are intended simply to familiarize the reader with an alternative frame of reference. Rather than attributing illness to external factors, be it virus, weather, or pollution of foodstuffs, I interpret illnesses here in terms of the person's early life decisions. The other factors mentioned probably also play a part, and they usually do.

I believe that our early life decisions are the most important, and certainly the most ignored of the causes of illness, and their exploration represents the greatest hope in achieving better health outcomes.

SECTION III:
THE TREATMENT OF ILLNESS

13
INTRODUCTION TO THE TREATMENT OF ILLNESS

I've attempted to establish a theoretical basis for the belief that people, through unresolved childhood conflicts, make themselves ill. I've tried to show that careful history-taking and equally careful observation will demonstrate which particular childhood decisions, leading to particular personality traits, are responsible for the illness. Those decisions, we've seen, are reflected in the person's body, his language, his posture and every conceivable major and minor idiosyncrasy, as well as his chosen illness. The personality can thus be used to establish the origins of the illness. Having established how the person makes himself ill, we now address what he can do about it.

The first option available to anyone faced with the prospect of continuing disease is to deny responsibility. We've seen previously how this choice will simply continue the illness. In this instance the client seeks out a practitioner whose interests lie in perpetuating the myth that the illness is beyond the client's ability to influence, and both doctor and patient collaborate to provide symptomatic relief without insight. This usually involves drugs or surgery, and guarantees that the illness will remain long after that particular fashionable treatment has been superseded or fallen into frank disrepute. Within fifty years of their introduction most drugs have been removed from the market, as their cumulative disadvantages begin to overtake their advantages.

The alternative is to seek a practitioner, priest, friend, guru or psychotherapist who can help to expand the options.

Ultimately, however, the only satisfactory answer to the client's problems are to be found within himself. We go through the stage of seeking others' opinions, if only to reject them. We must make the final decision ourselves, and that may be no decision. What follows is one biased person's subjective opinion about ways to change. Ultimately you'll need to reject it.

I work with people in therapy in two ways: individually and in groups. Because most people have several individual sessions before they go into a group, I'll begin by describing what happens in these individual sessions.

The immediate history, past history, family history, systems analysis, diet history, physical examination, and psychological profile have all been dealt with in great detail. It takes about two hours or two individual sessions to do this. I then engage the person on two levels simultaneously by discussing the role that they've personally played in their own illness and by discussing their diet. While these two areas of treatment may seem incompatible, in practice changing the diet will usually evoke the emotions. If you're having trouble believing this, you might try a three-day fast before reading further. You'll be feeling quite different in three days' time.

If you're generally racket angry (that is, anger is a common response for you), the change in diet will probably invoke your anger: "As if my headaches aren't enough burden without the additional imposition of this damn diet!"

If you're depressed, then eating may be one way in which you comfort yourself. Taking away one of your few pleasures may result in you saying, "I don't mind forgoing the white bread, but there's no way I'm giving up my morning coffee!" Or, if you're scared, "Where am I getting my vitamins and minerals from on this diet?"

Although under enormous pressure from advertisements to choose one product over another, we still decide what we'll eat. The more pressures we're forced to live under as a consequence of the restrictions of our world and our organized society, the greater the attraction of the supermarket. A great variety and availability of foodstuffs — especially those containing sugar, the great anxiety remover, and fat, the warmer of souls—are produced specifically to help us cope with the pace of life. We have become accustomed to this instant oral gratification and vigorously resist any change in that area of our lives.

When I change clients' diets, often substantially, they react.

This brings to the surface feelings of which they may be unaware, and injects energy into the healing process. Another way of looking at this phenomenon is from the viewpoint that if a person is desperate to return to "social eating," then they're motivated to understand the ways in which they're contributing to their illness. The loss of social interaction resulting from the diet (dining out with friends is difficult when you're eating boiled vegetables only) is more painful than an excursion into their own psyche. In this mood people are suggestible.

In the same way that emotions affect the internal organs, physiologically at first and then anatomically, changes on a physical level can affect our emotions. Most people recognize this. Most people are quite prepared to say, "Last week my back was aching, and I felt terrible. This week it feels better, and I feel great." They're prepared to state that their physical feelings "cause" their emotions. They're less willing, as a rule, to admit that the way they're feeling "causes" their physical pains. The reason for this lies in the belief that emotional feelings are less worthy of sympathy than physical ones. A quantifiable physical pain is good reason to feel terrible; sadness, on the other hand, is less valid.

The dietary changes also affect us physiologically, since the digestive organs are dealing with different foods, and these changes have psychological consequences as well. This isn't well recognized but then very few people have practiced remedial dietetics. Unless the physical and the mental, or the physiological and the psychological, are regarded as dynamic and continually interacting, therapy becomes a very one-sided affair, and ineffective. The physical therapies need to take the psychological state into account, and the psychotherapies need to take the physical body into account. When this is done, progress is enhanced. Practiced alone, the physical therapies tend to encourage non-responsibility and dependence, while the psychotherapies espouse responsibility but encourage transference, and then deal with it poorly. Transference is the phenomenon whereby a client puts Mother's, Father's or both parents' faces onto the therapist or therapists. It's the medium of psychoanalysis. As a consequence of doing this, people don't take ultimate responsibility for themselves but pass it from parents to therapist. Anyone who does this will never get better because to remain under the care of another they need to have a demonstrable incapacity. In order to guarantee this, they sabotage the healing procedures of each practitioner they attend. Unfortunately, patients are encouraged in this by most doctors and many psychotherapists who, for their own needs, encourage the transference by counter transference. Counter-transference occurs when the doctor tells, or implies to the patient, that he'll take care of him. An equally important element of counter-transference, is when the doctor needs the client to need the doctor.

Some commentators are of the view that as long as the doctor cares whether the patient lives or dies, the doctor is of no use to the patient. While this controversial and apparently insensitive remark seems inconsistent with care, on closer examination the value in the statement reveals itself. With each attempt of the doctor to take care of his patient, which is what many patients expect and require of their doctor, the chances of recovery are lessened. Many doctors are horrified at the thought of handing back responsibility for recovery to their patients, explaining it as uncaring, but their real motivation is to avoid becoming irrelevant. A doctor who "cares for" but refuses to "take care of" his patient is a doctor with his patient's well-being as his main concern.

While a change in diet affects us by evoking an emotional response, it's simultaneously, by altering the function of the organs, augmenting our reaction. The careful and detailed prescription of diet, taking into account both the physical state and the psychological profile, is called "remedial dietetics," covered in the next chapter.

14
REMEDIAL DIETETICS AND PRUDENT DIET

The first thing to clarify is the difference between "remedial dietetics" and long-term "prudent diet." The former is a detailed prescription of continually changing diets that are intended to alter body physiology and psychology in the short term. Long-term "prudent diet," or the "diet of best chance," is a general dietary prescription that will be beneficial to most people most of the time and, if followed approximately over a long period of time, will result in general well-being. The diet literature is incredibly diverse, because writers do not distinguish between these two forms of dietary practice. The majority of books—and there are thousands of them—are so general as to be completely useless for any particular individual who is suffering from a set of symptoms. They're written by people who have seen a narrow range of clients in a particular locality within a narrow time span, or, more usually, are writing of themselves. In addition, their views are invariably colored by personal preference. A writer who's cured her arthritis by eating boiled vegetables and brown rice will most likely recommend the same diet for others who are suffering from arthritis. At first glance this might seem reasonable, but in reality it's like treating everyone as if they're identical (a bit like a drug trial). The dietary recommendations end up being generally true but of little use to anyone who wants to change the course of an acute illness. To do this, it is essential to have an intimate knowledge of the client that you've ascertained via the previous detailed history-taking.

Clearly this is impossible to do in a book. I therefore intend to
discuss a few of the general features of remedial dietetics and
will point out that they're applicable to none of you. Then I'll
list a series of recommendations for long-term prudent diet;
these are of value to us all, but personal idiosyncrasy must
always take precedence.

A person's diet is yet another piece of information with
which to piece together the personality profile. Someone
who eats takeout six nights a week (and eats out of cans the
rest of the time), who drinks ten cups of coffee and smokes
thirty cigarettes a day, is not looking after himself. He needs
the instant gratification that his diet provides and will smile
perversely when he tells you that he always has a hot breakfast:
a cigarette and a cup of coffee! He takes pleasure in putting
his body to the test and seeing how long it can survive the
destructive urges of its master. To force this individual to eat
raw vegetables, whole grains, and lean, white meats or soybeans
would precipitate a crisis. Provided that the psychotherapy
backup system is effective, that's precisely the recommendation
I may make. Of course I cannot force him to eat anything,
but neither can he mislead me about those recommendations
he chooses to rebel against. First, there's no point in him not
doing what I ask unless he lets me know about it. Second, I
follow his excretory functions, sometimes on a daily level, in
such detail that I'm able to tell what he's eaten without having
any information from him. You may recall the questions about
bowel function (pages 100-01).

Conversely, and in my practice more frequently, I'm
consulted by people who have "perfect diets": a perfect
balance of cooked and raw foods with an ideal intake of
vitamins, proteins, carbohydrates, and fats. Their fiber intake
is sufficient to ensure good bowel function. They keep sugar
and salt, along with artificial additives of all descriptions, to
a minimum. Much to their horror, I recommend greasy fish
and chips washed down with liberal quantities of soft drinks
followed by chocolates and confectionery that are difficult to
distinguish from pure white sugar! Now, to remain on this diet
forever would be a disaster, but it can be used very effectively

in the short-term to energize a client who wants to stop being so perfect (and so unhappy, generally). These are two examples of prescribing diet to alter a defense system used in conjunction with psychotherapy. Remedial diet is also of great value in altering the course of an acute disease.

A client who complains of a stomach ulcer or of acute IBS (Irritable Bowel Syndrome) will recover in a few days on a diet of boiled vegetables and boiled rainwater. This will calm the intestine, calm the individual, and remove the symptoms far more effectively than antacids or anti-cholinergic drugs. As the symptoms abate, the diet is altered to keep the intestine exercised at a level that will stimulate recovery but not overload it. The boiled vegetables continue for a time, and other foods are added.

The program of recovery might look like this.

Boiled mashed carrots

Other boiled vegetables

Grilled white meat

White toast and white rice

Stewed fruit (apples and pears)

Yogurt and cottage cheese

Raw vegetables and herbs

Raw fruit

Whole-wheat bread and brown rice

Milk, cheese, butter, margarine

Nuts

Pulses, spices, hot condiments

Increasing gut irritation ↓

As you can see, the symptoms of the case described were such that I began the diet at level two: boiled vegetables. Had the symptoms been very severe, then I would have started with the cooked mashed carrots. The time the client spends at each level will depend on the rate of recovery, and if the client's symptoms disappear and then return, we may have to go back a step or two. With such a list, clients who suffer from these diseases can manage any acute attacks, should they need any in the future.

In such cases, other factors need to be taken into account. The client must chew thoroughly, especially when eating carbohydrates, rest before and after eating, not drink with meals, avoid eating fruits with starches as this may lead to intestinal gas, avoid eating anything which is irritating to him personally, eat slowly, in small quantities, and not immediately before retiring.

While the diet is taking effect, the bowels are carefully monitored, as is the urinary output and nature.

Notice how, in the case of IBS, the remedial diet begins by being very low in fiber; it gradually increases the fiber content once the bowel is able to handle the additional roughage. Now, the treatment of IBS is a high-fiber diet, as anyone will quite rightly tell you, along with some additional probiotics, bacteria which assist digestion and which our modern diet tends to remove from the gut. But there's no point filling an inflamed bowel with fiber when it's not functioning sufficiently well to handle it. It will simply make it worse. This is an example of how long-term prudent diet—that is, increased roughage—may be inappropriate in the short-term, when remedial diet is required.

In addition, other personal characteristics will require the diet to vary between individuals. A client with a stomach ulcer who also has sinusitis will not be allowed dairy products in this acute treatment phase, whereas another with a gluten intolerance will skip the toast in favor of the rice.

At the same time as the diet is taking effect the client is encouraged to look at the advantages of having decided to have this disease at this time. Whilst he's suffering pain and discomfort is a good time to propose a cure for the condition rather than yet another palliative, although proposing self-responsibility at this time may be met with hostility. An astute practitioner will intuitively pick his way through this phase, taking care of himself above all else. If the client is happy with the dietary treatment and isn't interested in removing the disease altogether, that's fine with me. I invite him to take responsibility for that decision: "I consciously choose to continue this disease (in a milder form) until such time as I feel safe to remove it."

Health is not an absence of disease, it's a willingness to take responsibility for any disease we choose to give ourselves. Self-responsibility implies a continuing improvement in those things over which we can exert influence. It doesn't imply we have influence, much less "control", over everything. If a client won't accept that responsibility then, after a period sufficient to demonstrate that clearly, I stop seeing him.

It becomes too great an effort for me to continually dodge the carefully laid traps intended to guarantee that I need him to get better more than he does. In this case I have no leverage and will certainly fail, as well as probably end up feeling bad. I choose not to do that, and may recommend a practitioner whose system of medicine would suit the client's current appreciation of his illness. He may return to me later.

As the immediate problem symptoms abate, so the diet expands, until eventually the client is eating and drinking what he wants. To reach this stage may take between three days, in the case of acute diarrhea, and two years, in the case of extremely severe acne. At the end of the stage of remedial diet, the client is offered the general diet considerations as the best way of avoiding a recurrence, while at the same time avoiding those foods that for him, are damaging. In the case of the diarrhea, this might be curry; in the case of the acne, it may be fried foods. In addition the amount of those foods that are eaten is significant. There's no such thing as a "good" or a "bad" food. Rather are there foods which that for a certain individual, at a certain time and in a certain quantity are not in his best interest. Writers who propose raw fruit and vegetable diets for all have presumably benefited from such an austere regime themselves. This doesn't mean that such a diet will benefit a single person other than themselves, devised as it was primarily in the service of their own psychological needs.

These are unlikely to be the same for any two people on this planet. Such restricted perspective (to which diet experts are particularly prone) demonstrates a lack of understanding of the continually changing face of nature, or the laws of yin and yang, i.e. that which helps can also harm.

On a physiological level, there are some generalities which will assist most people in keeping their bodies healthy. At the completion of the remedial diet, which the client has learned and can implement himself if need be, I hand out the following sheet:

GENERAL DIET CONSIDERATIONS

o Eat a large variety of foods.

o The least processed foods contain the most nutrients. For example, brown rice contains more vitamins than white rice.

o Eat the least adulterated foods: that is, those that contain as few artificial flavorings, colorings, antioxidants, emulsifiers, preservatives, and the like as possible.

o Fresh foods contain more nutrients, especially vitamins, than "stale" (or preserved) foods. Grow your own if that's possible.

o Those foods that are capable of life—for example, whole grains—will grow if planted; processed ones will not. That which is capable of sustaining itself is more likely to sustain you. Beans (pulses) are another example of such foods.

o Locally grown foods are generally best. The metabolism of a person who lives in the tropics is more capable, some would argue, of digesting a mango than that of someone who lives in the Mediterranean region. Similarly, if apples grow where you live, then you're more likely to be suited to apples than to bananas, which are tropical.

o Eat seasonal foods, for our bodies are as seasonal as fruits and vegetables and thus are more capable of digesting summer fruits in summer, winter vegetables in winter.

o Chew your food thoroughly.

- Rest before and after eating, since this facilitates digestion by not diverting the blood supply of the stomach to exercising muscles.
- Avoid drinking large quantities of very cold drinks with meals, since cold liquids reduce the blood flow to the stomach and may remove some of the digestive juices.
- Observe personal idiosyncrasy — this overrides all the other points. For example, a general diet consideration is that raw vegetables contain more vitamin C than cooked vegetables. If you have gastritis, however, then raw vegetables will be more irritating than cooked vegetables. An individual condition therefore takes precedence over general considerations.
- Socialize with impunity, knowing that your body can handle anything you choose to eat in certain quantities.
- Don't be a fanatic, since mental rigidity tends to negate good nutrition by influencing the absorption and excretion of the bowel.

This last recommendation includes all those dietary practices that receive considerable notoriety in the press and that people seize upon in their eternal willingness to dismiss their own intuitive feelings about what's good for them in favor of those of a higher authority. They try the new popular diet for a while and generally feel better for a while. Of course, the excitement of doing something new can temporarily relieve all manner of ills. Then the old problems begin creeping back in, and they realize that they're no better off than they were (or, more accurately, no happier). By this time, however, someone equally as clever as the proponent of the first diet has read the political and social mood so accurately that the next diet is on the newsstands and ready for the gullible. In this, the author is aided by commercial interests that are equally receptive to people's need to regularly be offered panaceas.

Until people dismiss all authorities (including myself) as offering no more than broad generalizations of passing benefit, and begin relying on their own internal resources, they will never be healed.

In order to maintain that they're in need of help, they cannot of course afford to be cured. Until they're ready to trust themselves, their faith in healers serves the purpose of maintaining their own illness.

I'm making the point that psychological need is the prime factor in people adopting most popular dietary regimes. Many of these regimes are a return to an eating pattern which was possible in the nineteenth century but totally impractical now. Organic vegetables grown in pure, unfertilized soil, watered with pure water and photosynthesizing pure air are not possible for most people. I believe also that they're not desirable. If our minds and bodies are continually interacting and mutually supportive, then the diet we eat needs to take our current stresses and personalities into account. A twentieth century diet will suit only those people who opt out of the twenty-first century. To drink soft drink, eat fast foods, dine out at restaurants and eat confectionery is part of the balance of twenty-first century living. It comes down to "posology" — the dose.

To exceed the limits of a body attempting to adapt to the new chemicals of the twenty-first century is to invite physical disease, while a moderate intake of chemicals will ensure that the body continues to modify itself to meet modem needs. As with all things, a balance is essential. I presume that if we eat junk foods to a moderate degree, then both our livers and, more particularly, our children's livers will be better able to process them. Processed foods are not going to go away, and neither should they. The fact that many people use junk foods to moderate their dissatisfaction with life and to suppress their fears is a matter I've discussed elsewhere. I mention it here for balance.

The practice of remedial dietetics is an art, and I've glossed over it here. The careful prescription for each client, taking into consideration who he is and who he wants to be, is a valuable ally in both assessing and treating the psychological component of his illness. Any treatment schedule is incomplete without an appraisal of the role of both short-term and long-term diet in the causation and maintenance of the disease.

The access provided to feelings by altering the diet is not surprising when the following is considered. The illness we're dealing with is a consequence of a grown-up person refusing to take full responsibility for himself and trying to cast someone as a surrogate Parent because of unresolved childhood fears. The greatest fear in childhood is the fear of not staying alive. Food is the prime vehicle whereby a mother passes love and life between herself and her baby. Everybody who's eaten has a food "issue." Food means different things to us all but everyone associates food with being loved and allowed to stay alive. It's logical that altering the diet will have a significant effect.

The beauty of diet in the long-term is the way it dovetails into the psychological notions of self-responsibility, self-love, and continuing self-education and self-care. People leave treatment with a firm connection in their minds between caring for themselves and nourishing themselves with health promoting food. They have a ready tool whereby they can practice self-care on a daily level, and also be aware of times when they feel ill disposed toward themselves. Nobody can force us to eat anything, and although the diet has been devised by another person, personal wants and individual biases are built into it in such a way that people understand it to be their own. It's still their decision whether to eat healthily or not.

Diet provides a safe way for those used to relying on the expertise of others to slowly experiment with their own power. They may rigorously apply the recommendations at first, before risking a few changes and seeing what happens. Eventually, they learn about themselves to such a degree that they're capable of devising their own diet to suit their changing needs. By now they really are best placed to construct their own diet.

No therapist sitting in his office, or author at his computer, can possibly have the data necessary for a meaningful day-by-day dietary prescription for everyone. Using his guidelines, it's up to you. By the client taking responsibility for his own diet, he's in effect parenting himself (parents feed children), and that's the end result of all successful psychotherapy. The lack of transference in this situation is one of the reasons why diet therapy is so unpopular with the vast majority of patients and practitioners. (Transference is the process whereby the client casts the therapist in the role of an all-powerful, all-knowing parent figure who he expects will take care of the client's problems.) I believe that there can be no transference without counter-transference, which is the part the therapist plays in taking on the parent role. I'm concerned with transference because, like most of us, I struggle with the fear of being totally responsible for myself. Diet therapy provides a way in which clients can break out of their dependence on therapists. Some therapists don't like that.

In summary, diet as a treatment modality has the following advantages. It provides a physical component to the psycho-therapy, thereby balancing the treatment. It involves the client in taking full responsibility for the treatment at an early stage, since he's preparing, administering and taking the prescription. In the long-term, diet represents self-nurturing. Clients learn about their reactions to diet in such detail that they equip themselves with skills that they can use in the event of future illness. By so doing, they lessen their dependence on other healers. Diet is the perfect adjunct to psychotherapy as it mobilizes the emotions. Because diet is closely associated with self-worth, self-love and the desire to stay healthy and alive, it can be used diagnostically and predictively. Correct, sensible diet is a readily available method for keeping our bodies healthy on a purely physical level.

The microbiome—the internal environment in our gut populated by micro-organisms—requires a healthy diet. We remain in symbiotic relationship with trillions of organisms both within our guts and on the surface of our bodies. Our relationship with these organisms is vital to our health and is affected both by our diet and by any drugs we may take. Our relationship with this teeming life outside and inside us has evolved over millions of years. Our immune and endocrine systems maintain this relationship; as indicated, these systems are profoundly affected by what we think and feel. In a very real sense, our thoughts and feelings, the organisms with which we cohabit, and our diets and lifestyles are all in a never-ending dance, all affecting and being affected by the others. Thus what we think and feel about ourselves and our lives affects various organisms' capacity to fulfill their roles in our physical health, our mental health, and our personalities via their impact on the immune and endocrine systems.

This can be a profound realization. We are part of a holistic system of life much more complex and inter-related than may appear to be the case at first glance. If we can embrace this bigger picture, and explore our evolving relationship with it, we can make use of its healing capacities which have themselves evolved over millions of years. We are not isolated from our Universe, any more than a drop of water is isolated from the ocean.

Just as the mind affects the immune and endocrine systems, so do those systems affect the mind, contributing to our personalities in the process. Our personalities are not only a consequence of early-childhood conditioning and current social circumstances but have evolved from the interaction between our immune systems and the organisms and extended universe that surround us and sustain us. Without the sun, for example, we'd snap freeze in a millisecond.

The human organism cannot survive in a vacuum. It's dependent upon, and constantly interacting with, every other living organism in its environment. These organisms are not only impacting us physically, but also mentally. Put broadly, we're part of life and cannot be separated from it, any more than we can separate our bodies from our minds.

Re-acquainting ourselves with a broader view of nature and of life, offers us a unique healing opportunity.

15
INDIVIDUAL PSYCHOTHERAPY

My skills as a psychotherapist are derived from my childhood need to survive in a sophisticated, disrupted family. I believe the same to be basically true of all psychotherapists. It seems ironic that these people, who struggled for survival as kids and are now therapists, are deified by clients wanting to attribute wisdom and peace to those who perhaps least have it, certainly who least had it. I won't accept those accolades offered to me by clients wanting me to look after them. Rather do I accept my skills (and my sadness at having needed to acquire them) and use them to assist others to assist themselves in their quest for autonomy. Perhaps the real test of me having forgiven my parents will be when I cease being a psychotherapist. Until then, this is what I do.

By now the client and I have minutely detailed the physical ramifications of the client's defence against his fear (termed his illness) and using the script questionnaire have ascertained what that fear is in general terms. We have some details about how this particular illness specifically allays those fears, for example, how his acne keeps the teenage boy safely away from those women he fears. We've implemented a diet to begin correcting the physical imbalance of the acne, and in so doing have mobilized some feelings. By this time the client is either eager to assess his role in this illness and looking forward to an analysis of it, or rejecting the notion of self-caused illness altogether. Let's look at the former situation, a willing client using a private session. You'll recall that I work individually and in groups.

James is twenty-four and has been suffering from severe acne since he was fifteen. He's consulted with several dermatologists, all of whom have described his case as one of the worst they've seen, and all of whom have administered treatments of dubious safety, with various degrees of desperation and with uniform lack of improvement. James says he's fed up, and that the acne is ruining his social life. He's a computer operator who plays football. His frame is slim and muscular and the rest of the skin on his body is fine and slightly dry. In his face I notice fear, anger and sadness. The anger is most apparent, evident in the thin upper lip and the large jaw muscles. The sadness and fear show in the eyes, the former in the blue discoloration below the eyes and heavy lower lids, the latter in the tension of the surrounding muscles and the intermittent glazing over of the eyes. There's a little dermatitis behind the ears, also indicating fear.

I remembered that James undressed willingly for the physical examination, and that I was surprised to find how large his shoulders were. He was clearly used to carrying a considerable burden. His chest muscles were powerful and he held them more for protection of his heart than for display, although he obviously derived some pleasure from his own physique. He moved with purpose, holding his buttocks more tightly than most twenty-four-year-old men. When I touched him on the back he tensed up with a control with which he was familiar. His testicles were normal, and his penis, although of normal size, felt and looked enervated. He was more aesthetic than sexual.

The worst scene he described during the personality profile was of him being beaten by his father for something that he didn't do, and then feeling ashamed when he cried. His best scene involved sexual exploration with a girl he knew when he was seven and she was six. This scene, however, was interrupted by his mother, who had obviously waited for something to happen before "discovering" them. He had an erection at the time and once again felt ashamed. He fantasized dying at seventy-five from "old age," and his wife and two children, all of whom loved him dearly, were at the funeral. His

gravestone read "Loved by his family." His favorite character
was Batman.

An edited account of James's first treatment session
follows:

> "Hi, James, what would you like to do today?"
>
> "Well, I've been thinking about how I might be giving
> myself acne, and I keep coming up with the same
> thought—all I want to do is get rid of the damn
> problem!"
>
> "How is the acne a problem for you in your life right
> now?"
>
> "Well, take Saturday night. I'm really looking
> forward to going to dinner with a friend of mine and
> his girlfriend. There's this woman at the bar who I've
> secretly admired for months now, and I think she might
> be interested. What happens? Saturday morning, I
> wake up with a face full of pimples. I call up my friend
> and tell him I can't go, but he says 'Don't be such an
> idiot,' so I go anyway. There's mirrors all over the
> place, but thank God the lights are low enough so I
> don't look so bad."
>
> "How are you feeling as you enter the club?"
>
> "Pretty awful. I guess I'm not too confident."
>
> "And what are you saying about yourself?"
>
> "That no one in her right mind would want to know
> me."
>
> "Go on."
>
> "Well, the girl's behind the bar, and after about an
> hour I pluck up the courage to go and ask her for a
> drink, hoping to start a conversation. Just as I get to
> the bar, another guy—who I was sure liked her, too—
> sidles up and asks her out next week, just like that!
> Of course, the bastard's got a flawless complexion. I
> just kept on walking and hoped she didn't think I was
> going to stop."

"Think carefully. Did you see this guy about to make his move before you made yours?"

"I guess I did, when I think about it. Yes, he'd just begun to move toward the bar when I decided it was now or never."

"Does that timing mean anything to you, James?"

"Do you mean, did I deliberately let him get there first?"

"It sounds like it. What were you thinking when he asked her out?"

"Lucky bastard. It's hopeless; she would've rejected me anyway."

"And what were you feeling?"

"Ashamed and angry."

"Can you remember feeling like that as a little kid?"

"Well... yes, in the exercise you gave me to do the other day, you know, when I was caught with Suzy next door by my mother."

"Just let yourself remember what that felt like. Close your eyes and be there, with Suzy, and be aware of your mother coming in. Are you able to see or hear her?"

"Yes."

"Good; let's try a little experiment. Please open your eyes and move into this chair; act as if you are your mother. Now, Mother, tell little James, in this chair, what you're feeling and thinking."

"You said that I was..."

"Be your mother."

"'You're a filthy little boy. You should be ashamed of yourself pulling down a girl's pants. I'm going to tell your father when he gets home, and I hope he gives you a thrashing.'"

"Come back to this chair and respond to that, James."

"You stupid bitch; leave me alone, why don't you!"

"What might you be feeling if you weren't angry, James?" I ask, noting the tears welling up in his eyes. "Tell your mother how you're feeling."

"I'm really sorry that you keep picking on me," James sobs.

"Go back and be Mom and reply to that, James."

"'Well, you're such a naughty boy a lot of the time; you need discipline.'"

"What's your name, Mom?" I inquire.

"'Betty.'"

"It sounds as though you're pretty angry yourself, Betty."

"'Well ... yes. James's father is away half the time, and I have to look after the boy. I even have to do some cleaning to make ends meet.'"

"Mom, do you know that it's very healthy and normal for children to want to inspect each other's genitals? You probably did it yourself."

"My brother forced me to touch his; that's what happened."

"It's usually exciting whoever suggests it, Betty, and I'm wondering if that's what you're feeling when you sneak up and catch James doing it. Children naturally explore each other."

Betty's silent for a minute. She considers the ramifications of what I've said of her relationship with her brother, her husband, and James. Tentatively, she admits to having a new perspective.

"I suppose there might be something in what you say."

"Are you prepared to tell James that it's OK by you if he plays with Suzy and if she plays with him, Betty?"

Again she hesitates. "'Well, he does have a beautiful little body and so does she. Son, it's OK that you explore each other, and I love you.'" Mom begins weeping.

"Switch chairs now and respond to your mother, James," I whisper.

"I love you, too, Mom. Dad's away so much, and I need you to look after me."

"It's good to cry at times, James. Are you aware of deciding to do things differently now?" I inquire, as the crying stops.

"I feel so much lighter!"

"Maybe you no longer feel guilty?"

He nods in realization. "I still think I'm a bit scared, though."

"I'm sure you are. But as an adult, there's a grown part of you who's very capable of looking after the little kid in you who's still scared. How might that grown-up part of you make sure that the kid's safe when he's around women?"

James makes a few suggestions.

I continue. "What benefits do you see from having your acne?"

"Well, it's given me an excuse to feel angry at myself and my mother, and at the same time it's kept me away from women. The closer I got to them, the more guilty I got, and I guess I felt that acne was better than guilt."

"And safer for you to feel angry than sad."

"Yes. I'm beginning to see how I was desperately trying to get Dad to stay at home, but of course not succeeding."

"We can deal with that another time."

"I'd like that."

"Right now I'm wondering if you're prepared to pat yourself on the back for looking after yourself so well by giving yourself acne."

In this, the first session, James has moved from a position of believing that he personally had nothing to do with the initiation or the maintenance of his acne ("All I want to do is get rid of the damn problem!") to a part understanding of the role that the disease has played in keeping him safe. Such rapid awareness will not be possible for all of us. Nor is it always necessary, for many people, as I've said, make changes in their lives at a subconscious level, from whence they proceed to work effective and desirable behavioral changes. In a similar manner the hypnotherapist may evoke a healing response from the client.

At this point James is nowhere near done with the acne. The likelihood is that between now and when I see him next, he'll have used the experience of the first session and the insights he gained to reinterpret the data, strengthen his defenses and end up with the same feelings of insecurity and anger, albeit better defended. Some therapists believe that if the client is not cured in one or two sessions at the most, the therapist lacks skills. I can't help feeling that they're the same therapists who travel a lot, never following up clients for long enough to see the final result.

Instead I believe most people's defenses are well ahead of most therapists' skills, and that the client is in charge of the rate of personal change.

Not only is the client in charge of the speed with which he's prepared to resolve his issues but he also decides whether he'll continue in therapy at all. As soon as the therapist wants more for the client than the client wants for herself, therapy is a lost cause. In this situation the therapist has no therapeutic leverage, since the client quickly recognizes the therapist's need to cure him as being greater than his own need to be cured.

In response to such an invitation, the client will most likely hand responsibility to the therapist, and having accepted it, the therapist is then in an impossible situation. She's likely to become very frustrated from the effort that she's putting into curing this person with no results — or, more commonly, results that are just encouraging enough to keep the game going. The client plays victim and the therapist plays rescuer. Many doctors, other health professionals, and therapists are like this. They may have developed skills to hide their rescuing roles, but the client's little kid will detect these roles easily, since her very existence depended in the past on recognizing parental caring.

The positions of victim, rescuer, and persecutor are interrelated, as shown in Stephen Karpman's 1958 *Transactional Analysis Bulletin* article "Fairytale and Script Drama Analysis"; Karpman shows the diagram below of the "drama triangle" or "game triangle."

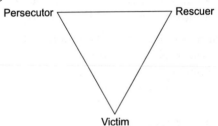

As the game that the doctor and the patient are playing evolves, they change positions within the triangle. The following is an example.

Victim: "I'm feeling very low, doctor. My sinusitis is terrible. It would have to develop just as I was going on vacation."

Rescuer: "What terrible luck. It must be awful; I'll see if I can help. Take these pills three times a day for five days. That should work."

Persecutor: "Not more pills. Every time I come here, you fill me up with pills. I think it's time I consulted the naturopath down the road."

Victim: "I'm sorry, but that's all I have to offer," or,

Persecutor: "I told you. If you insist on continuing to smoke, you'll pay the price. Stop smoking or have sinusitis. It's that simple."

Both parties end up feeling uncomfortable, because they're involved in a game. In this context, a "game" refers to a series of transactions that end in both parties experiencing racket feelings.

With James I'm careful to emphasize the following points. His current state of health, including both his psychological state and his physical condition, is the very best that he could do for himself up until this point in his life. Similarly, I believe he'll continue to care for himself as best he can. If it had been safe for him to be around women and have no acne, then I assume he'd have done that.

It was obviously less painful for him to have the acne than to confront some of his fears. Those fears concern his mother's anger at his sexuality, as well as his father's absence. Most clients take a long time to accept this notion. I know I did.

If everything we did was done to look after ourselves best (given limited options and even less power), then everything we have done and will do is OK. To accept this is to believe that we're OK. If we believe that we're OK now, as we are, then we don't have to change anything. That's unattractive to us for the following reason.

When we were children, we desperately sought our parents' approval, and this meant adapting in certain ways. Much has been made of this elsewhere. If we now make a declaration that we're OK as we are, then we no longer need to adapt. As kids we did need to adapt or suffer the consequences (death, we fantasized), but as adults we no longer need to. However, if we stop paying attention to what Mum and Dad want, either the real Mum and Dad or, more commonly, the parents in our head, we still risk losing their love. If they stop loving us then who will love us? We therefore cling to the need to be not OK and therefore the need to change, in order to keep our parents loving us (even though they may be dead). And of course it doesn't matter how much we suffer, or how much we change, the love we're seeking, that unconditional love of perfect parents, will never be forthcoming because it's a myth. We created it because we want to be cared for perfectly, we're afraid to be responsible, we're afraid to love ourselves and we're afraid to be alone.

If we accept that we're perfect as we are, and we stop making ourselves not OK, we'll need to drop the notion that if we were just that little bit better, Mom and Dad would give us the love we crave. To drop the need to change is therefore to drop the hope of turning back the clock and undoing history. As we become adults, we replace our real parents with surrogates such as spouses, our football coach, Jesus Christ, Buddha, the doctor, the psychotherapist, the queen, the prime minister, the president, Karl Marx, the guru, and even our own children. We create problems within ourselves as offerings to these surrogates, hoping that they'll see our pain and come to our rescue. We cannot afford to be well.

This is often a bitter realization, and people need varying amounts of time to adjust to it. In the meantime they undergo therapy or continually manipulate their circumstances to protect themselves from facing their own aloneness. James will be introduced to these ideas slowly and gently. They will not be forgotten through the hurly-burly and excitement of therapy. Nor will they be accusingly thrust at him, for he'll accept them only when he feels safe to do so; if he's like the rest of us, his temptation will be to never accept them. Meanwhile his therapy continues.

Therapy has two major components, and therapists tend to broadly orient themselves into two camps: the "thinkers" and the "feelers." Thinking therapies include psychoanalysis and its modern-day offshoot, transactional analysis, while feeling therapies include Gestalt, radix, bioenergetics, primal therapy, Rolfing, and other breath and bodywork therapies. Most therapists tend to use a combination of both feeling and thinking. Hypnotherapy may include both. Cognitive Behavior Therapy (CBT) is a combination of thinking and feeling, while practitioners of mindfulness attempt to become aware of their thoughts and feelings and not judge them as either "right" or "wrong." Those therapists who were brought up to think and not to feel will generally be expert thinkers and poor feelers, while those who decided under parental pressure to express their emotions and not to think about it a great deal will generally be attracted to the physical therapies, including the breath therapies. If the therapist strongly favors one modality and rejects the other, then you can be sure she'll be repeating her childhood circumstances or rebelling against her parents. That will suit some clients and not others.

James will firstly be encouraged to understand his need for his acne, because I'm more comfortable with thinking than with expressing emotions. He will, however, be given ample opportunity to express the rage and sadness that he feels toward his parents. Emotional catharsis, the outpouring of feelings stored up from childhood, can be very powerful and often frightening to watch. There's no point in James confronting his real parents with the "injustices" of his childhood. It's not their problem. Therapy offers the opportunity to direct his anger towards his parents. James may be invited to punch or kick a bean bag, or beat a mattress with a tennis racket or a soft baton. I make sure that he doesn't hurt himself, for that would confirm his childhood belief that to be angry is dangerous. Equally important is that he doesn't hurt me or anyone else. All the necessary safeguards are taken before he does his anger "work-out." Initially he'll be most comfortable expressing his racket feelings, and as he tends to swallow his anger, he'll be invited to express it openly and directly. If he has no difficulty in yelling at others, and does so excessively, I'll explore those feelings that he's avoiding by being angry all the time.

Much anger, apparently expressed in response to an immediate stimulus, is in fact old anger left over from previous incidents. James may be feeling sad beneath his covering anger and, in that event, I'll know his therapy is progressing well when he cries in front of me, or he reports crying.

In theory, if the old emotions can be mobilised, then they may be expiated and the person will re-establish emotional balance. In practice this will not happen unless the bottom level of feeling is unearthed, and that, I believe, is always fear. When fear is dealt with, which means that the client has come to trust himself to keep himself alive and to love himself and get himself loved, he'll no longer need the racket feelings and he'll drop them. They've served him well, effectively preventing his fear from surfacing. The physical ramifications of these racket feelings, those diseases whose role it was to maintain the old feeling states, will similarly no longer be needed. When James no longer needs to be angry (toward himself and his parents) he'll no longer need the acne to maintain his rage.

The racket anger moves freely around the circle and draws in outside issues as well: for example, anger at lovers, work colleagues, or the government. It may be primarily in any of those three positions at any time and could be available to the therapist in that position or indirectly through the other two. The client will regularly move it around in order to thwart a therapist's efforts to contact the underlying fear.

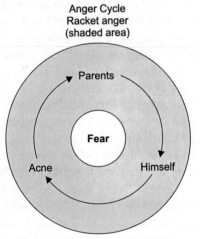

Anger Cycle
Racket anger
(shaded area)

Since therapy continues over a considerable period of time (on average about six months), the reader will appreciate the difficulty in describing the overall process. To report each phase the client goes through in reaching a level of operating that is satisfactory to her, and to fairly describe the therapy of those phases, would mean transcribing the tapes of the sessions. Each client's therapy would occupy a large volume, since no two are alike. Verbatim reporting would show the ebb and flow of progress, for between the "ah ha!" advances — those exclamatory leaps forward in awareness — is the terror of doing things differently as a consequence of new awareness and the tendency to return to the old safe ways of behaving. James, our man with acne, may find that mild acne returns at those times when he's most apprehensive. He'll learn to use this as a sign that he needs to look after himself.

People will always make changes at their own pace, even though the therapist may want them to go more quickly. I've had trouble coming to terms with this. When a client starts in therapy, I'm able to detect her basic blocks within the first session or two and will have some idea of what she could achieve. What I really mean is that I can see how dramatic a difference I could make to this woman, and I know how good I would feel to see her leave therapy with her cancer cured. Now, what I want for her may have little to do with what she wants for herself, and if I fail to detect my investment in her early recovery, I'm going to be very frustrated indeed. When the therapist is going too fast, the client will thwart the therapist's aspirations every time, even though she'll seduce him into believing that they both have common goals. Subconsciously, the client is sabotaging the therapist's every move. This leads to the often-heard cry among doctors, helping professionals, and therapists: "He didn't want to get well." Of course the client wanted to get well, but not in the same direction or at the same speed as the therapist wanted him to. Some clients need to test the water at every step, and that's why for them, therapy is a long, drawn-out affair. It's also why, if the therapist can resist the temptation to push too hard, therapy can be so effective. Clients appreciate having the time to practice new thoughts, feelings, and behaviors before undertaking further change. People don't get better in straight-lines. They take two steps forward and one step back, two forward and one back. Biofeedback mechanisms, the very architecture of biology, all work like this.

Diagrammatically, the progress of therapy looks something like this.

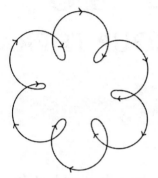

But you end up in the same place you began! What's the good of that?

I assume that the place you began, before the adaptations were made necessary and the illnesses started, was a good place. The illness cycle has been just part of the meanderings made in an effort to understand who we are and to accept responsibility for our lives. There's no fixed time that we need to have illness, be in therapy or continue searching.

We're searching for something that we misplaced, rather than lost.

16
GROUP THERAPY

A lone guitar rises above the sounds of the room, struggling to be heard. The audience settles, the tempo and the timbre of the instrument become sure, obeying every nuance of the master's call. The percussion enters, slowly at first, then gaining in empathy, an accompaniment on a sometimes hazardous journey.

Aware of its fellow traveler, the guitar courses up and down the scales with an added confidence. Sometimes in lead, and sometimes in answer, it will engage its fellow, and together they create a new dimension. Their call for others is answered by the bass, a low, rhythmic reply from long ago, before the course was sure, before the celebration began, a reminder of their roots. A violin is the last member of this ensemble. The players' momentum is carved from individual experience, honed by immediate needs to give expression through their instruments, and the need to take part, to share their dreams.

The melody becomes clear, the variations and leads are taken and given in nods and smiles as the momentum gathers. Together they see an opening, a way to the unfinished part of their symphony. They combine in harmony against the discord of failure. The audience wills them on. We can feel the dangers, smell the excitement, see the goal. They're in the tunnel, they're racing for the light. The beat reaches for the fury of the occasion, the violin is on the edge of freedom, the guitar hurtles into the void. They explode into sunlight, rejoicing in the singleness of their purpose, in the oneness of its expression. They've made the peak. The breathing becomes easier, the faces peaceful. As the music winds down the audience erupts into a spontaneous acknowledgement of the fear, the risk, the journey, the power and the victory. For a while we're in triumph together. In a few moments we resurface alone.

Group therapy can be very exciting. I enjoy it because of the increased dimension of people, whose only common ground may be a struggle for love, interacting in a way which shows you rather than tells you how they're feeling and thinking. Individual sessions, although no less penetrating in their analysis, and no less effective in their treatment of an individual, lack the fellow-traveler spirit. Since clients leave the office or the group room and return to a world occupied by others, groups preempt reactions to or by the outside world, by providing a microcosm of that world. This is valuable for clients wanting to practise new behaviors in a safe environment. Every group member, including the therapist, will react to everything said or done by any group member. It's impossible not to react. No reaction is reacting by doing nothing.

Clients are invited to respond on a gut level to the proceedings around them. Those who appear to not be reacting may have suppressed feeling to a level at which they're apparently unaffected by external happenings, or are frozen by fear. Either way it's obvious in their faces, and can be used by both the clients and the therapist in resolving the client's problems. Members will clearly be affected by the issues being worked on by others, and will advance their own inquiry as a consequence. This level of interaction isn't possible in individual sessions. Take the following example.

Bill, who has severe asthma, had been talking to his mother in the therapy sessions for some months, on and off. This involved imagining his mother was in a chair in front of him. Bill would converse with his mother by moving from his own chair, where he was himself, to the chair where he played the part of his mother. This technique is referred to as "two chair work." He was still very angry with his mother and blamed her for his asthma. He was also secretly angry with his wife but wasn't ready to admit it, as he believed that to be angry with her was tantamount to saying he didn't love her. Until Bill was prepared to confront his anger toward his mother as being the way he remained dependent on her, face his anger toward his wife and drop both, I couldn't see his asthma going. I resolved to make him uncomfortable.

"Your wife's obviously a real bitch," I suggested.

"How the hell would you know? You don't even know her!" Bill fumed.

"She married you, didn't she? I'll bet she's like your mother, who kicked you around all day."

"What a terrible thing to say," another voice said from across the room, more in righteousness than in anger. "You just don't say those things about people."

"Who's a real bitch in your life, Deborah?" I inquire.

"Nobody," she replied. "I wouldn't say that about anybody!"

"If you would say it about somebody, who might that be?"

"My mother makes me so mad at times," she replied.

"Will you see your mother there in front of you and tell her you're mad with her, but you won't call her a bitch?"

"Mom, sometimes you..." Deborah began to cry.

"It's OK to be angry with your loved ones," I told her gently, since I was dealing with a young child here who wasn't permitted to express her anger directly.

"The people we get mad at are often those we love most. Women are taught to cry instead of being mad. When you're ready, you might tell your mother that you love her and that you're angry with her. Meanwhile, you're

really looking after yourself by not letting yourself get mad... Bill, how are you?"

"I'm not sure; I'll think about it."

"Take your time."

From the rest of the group's interest in these proceedings, I know people are in the process of internalizing what's happened.

"What's happening to everybody?"

"If my husband fusses over me once more I'll scream," says Judith Miller, who's almost confined to a wheelchair because of her arthritis. *"He means well, but he makes me so damn angry at times."*

"My boss is a real pig," says Stephen, *"an arrogant bastard who shoves me around and gets a real thrill from it. I'm tempted to tell him to get stuffed."*

"Then what would happen?"

"I'd get fired."

"Do you want your job?"

"Sure. Right now I can't afford to lose it."

"Then congratulate yourself on keeping cool. How could you keep the job and feel good about it at the same time?"

"I don't know."

"Think about it this week, and report back when you come up with something."

"Yes, I will."

By confronting one group member, other transactions have yielded valuable information and started others on the way to a resolution of their own problems. Deborah, who's a social worker and rescues her helpless charges—just as she attempted to rescue Bill in the group—will benefit from getting in touch with her anger. Everybody who rescues others is angry at having to do it. Once they realize that they no longer have to heal the world as they were encouraged to do in childhood (at a time when they were least capable of doing so) and that they're far more effective if they let people take care of themselves, they become much happier.

None of the above would have transpired in an individual session. It's generally scary for people to take part in groups, since they feel exposed and vulnerable. Individual sessions are safer for most people, because in those situations they only need to contend with the therapist (and they've been conning doctors for years). It's no big deal for them. The group's another matter, however, and is therefore threatening. If people want to move from where they are, they have to take risks. I emphasize that groups are great fun and that a real sense of communion develops in a short space of time. Ultimately, I believe it's very important for people to be able to gradually expose themselves to others. There's something much less effective about telling a client that she's worthwhile despite her being sexually molested by an uncle when she and the therapist alike treat it as a secret—similar to the secret that the client and her uncle maintained between themselves for all those years. In a group it becomes obvious by the failure of the other members to reject the client—and their good wishes for having had the guts to tell them—that the matter defuses more rapidly. The added dimension of hearing other people to whom exactly the same thing has happened tell their stories further removes the shame, guilt, and, even more importantly, anger that remains toward the perpetrator of the alleged crime. Sure, it was sad that the little girl had to have sex to feel loved; sure, she can be angry that her uncle needed her to feel guilty in order for him to remain undetected; sure, she can scream at her mother for knowing it was happening yet doing nothing about it. That's all necessary. Also true is the fact that not forgiving her uncle will end in depression and martyrdom. I don't condone the act, but I also cannot rescue the victim. Unable to tell people of this childhood secret, many people who wish to maintain the energy of the affair will instead make themselves seriously ill and carry on bravely. As mentioned previously, arthritis serves a martyr well, although in the case above, a sexual disease would be more likely. Both illnesses will resolve themselves when the victim drops the pretense of not being responsible for her own life, no matter what happened to her as a child.

The mention of group therapy often meets with a strong reaction—mostly anger and fear. This isn't surprising, when you consider that people have been harboring their greatest fears for as long as they've been alive and have become very proficient at it. The thought of becoming less defended naturally provokes anxiety. They may mention someone they know who's done "groups" and who's "never been the same since." Some people will attend groups for exactly the same reasons that they've been attending doctors for many years: in the hope of either getting someone else to take responsibility for them or to blame the practitioner's incompetence for their continuing illness (when in fact they're simply not ready to resolve their problems). When competent group leaders refuse to take responsibility for their clients, this reaction may be the clients' way of maintaining their dependence.

To acknowledge that the expertise of the practitioner is less important than our will to be healthy is to take full responsibility for ourselves.

Physical closeness is facilitated in group sessions, and people often establish an intimacy that they've previously denied themselves. Getting close to other people—both emotionally (i.e., trust) and physically—is very frightening to many people, which is another reason why those who do not want to take risks often criticize group therapy. I remember a woman who'd suffered a debilitating illness for many years saying to me in a group session that she'd do "anything to be free of my pain." I replied that she didn't need to do anything drastic; all she needed was to get herself hugged by any member of the group. She refused.

I also encourage people to take responsibility for their sexuality, which means that they decide whether they want to become sexually active or whether they want to suppress their sexuality in favor of a personal contract (or perhaps a religious belief). Those who want to practice being sexy in the group can do so. I make allowances for the prevailing community attitudes to sexuality. Nevertheless, people often dismiss group therapy due to the implications of sexual wrongdoing involved, which unfortunately is yet another excuse for these people to fail to evolve. I say "unfortunate," because people do not need an excuse to look after themselves. If they aren't ready to accept responsibility for themselves and their diseases, then that must be what's best for them right now. If they can get somebody to look after them, that's all well and good. If they want to do something different later on, they can.

I believe that group therapy has the following advantages over individual sessions in the treatment of illness. First, it's novel. The assessment of illness using psychological methods (including vocal, facial, and muscular diagnosis) is different enough, but using group therapy to cure people of physical illnesses without drugs is really exciting. When clients face a serious illness and an exhausted orthodoxy, the thought of doing something different, however scary, becomes attractive. A group of people who gather to forge major changes in their lives—such as healing themselves of serious illnesses—generates considerable energy. This may be contrasted with the lethargy that is induced by doctors' resignation toward diseases that they regard as incurable. The group energy invites possibility.

Second, group therapy is a social event. A client may have an intimate relationship with his doctor that both doctor and client value, but given the great spectrum of personalities who are present in a group, the atmosphere becomes even more expectant. Not unlike what happens at a good party, many people use groups to establish long-term friendships. Groups afford one of the few opportunities to learn a great deal about another person before establishing a relationship. Because of this, experienced group leaders will require that group members not reveal anything that happens in the group to people who are not present. This is called "contracting." Group members can only discuss what happens within the group among themselves, but they are at liberty to discuss what happens to them personally with whomever they wish.

Groups are great fun. I use humor a lot in treatment, and a responsive gathering of people is very beneficial in taking the drama out of serious illness. Hanging on to the tragedy of illness becomes more difficult when neither the therapist nor the group is enticed into feeling depressed about a disease that someone has chosen to give herself. People usually drop their martyrdom very quickly when playing this role fails to have the desired effect. I've found it much more difficult to keep clear of rescuing such people in private sessions, since most people are generally very skilled at getting others to sympathize with them and will exploit my need to help them if they can. Because I was raised to care for my mother, I have to be watchful of this.

Group interaction, as I've mentioned before, is one of the major components of group therapy. When one woman in the group looks jealous because I'm hugging another, or the one I'm hugging shoots a guilty sideways glance at my female co-therapist, then I'm dealing with a couple of little kids who are responding much as they no doubt did in childhood. Both jealousy and guilt will be reflected in their physical health.

By monitoring the reaction of other group members, the therapist is better able to gauge the reality, reason, frivolity, or truthfulness of what's being said. I can be sure that if a woman is describing herself being sexually molested but the group is uninterested, restless, or, in extreme cases, yawning, then her story has an element of self-aggrandizement or insincerity to it. If, on the other hand, the group is listening intensely, they've subconsciously registered that this is an important issue, accurately reported, and react accordingly. In the first case, I may point out the client's game of "Ain't it awful?" in such a way that she understands that she can do things differently while still being supported for having cared for herself; the game was a very necessary defense when she first adopted it. In the second example, I may invite the woman to engage in an imaginary dialogue with her rapist in which she expresses her feelings of rage, forgives her rapist, works out how not to let it happen again, and stops feeling guilty; as a consequence, she'll stop her dysmenorrhea (painful periods). This will probably take some time, although if she's been allowing her feelings to surface, then she may cure herself overnight.

I may put my arm around a client's shoulder in an individual session—in fact I do so regularly—but a group offers a safer environment for practicing physical closeness. It also provides information on the fears that people have of being touched. Men with a fear of women will get their shoulders rubbed by other men. A woman who's angry with men may snap a refusal at a man who's asked that she rub his shoulders. In turn, a man who likes to be yelled at by angry women will ask such a woman for a back rub; the sagas of childhood adaptations are played out before the therapist for the rest of the group, the client, and the therapist to see.

In order for therapeutic interventions to work, and for the clients to feel safe to evolve, it's necessary to establish a caring environment. The tone of voice, the body postures, the honesty of the therapist in pointing out his own areas of difficulty, all play significant roles in this. No acting or misleading of clients is possible. Since the client will interpret anything the therapist says to him in terms of his own experience and needs, there's no point in trying to appear what you are not. The greatest factor in any transaction, the need of the client, is thankfully totally beyond the control of the therapist. Were that not the case, a situation would exist in which the therapist was in control of the client's destiny. That's not possible. My concern for the pain of another involves using my skills to facilitate him achieving what he wants for himself, and in relating to him as an individual who's done the very best he could in the circumstances.

Cure is the hallmark of group therapy. People actually cure themselves, and it's obvious to all present when that happens. To watch a person become happier during the course of group therapy is a very rewarding experience. The whole body changes. The face becomes open and softer. The eyes are untroubled, the voice becomes powerful and well modulated, there's a full range of emotional expressions, there's a willing exchange of physical contact, and compliments are both given and received joyfully. The symptoms of the disease gradually abate and eventually disappear, or they disappear between one session and the next. To watch this happen is enormously encouraging, or frightening, depending on whether or not the other clients want to cure themselves. Either way, it's very effective in mobilizing their energy to accept or resist the invitation of a cure.

17

SUMMARY OF THE CAUSE AND CURE OF ILLNESS

The trauma of the birth process confirms the world as potentially dangerous. The unborn infant monitors and responds to maternal anxiety. The adaptations begin.

Basic needs which are unmet or met unsatisfactorily, and which the infant is powerless to meet himself, confirm the need to adapt to survive. The child decides that some of his own needs must be modified to meet the requirements of his caretaker. The modifications guarantee continuing care. Some of those decisions lead to illness. Physical and psychological pain develops. The client seeks relief. Drugs or symptomatic treatments modify, or temporarily relieve, the discomfort. The disease process continues. The client becomes disillusioned with the treatment. A level of discomfort is reached at which the fear of the original adaptation is exceeded, that is, it becomes more painful to have the illness than to look at what needs to happen to remove it. Many people never reach this point.

The client seeks a healer. He's introduced to the notion of self-cause and self-cure. The client begins to accept responsibility for the illness. He becomes aware of the basis of the illness. His new-found awareness leads him, with the help of his therapist, to expand his options. He decides to do things differently. He retains the old ways until he's familiar with the practice of the new options. He satisfies those needs, which resulted in the illness, in other ways. He no longer has any need for the illness.

His mind and body are released from the restraints of early childhood adaptations, and freed up to respond with their full healing potential.

He cures himself.

18
PSYCHOTHERAPY—
THE TRANSITIONAL STAGE

A claim of a cure warrants careful examination. We're all extremely wily when it comes to doing things that make us feel safe. So great is our need to feel comfortable that we develop a very complex system of defenses that are mostly unknown to ourselves, let alone to an outsider such as a therapist. We suppress our fears, our knowledge of those fears, and our knowledge of our defenses of our fears. We're unwilling to admit that certain of our behaviors are defensive, because it's unsafe for us to do so. While we're unlikely to inform a therapist of these matters, an astute therapist, by observing the outward signs of the internal processes, can get a good idea of what the client is thinking (although never a complete picture). Therapy is similarly incomplete; any therapist who believes he can predict what a client will do in the future is deluding himself.

When I say that the client has decided to remove his illness, I mean for whatever reasons. Those reasons may be to please the group leader, the group in general, the client's wife, his boss, or his children. He may have readapted in order to remove the symptoms but still be complying with or rebelling against his parents or parent figures. If the parent figure is the therapist, which is very common, then transference hasn't been resolved, and future problems may arise. Withdrawal of interest on the part of the therapist may precipitate a new wave of fears in the client about who'll care for him now. Having removed the original illness to please the therapist, he may now have an acute need for something to take its place. Asthma then often takes over where migraine left off. There may be no reason to doubt the reduced support of the substitute parent, however. Many people stay very well under the umbrella of Jesus Christ, Buddha, or Allah. Multiple renowned therapists or a large number of Tibetan Buddhist gurus play the same role for a generation of people who need to rebel against their parents' values but have the same need to be cared for that all people do. People who stay happy and well within religious or other organizations have clearly found something that suits them.

When a part of our future happiness depends on the good offices of another, however well meaning, we're in the position of children. Jesus said, "Else ye turn and become as little children, ye shall not enter the kingdom of heaven." This may be interpreted to mean that we put ourselves under the care and guidance of a benefactor, in his case the church, or at least its teachings. As long as we remain true to those teachings, then we'll be happy and safe.

I prefer to believe instead, however, that as long as we remain accountable to another for our actions—and in return receive guidance and protection, either real or imagined—we're limiting ourselves. Certainly we can take into account anything other people say in an attempt to work out what's safest for us, but to slavishly follow someone else's advice on how to lead my life doesn't appeal to me. It may be necessary, however, to do that for a while. Surrendering to another human being, or a deity, may be a necessary step toward taking full responsibility for ourselves. Eventually we realize that our godhead does not have the answers for us that we hoped, and we become our own masters. This may involve the anguish of accepting our personal responsibility.

In psychotherapy a similar process may occur. Clients go into psychotherapy hoping to find someone with the answers for them, someone who'll do better than their original parents. This new parent will teach them new skills with which to protect themselves against the world. Very often this is exactly what happens in therapy. The client comes out better defended than when he went in, albeit very much better at hiding his fears. In this case he would appear to have achieved nothing.

If however, he realizes that he's no happier with his new skills, and it may take some time (it took me three years), he can use the experience to begin to really achieve autonomy. In so doing he'll need to reject the therapy as being no more than an incomplete theory emanating from the needs of a fellow sufferer (the therapist) and begin trusting himself. Most people appear to need to go through the process of hope, disillusion and then rejection of the therapy.

As I see it, we're left with a choice to make. That choice is to remain under the umbrella of another's wisdom and love or to be our own ultimate master. As our own guide we can allow the "grown-up" part of us to choose another person or persons to help us look after the "little kid" in us. The decision to be our own final authority doesn't imply being lonely. We can surround ourselves with whomever we choose. It does mean accepting that we're alone in the sense that we cannot rely on anyone else or any guru to look after us. In a similar manner, we're unable to ever get inside the head of anybody else to feel as they do. Such self-responsibility means accepting that from time to time we may need to be unwell.

Some people who find the notion of being their own ultimate guardian appealing, may do so because they've experienced inadequate caring as children. They don't trust others anyway, so they aren't enthused by the idea of placing themselves in the hands of another person. They don't believe that anybody else can know their needs, or if they do that they will care for them as they wish. They have no experience of this kind of care as a child. Their belief that "I'm responsible for myself" comes from both their anger and their fear that "no one else will care for me properly." That's not autonomy, for their belief is motivated by fear. In a treatment setting, they'd be offered the opportunity to place themselves in another's care so that they could resolve their fear. When they trust others to do their best to look after them, then they'll believe that they're worth looking after. They're now in the "I'm OK — you're OK" position, from which they may choose self-responsibility.

Conversely, others are attracted to the idea of always having an authority whom they can turn to for guidance. They may in many aspects of their lives be self-fulfilled, be successful and responsible members of the community who choose to worship a god, maintain a guru, or stay in psychotherapy forever, sometimes as a client but more often as a therapist. They have a sense of great warmth and comfort from believing in a benevolent god. Without such a belief, they feel scared. Many people adopt religion during stressful times in their lives and drop it once things get better. They keep their beliefs at the back of their minds, to be called on when needed. I've been speaking of religious devotion, but numerous figureheads and organizations out there serve exactly the same function. Devotees vociferously defend political parties or political beliefs as being the repository of ultimate truth. Diet fanatics will attribute healing properties to certain dietary truths, paying homage at the feet of whole-wheat bread or organic vegetables. Authorities and figureheads serve a purpose: to allay the fear of accepting that there's no higher authority than ourselves.

The people who believe in higher authorities are those who as children have been told, usually indirectly and therefore more powerfully, that the world is unsafe. They're never encouraged to believe that they're powerful enough to care for themselves, and never have the reins of self-responsibility handed to them in a safe and caring way, as they become capable of taking them. They're encouraged to remain under the influence of others, sometimes parents, sometimes the church, or are left to find their own godhead. If they're angry with parents, they'll pick a belief as visibly removed from that of their parents as possible, for example, if the parents are Christian, they may be fervent Hare Krishnas. In reality they've adopted the parental belief system, that is, it's necessary to believe in something more strongly than you believe in yourself. This re-creates their experience of childhood, when they were unable to look after themselves. To maintain it forever is to always deny our own influence over destiny, which is the traditional illness position. Lived like this, life is at least consistent. There's no need to change just because we're now adults. It's consistent and, above all, it's safe. It provides a ready community. It clearly suits many people.

The alternative is to regard life as consisting of two general phases. The first phase is childhood: a period of diminished responsibility. The second is adulthood: the period of full responsibility. During the first phase, our parents are the ultimate authority we know. As grown-ups, we become the ultimate authority, although the law may frustrate us. In this model, we're faced with two changes, just as there are two phases. The first change we make is to adapt to our parents' wishes.

We become either what they want us to be or its opposite. Either way we've still modified our behavior in response to our parents' demands. That's the first change we make. The second change is the change back. Having modified our thoughts, feelings and behaviors out of necessity in childhood, we now change back to thinking, feeling and behaving as we, our own new parent figures, want. To do this we need to drop those parts of our childhood conditioning that we adopted for safety, but which we no longer require. We no longer need a figurehead to keep us safe or alive. We are free. That's the second change, the change back. Perhaps that's what Jesus Christ meant when he said, "Else ye turn and become as little children, ye shall not enter the kingdom of heaven."

This interpretation refers to the "free child" and not the "adapted child."

There's a transition period between the first and second phases that occurs usually between adolescence and young adulthood. When parents are aware of handing responsibility to their children, or they do so intuitively, then the transition phase will be successfully accomplished with a minimum of trauma. The new adult may have plenty of adjustments to make, but she'll have the confidence and skills to handle them. She'll believe in her ability to take whatever steps will benefit her most. She'll have little need for illness to help her through this phase.

For those of us who didn't get what we wanted in childhood and who were forced to adapt more of our own wants to meet parents' needs, other methods are available to us to make the change back. It may be frightening, because the level of adaptation may have been so great that we don't know what it's like to be who we are, to be ourselves, to be free. We can't remember or conceive of such a state. We may not be motivated to try for it unless the pain of our present circumstances becomes too great. Illness may be one of those motivating factors. It may feel much safer to accept a level of discomfort and try to ignore it, focusing instead upon work, family, politics or religion. We may not want to address the possibility of dropping our defenses and risking the unknown. We may have carved out a niche of caring which, despite needing the occasional sinus attack to keep it operational, serves us well. We settle for it.

For those intrepid souls who reach for the sky, psychotherapy, meditation, religion, fanaticism of any kind, a guru or a friend may serve to keep us safe through the transition period between dependence on parents and dependence on self. We're like a caterpillar entering the cocoon from which, in order to achieve its life destiny, it must emerge. To emerge from this phase is to drop the transitional belief system and to create one of our own. The psychotherapy is no longer relevant, the leader's beliefs become his own. We reject him with love. We are free.

SECTION IV:
THE PREVENTION OF ILLNESS AND THE CREATION OF WELLNESS

19

LEVELS OF PREVENTION

Prevention has several components. An illness that has taken hold may be prevented from becoming worse. An illness that has been removed completely may be prevented from recurring. An adult may prevent illnesses that other members of her family have suffered from by taking preventive measures. She may elect to do this at any time in her life. Finally, and I think the aspect of prevention that has been virtually ignored, is the prevention of illness in children and adults by preventive or healthy parenting. This involves relating to our children in such a way as to encourage wellness and to discourage the need for illness. To do this would significantly alter health outcomes.

Meanwhile, let's look at those measures that we adults, who perhaps were not taught how to avoid illness, can take for ourselves now. In previous chapters I've described how we give ourselves illnesses that confirm our early-childhood decisions about ourselves, our parents, and the world. Rather than face the fear of doing things differently, we choose to continue with the old beliefs and behaviors, even though they're damaging to our psyche and our bodies alike. In this way, illness takes care of our greatest fears and may be regarded as an ego-defense mechanism. If we're prepared to risk being scared, we can investigate the origins of our disease and learn what we can do to remove it. This may vary from changing jobs to admitting and expressing (indirectly) the anger toward a parent — perhaps our father for deserting us. Having learned the cause of the illness—that is, why we've decided at that time to become sick—we then choose whether or not to remove it. Both choices, taken with awareness and responsibility, are equally valid. For example, we may choose to understand why we've made ourselves ill, choose not to proceed with those behaviors that would make the condition worse, and choose to retain the conditioning that maintains the disease. There are many good reasons for adopting this attitude, and in practice many people do choose this level of prevention. Some of these reasons include financial commitments, family responsibilities, or, most often, the fear of loss of love.

Here's an example. A thirty-year-old woman who was supporting her three children consulted me with a complaint of pelvic inflammatory disease, a long-term problem she'd suffered since the breakup of her marriage three years before. She'd been given eight courses of various antibiotics during that time, all administered by a gynecologist who hoped to settle the inflammation. The pain lessened for a while, then recurred. She also tried hormones, in the form of various brands of the contraceptive pill.

We established that she felt guilty about depriving her children of their father. She'd had an affair and took responsibility for the ensuing breakup of her marriage. When I suggested to her that her pelvic inflammatory disease would improve if she slowed down at work, she began to cry and said that since it was her fault that the children were without a father, the least she could do was to ensure that they didn't want for anything material. She wasn't prepared to reduce her working hours. She was prepared, however, to stop feeling guilty about having an affair (realizing that it was a symptom of the marriage, rather than the cause of the divorce) and to stop taking responsibility for the actions of her previous husband. In particular she stopped regarding her sexual infidelity as the reason for all her problems. The disease settled and, since she didn't take a rest, continued in a mild form for the next year. In this case, the woman arrested her disease's progress and prevented it from worsening.

This example can be extended to cover the second type of prevention: preventing the recurrence of a disease that the client had removed completely. If the woman with the pelvic inflammatory disease had taken a vacation or rested more often as well as ceased feeling guilty, she would have stopped inflaming her own reproductive organs, thus resolving her condition. If she were prepared to become aware of those times in childhood when she decided, in response to her father, that she was responsible for men leaving her and that this was because of her sexuality, she might cure her disease forever. This would involve disowning the responsibility she took for her mother's jealousy of the way in which her father cared for her. She was not to blame for her father leaving home, despite her mother's insinuations, and to be loved she need no longer feel guilty, as she had decided to at the time. She had of course repeated these exact conditions in her own life, which demonstrates the power of scripting, or the fear of loss of parental love. If she marries a man who will not leave her, will not hold her responsible for his own feelings, and who's happy to tell her how wonderfully sexy she is, then she'll have resolved the matter. She may, of course, resolve it in other ways.

As adults, we can improve the general quality of our health in nonspecific ways. We can practice general prevention; by doing this, we can avoid degenerative diseases or perhaps prevent those diseases that our family histories almost guarantee we will contract: every member of a family over fifty may have suffered from arthritis, for example. In practicing this sort of prevention, we take note of such factors as diet, lifestyle, recreation, exercise, spirituality, sleep patterns, rest, interests, retirement planning, meditative practices, and interpersonal and family relationships. These are the general considerations.

We've previously looked at preventive diet. The "diet of best chance," the "prudent diet," the "long-term general diet," and the "preventive diet" are all the same thing. This, I took pains to point out, was completely different from a "remedial diet," which is the acute treatment of specific disease in specific people by altering their physiology and psychology using constantly changing diets. I will briefly discuss the other factors in general prevention before examining the area of disease avoidance I consider most important: preventive or healthy parenting.

The general consensus appears to be that a person who eats a prudent diet, sleeps between six and ten hours a night so as to awake refreshed, and takes a certain amount of exercise will be healthiest. Such a person will have a loving spouse; between two and three well-adjusted, loving children; have interests outside the home; be intellectually stimulated and stimulating; have great sex at least three times a week; and will be unafraid to masturbate. In her life will be a fine balance of commitment, rest, and recreation. Spiritually, she'll be both surrendered and flexible, perhaps a member of a church group or interested in meditation. Others will notice her inner peace. She'll be receptive to the political and social troubles of our times, have the strength to change those things she can, and accept those she can't. She'll be both existentially content and continually evolving as a personality. Above all she'll accept her own power to do as she wishes, while both considering others and not accepting their burdens as her own. Among her friends will be soul mates (perhaps one or two), up to four close friends, and a number of acquaintances with whom she spends a little time. She's learned to live with paradox.

What was your reaction to the above cameo? Were you wishing you were there; not believing some or much of it to be possible; angry at not being like this woman, positively nauseated by the thought of it; thinking it was a hoax, wanting some of it for you but rejecting other aspects of it; not wanting any of it; confused about what you do want, seeing it as idyllic but scared that you may never make it; dismissive of it as a conspiracy to return you to peace, love, and sisterhood; sad that you have a long way to go and are resigned to mediocrity; wanting to forget the whole thing; angry that religion was mentioned at all, or not enough; wondering if it's the same for a man; or wanting to adopt it as a good way to be?

Is your response some of the above, all of the above, or none of the above?

The likelihood is that you already have some of those things, are in the process of acquiring others, and are disinterested in the remainder. By using such an exercise, it's possible to see that a general description of health and happiness in one fictitious person actually describes no one. This doesn't mean that no one has achieved that degree of fulfillment but that fulfillment, health, and happiness are different things to different people. That's hardly an earth-shattering statement. We're all aware that we have quite different tastes, dislikes, and aspirations from those of our neighbors (even our spouses) and that this difference in tastes causes us no problems. Few of us would welcome changing so that we all became the same. If we apply this same reasoning to health, it becomes clear that some readers will consider certain aspects of my mind-body that I regard as "diseases" (i.e., I'm "un-easy" about them) as minor inconveniences or of no significance. Certainly they wouldn't bother to do anything about them, whereas I'm searching for the way and the will to change them.

Similarly, conditions that you and I both suffer and that are of great concern to you may be of no importance to me. In addition, we all forgo a degree of health in order to achieve other things. A woman who is supporting her children may have dermatitis of the hands from the need to do extra cleaning, and she may accept that; to another woman that would be intolerable. I've spent most of the past thirty summers on the beach surfing. To experience the exhilaration, the fear, and the triumph of riding waves is important to me, and I'm prepared to accept the premature aging and drying of my skin that is an inevitable consequence of such an activity. I take the precautions I can, but I'm not prepared to stay indoors just because my blond complexion evolved in milder, less sunny climates than Australia, where I was born and have lived for much of my life. I take full responsibility for that decision and take what steps I can to minimize its significant consequences.

It's because we all differ so much that general recommendations are, at best, of little use. This makes real nonsense of the fanatics reported in the news who've decided that we should all eat fish and no red meat, or we should all play squash or handball, or that we should all sleep from 10:00 p.m. until 6:00 a.m. They've also decided for us that we shouldn't smoke, that we need multiple examinations for cancer every year, and that eating organic vegetables is the only way to keep our bodies free of pollutants. What they really mean is that *they* need to eat organic vegetables and not smoke, because if they didn't, then they would be imbalanced. This, of course, has nothing to do with us. They undertake their efforts to convert others to their ways of thinking for their own benefit. Often they're seeking approval for their discovery, which isn't dishonorable, but of limited relevance to others.

People get acknowledged the best way they can. What it means for us, the readers, is that we accept only those theories and practices that agree with our own assessment. From time to time, in order to advance, we may need to risk those old assessments, but we don't have to take anyone else's word for it. We can listen. We can decide.

20
HEALTHY PARENTING

I believe that the most important aspect of preventive medicine, or health promotion, is healthy parenting. It's probably also the most difficult, and it comes at a time when we may be immature ourselves. This refers to the messages that parents give their children in the early years (the first six are the most important) that shape the child's personality. These years are most important, because young children are the most vulnerable and the most impressionable. If children are raised to be autonomous, they won't need major illness. What does being autonomous involve?

Autonomy, according to Eric Berne in *Games People Play*, has three components: awareness, spontaneity, and intimacy. Awareness has two components: sensory awareness, which means intact taste, touch, sight, smell, and hearing, and psychological clarity. Spontaneity refers to the willingness to feel and express joy, anger, sadness, and fear. Intimacy refers to loving and being loved in warm, caring, and satisfying transactions. These three characteristics are considerations of both parenting and therapy. I'm inclined to add "interconnectedness." Autonomy implies a willingness to interact, to be part of a bigger whole.

In chapter 2, "The Childhood Basis of Disease," I discussed ways in which children act on their injunctions and drivers, along with the subsequent development of disease, while the permissions and allowers promote autonomy and health.

The most important of the permissions is "Exist." A child who's uncertain whether her parents wanted her will substantially modify her behavior in order to be "allowed" (as she sees it) to remain alive. These specific thoughts are rarely formulated in the child and are rarely recognizable to an adult. These modifications cause disease in both the short and long terms via mechanisms that have been elaborated on elsewhere. The injunctions and drivers are modifications of the right to exist; for example, in the case of the injunction "Don't be a girl," it's OK for you to exist, providing you aren't a girl. Or, in the case of the driver "Be strong," it's OK for you to exist, as long as you're strong. A child who believes that one or both parents are not totally happy with her being alive will begin life on a shaky foundation. Someone who believes that her right to exist is significantly qualified will not influence her own body positively; her physique will end up an accurate reflection of her fears and insecurities. Illness is practically guaranteed.

The first step in preventive parenting, or more accurately "healthy parenting," is to affirm and reaffirm children's right to be alive. Parents will feel comfortable in doing this in their own ways. The overall message will be the equivalent of "Sweetheart, I love you, and I love having you around." If parents repeat this frequently in the early years, and say it at impromptu times when the child has done absolutely nothing to "deserve" it (that is, it was totally unsolicited), then the child will believe that truly she's a joy to her parents and that they want her. Needless to say, the child will detect any falseness in this and any other messages she receives, so there's no point in lying to her. Better to say nothing, or tell the truth if you're not feeling like approving her. Our body language, voice intonation, and of course facial expressions will tell the child, well before she's acquired language, what we mean. If our words are different from the way we express them, children will believe their own interpretations. A child whose parents told her that they loved her but did things that would suggest otherwise will not be convinced by their words. She'll end up not trusting anything she's told and will become very confused indeed. If the parents didn't want the child and now regret her existence, then it may be better for them to adopt her out to someone who will love and cherish her. If that opportunity has passed, then the child may be better off if she's not lied to. There's no point in telling her that she's not wanted—she'll pick up on that anyway—but it will be less damaging in the long run to be a real parent, however unloving, than a false parent. It will be painful, but she can work through it later.

More common than parents who don't want their children are parents who love their children but don't tell them. For example, many men believe that to tell children they're loved is to be an unmanly father and that if the child's a boy, such a statement is unbecoming. They may be afraid of telling their daughters, perhaps equating love with sexual intimacy. They believe that children can be spoiled by love, or demonstrated love. I don't agree with them but I respect their own personal need to withhold the verbal affirmation of their love. They do this because of their own fears and not for the reason they usually give, which is that it's good for the children. I encourage them to resolve their fear and to start verbally and physically affirming their children, for I know from experience that their children will be much healthier, knowing and hearing they're loved.

Feeling loved is not the same as being inconsiderate of others or believing that you can always have your own way. Many parents believe that to continually reaffirm their love for their kids by telling them so and hugging them will mean the kids will grow up to be demanding monsters. On the contrary, it's much easier and more effective to say, "You can't have that, because we don't have the money" in a loving way—i.e., "It's OK to ask; you can't have it, but I love you"—than to refuse children who ask for things out of the frustration of not knowing whether they're loved or not. They ask in anger. Their anger is not at being refused what they want but at not feeling loved. The former is a short-lived disappointment, the latter an ever-increasing antagonism that only love can cure.

Those children who appear obnoxious, arrogant, or spoiled are protesting at the way in which they've been bought off by parents who are willing to indulge their every whim rather than love them for who they are. They're responding to a need in the parent—a need that the children are in no way capable of satisfying. They struggle to do it, however, in their quest for survival. Spoiled children may be the result of parents who are so in need themselves that they desperately long for their children to love them, and they try to buy that love. A child often responds with anger at this blackmail, since she loves her parents anyway and recognizes the ulterior message to her, which is that her love is not good enough to satisfy her parents. This contrasts with the child who's convinced of his parents' love and is under no obligation to love them back in a particular way. Children will love parents without having to be coaxed into it.

Love doesn't cause spoiled children; it cures them.

The other permissions and allowers naturally follow the unqualified right to exist. In fact, they *are* the unqualified right to exist. Look at these a moment (go back to page 30) and ask yourself about you and your children. Do you encourage them to feel their emotions—cry when they're sad, get angry at you when you do something they don't like—or do you use your physical power and greater experience to keep them subservient? When you've asked yourself that question, you might ask whether the pattern of your own childhood is not repeating itself; remind yourself of how you felt about it at the time. If you're like the rest of us, the likelihood is that you'll have repeated some of your own childhood messages to your own children even though some of them were distressing to you at the time. Or you may have decided in childhood that when you had kids, you were sure you weren't going to make your kids go through what you went through. You might be telling your kids that you love them, just as you wished your parents had told you; allowing your daughter to become womanly and sexy, just as you wished you'd been allowed to; or letting your boy cry, just as you were encouraged not to. Will you consider giving yourself the same caring permissions you're giving your kids? After all, you're now your own parent as well as theirs.

If parents give their children the sorts of affirmations I've been speaking of, the children's need for illness will be reduced. If illness is regarded as a defense mechanism, and the individual has little need to be defended, then she'll have little need for illness. Because we're all defended to some degree, and because we're living in a hostile environment, we all suffer intermittently.

Pollutants in the form of colorings, flavorings, preservatives, car fumes, industrial fallout, microwaves, genetics, noise, chlorinated water, excessive dairy products, poor bowel function, tension in children and their parents, and a lack of fresh green vegetables all play a part in the development of upper respiratory tract infections in children. They're almost inevitable, even in children who are loved. When the first stage of prevention, health-promoting parenting, fails to prevent the development of disease, we need to isolate those factors that are maintaining it or making it worse. This prevents future, more severe attacks from occurring by minimizing the influence of those factors that are beyond our control and addressing those factors that we have some influence over. We can minimize the effects of those factors that are beyond our control by not adding to them.

When a child develops an infection, or more often an inflammation, her caretakers must attend to her immediate needs: they tell her to rest, feed her a remedial diet, ask her about any problems, and give her the same amount of caring as if she were well. The illness doesn't attract increased parental energy and support; to do that guarantees its repetition. Particularly if brothers and sisters demand equal attention from the parents, children will be very quick to seize on any activity that increases their share of the parental caring. Illness is a favorite. Initially it may be necessary to give the child less caring than if she were well in order to encourage her to change her illness pattern, although this may result in attention-seeking behavior that is equally as undesirable as the disease itself. Future attacks may jeopardize the long-term health of the child, in which case immediate and strong measures may be required. At the same time as the patient is offered minimal caring, other children in the family may be stroked and congratulated on keeping themselves well. Wellness is therefore rewarded, illness is not.

Children respond very quickly to a change in the reward system and are very aware of its ramifications, as demonstrated by the five-year-old client of mine, whom his parents overheard telling his three-year-old sister: "If you want Mommy to look after you, just get sick—that's what I do." When children come into my office and one member of the family is ill, I'm careful to pay attention to the healthy children. Since some of them enjoy coming to see me, I arrange times for them to visit when they're well. This is a rewarding thing to do, and, with a little bit of arranging of my schedule and that of the parents, we can organize casual, short-term drop-ins. The children begin to replace illness with wellness.

It may be necessary for parents to examine and change their own patterns of illness if they wish for their children to become well. There's little point in parents complaining about seven-year-old Mary always having stomach cramps and staying away from school before an exam if the mother takes to bed with an aspirin or two whenever she's feeling tense. Similarly, little Freddie's foot is unlikely to improve enough to allow him to take part in sports lessons while his father is still at home with an "industrial back." We're creating the illness patterns of our children every time we suffer from an illness ourselves. We can minimize the effects of this modeling by being truthful about what's happening to us: the equivalent of, "Son, when I was your age, I lost my father in a car accident. Since that time, I get asthma whenever I'm scared about something; as you know, right now I'm in line for this promotion, and it's scaring me a little. I'm not sure why I hang on to the asthma, but I do know that only I can remove it. As for you, well, you can decide to be well." By owning our power to be well or ill, we model that for our offspring.

Paradoxically, permitting illness is a necessary part of promoting wellness. If we're overzealous about discouraging illness in children we may be inadvertently telling them to not look after themselves. Illness is a legitimate way of meeting needs, and when we attempt to discourage it on the grounds that it causes long-term harm to our bodies, we need to be clear that we're not telling children that they're not OK because they've chosen illness to meet their needs. Rather can we isolate the need, attend to that part of it which is our responsibility as a parent and teach our children to take care of themselves by asking for what they want if they're unable to provide it themselves. As support for this, we need of course to be willing to provide the caring in other ways. We support them for doing something to improve their lives, while recommending a less damaging way of going about it.

Consider the following exchange.

"Why aren't you at school today, David?"

"I hurt my knee."

"How'd you do that?"

"Playing football."

"What's going on at school today: Anything special?"

"Just another football game, that's all."

"Don't you want to play?"

"No. It's too rough. Peter Smith is a big bully, and Tom's always after me, and he's about twice as big as me."

"Don't play if you don't want to."

"Then Tom's father will call me a sissy. He says only girls don't play."

"Are there any others who don't play?"

"Sure—lots of 'em."

"Are they sissies?"

"No."

"It's OK by me if you don't play football. I loved playing tennis."

Taking care of children's needs and then handing responsibility to them when they're capable of taking it is an art. It's also one of the main factors in the creation of wellness, or the prevention of illness. How might we go about this?

Children begin to acquire skills at a very early age. By the age of six months, they're able to hold objects in their hands and to pick up those things they've dropped, provided they can reach them. They may not be able to crawl or sit properly at this stage. The art of letting them do things they're capable of or that they want to practice begins in infancy. When the child drops an object that is of interest to her and her hand control is sufficiently developed to enable her to pick it up, let her. By so doing, the child develops the skill, becomes surer that she can get the things she wants, confirms her belief that her parents are interested in her developing skills, believes that it's OK to do things for herself, and continues to mature. At six months she'll need help to be placed where she can retrieve the object; by a parent putting her there and letting her pick it up, she learns about asking for and receiving help. She grows safe in the belief that she'll be permitted to benefit herself when she's able and that she will receive help when she needs it. She figures the world is a safe, caring place.

A child who lets her mother or father know that she's interested in an object by reaching for it, or by making a noise, and receives no help in getting it will start believing that she has little power over her life. She hasn't the skills to do it herself and nobody seems interested in helping her. If this happens often enough, she resigns herself to powerlessness. She may also make the decision that she's helpless and loveless. I've outlined previously how these feelings soon express themselves in physical disease.

Alternatively, a child who has her needs attended to but isn't allowed to help herself—that is, she wants the object and although capable of picking it up has it repeatedly picked up for her—understands that her needs will be met, but she'll probably decide that there's something scary about meeting those needs herself. Such a child grows up feeling loved but incapable: the world is safe only as long as someone else is there to take care of things. She accepts her parents' fears about life being dangerous. As an adult she'll be tempted to become ill to be cared for, since society condones this option.

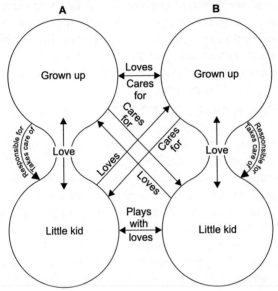

I've described a six-month-old infant, but the process of striking a balance between caring for children and letting them care for themselves occurs between birth and when the offspring leave home, and even after that. As the child becomes older, another hazard arises; encouraging or even forcing children to take care of themselves and others, usually parents, before they're able. This creates enormous anxiety in the child, and usually means she suppresses her own needs and feelings in favor of those expected of her. Eventually, the little kid inside her becomes exhausted from the burden and collapses, physically and mentally. This may happen at any age and until it does, these people are often bastions of caring for others. I've known upstanding physicians to be heroin addicts, for instance. In fact there's a high level of substance abuse amongst the medical profession. Therapy involves the client's own grown-up taking care of her own little kid. Prevention involves having expectations of our children that they can handle.

The task of steering a middle course with teenagers becomes seemingly impossible at times. Teenagers' need to rebel, and the influence of peer groups and societal messages that conflict with those of their parents (especially in the world of the Internet and social media), makes for difficult communication and family harmony. These years have less to do with the prevention of illness, since the crucial period for establishing a pattern of caring and safety and encouraging self-responsibility is accomplished before children reach the age of ten. In later years that pattern is refined.

Another component of healthy parenting is teaching children to pick someone with whom they'll be happy to spend their lives. This will indirectly prohibit illness by meeting needs before the need for illness becomes necessary. I refer here to a partnership between two people who are of opposite sexes or the same sex, bound by law or by private contract, or who intend to have children or not. We may regard the partners as two adults with two children in their charge; better still, two grown-ups with two little kids in their charge. The two little kids are, of course, their own internal kids. The little kid in us represents our needs, wants, loves, feelings, hopes, and fears—the part of us that needs protection to be provided by the grown-up part.

The grown-up takes responsibility for her own little kid and also takes responsibility for finding another person who has grown up who will help her own grown-up look after her little kid. In other words, we each find a grown-up who will help us look after our own little kid. Our little kid plays with our partner's little kid, and our grown-up helps look after our partner's little kid. Our little kid doesn't need to look after our own grown-up or the grown-up of our partner. Nor do we ask our partner's kid to look after our grown-up. By such an arrangement, each partner remains responsible, cared for, caring, loving, and loved.

How do we teach our children to do this? If we ourselves are in such a relationship, it's easy. We simply model being loving by simultaneously having fun, taking care of ourselves, and caring for our partner. At the same time, we adopt the attitude to our children's needs as described previously. If we aren't in such a relationship, then it may be more difficult. We may use metaphor or storytelling and, as the child becomes more able to understand, explain our position directly. We can place our children in the company of adults who enjoy a partnership that models the behavior, and we can comment favorably on the behavior of others to whom the child has access. We can allow the child to choose differently from ourselves by recalling the allowers and permissions mentioned previously. Above all, as they leave childhood, we can confirm the love we had, and still have, for them.

We can instruct our children in those lifestyle factors that we found to be helpful for us and make available information that we haven't tried or used ourselves but we believe may be of value. We can encourage an attitude within the child of respect for her own individuality and the idea that any decisions she makes about herself will ultimately need to be her own.

Because she's different from every other person on the planet, those decisions will be necessarily unique and untried.

We'll have prepared her for the risk.

21

AT YOUR INVITATION ONLY

Whenever I read a psychotherapy book or attend a lecture by a fellow therapist, I constantly modify what's being said with my perception of who's saying it. My assessment will be based on my observation of his body language, his general state of anxiety, the way he relates to his colleagues or spouse, his use of language, his major representational system, and so on. I've previously discussed in great detail diagnosis by observation. As the personality of the therapist emerges, what he's really saying becomes clearer, and I'm able to assess its relevance for me. I use my skills of observation to sift rapidly through an otherwise formidable amount of theory about health and healing.

All theory arises within the theorist's own experience. That may sound obvious, but if we use that maxim, several well-accepted theories and practices become recognizable for what they really are—a person writing not of some universal truth, but of herself. Medicine abounds with scientific hypotheses that are statistically "valid" one year and disproven the next. For the brief period of their acceptance by the scientific fraternity, they are the only truth, maintained if need be by the scurrilous deposition of alternative views. Then someone, working from her own internal needs as did her predecessor, discovers something that is more true—that is, more fulfilling of both her own needs and the needs of those responsible for accrediting new theories and practices.

Man interprets what he sees, rather than describes it. Red to me is a collection of colors that I've seen over the years which were called red by my parents and others. To you red will be almost the same, but not quite, since your experience will have been different. If we both saw a color which was borderline red, then it's likely we would differ as to what we called it. I might say "sort of red" and you, "sort of yellow." Similarly, an individual living in Ireland all his life has a quite different notion of what constitutes "green" flora than does someone living in Australia. A tree described as "green" by the Australian would be considered "gray" by the Irishman. Hardly scientific. In a similar manner, patients are diagnosed and treated differently by different practitioners.

As an example, I believe that if an individual isn't having sex (either intercourse or masturbation), that requires exploration. The therapy I offer to that person will take that into account. Another practitioner may view that as contentment, and call it balance. The client concerned will be attracted to me because of my views, or will reject my approach and go elsewhere. No practitioner has a mortgage on the truth. There is no truth, simply a subjective, biased interpretation of unverifiable, fluctuating data. The interpretation the client accepts will be the interpretation which suits him at that time. It will be the one with which he's most comfortable (or least afraid). Later he may be prepared to risk more, and increase his level of discomfort in order to achieve something he considers important. Then he may need to change practitioners. Any investment I have in him accepting my ideas about his condition will ultimately stand in the way of his resolving his problem, and he must realize that. If he doesn't want to take responsibility for himself, he'll invite my interpretation and take it as gospel, rather than use it to clarify his own beliefs. By so doing he hopes I'll relieve him of the burden of looking after himself. The value to me in being regarded as fallible by the client is that I don't have to pretend to look after him.

I believe that the energy for a hypothesis comes partly from a denial of its opposite. If I'm afraid to express my emotions, then I'm likely to develop a treatment modality which is intellectually orientated, and I'll try to "prove" that expressing emotions is of little value in psychotherapy. The more strident I am about my beliefs the more likely I am to be afraid of their opposites. When I campaign long and hard for the death penalty for murder, I'm denying the part of me that would murder. Much bigotry has its roots in the fact that the proponent of a viewpoint fears he's the very thing he finds so abhorrent. None of this would matter so much if it weren't essential, in order to deny the fear, that some people attempt to inflict their attitudes on others. Because of this I'm denied seeing and hearing what I deem to be healthy for me because a censor, afraid of his own lasciviousness, needs to believe he knows what's best for me. He imagines my impurity as a way of denying his own. My way of life is affected by others needing to justify their own actions taken as they are, not in the light of knowledge and objectivity, but in the service of their fears. Pity those who trap themselves in the medical system, are too afraid to abscond, and who wake up without their gall bladders. They'll get little comfort from the knowledge that they've helped a surgeon stave off his fear that there was a less invasive way to cure the patient.

Current medical practice may be regarded as the result of the medical profession and the public combining to defend themselves against the fear of self-exposure and alternative views. It has little concern for those theories and practices which could keep most people free of physical and mental disease. The more mechanistic and strident the conservative element in the medical profession becomes, the more afraid they are. Change, flexibility and human concerns become increasingly dismissed in favor of spending large amounts of money to shore up a system which was never effective in curing people. It does, however, temporarily allay the feelings of impotence of those claiming responsibility for the health of others. The alternative is self-responsibility. Some doctors and members of the public may not like it, for it means no longer telling people what they should do and letting them do what is right for them. Bureaucracies, like medical hierarchies, fail to survive when they are no longer funded by fear.

So too is this book a reflection of both my aspirations and my fears. That I should propose self-responsibility for you comes from my reluctance to accept my own, or my unwillingness to trust others. Am I not, by writing this book, seeking your tacit approval for my ideas and, indirectly, your admiration for me? Do I only feel safe if I know that you, my public, loves me? I'm both yearning for you to need my advice and caring and angry that I've put myself in a position of taking care of your needs. Like most doctors, I've been raised to care for others, and I do it very well. From the paradox of my feelings, and from the honing of my perceptions and interpretations in childhood, comes my therapy.

I can't tell you what to do, because I don't know. What I can tell you is what I've found in living my life up to this point in time. I'm subjective, and my conclusions constantly change. Therein lies their value. You can read them, allow them to affect you, dream about them, and ultimately discard them in favor of your own immediate truth.

The notion that people who intend becoming well must decide for themselves is, for many, a bitter pill to swallow. We all twist and turn in order to avoid that realization, searching often all our lives to find someone or something to take care of us. And yet there's a part of us which is continually rejecting advice from authorities, even after we've expended much effort in obtaining it. Clients almost seduce doctors into advising them, promising to be good, reliable patients, "I'll do anything to get rid of it, Doctor," only to dismiss the recommendations. I've argued before that this well-recognized phenomenon is often in the service of continuing the illness, a part of the contract between the patient and his practitioner. But there's another component to it as well.

We encourage a prophet to promote his views, give him credence, patronize his practice, spread the word of his wonderful cures, and lure him into believing that he's infallible. We promote him to a position of power, often forgiving minor transgressions of his stated aims along the way. He becomes a figurehead, and people look to him for guidance. He cannot assume power over people or over their views; they must give it to him. Secretly, people regard him as a fool, though they take care until the time is right to not publicize their view. And then he stumbles, often with the help of someone who is apparently sympathetic but is secretly aspiring to his position, but mostly because the prophet can no longer stand the solitude and fear of being top dog. His fall from power is often dramatic, generally aided by scandal of some sort. We strip him of his power just as we gave it to him, musing in his passing at what had possessed him to make the oldest mistake on earth. We've made him a fool. The sorrow of the occasion is tempered by memories of the early dream, when we hoped he would save us. Soon both sorrow and memories are lost beneath the crushing inevitability of his demise. We settle back to defending ourselves against the realization of our own aloneness, quietly plotting to whom we'll next give the mantle—the poisoned chalice of hero. Before long he appears.

We do this in the hope of avoiding responsibility. Our fear is that we're not good enough, since we didn't attract the perfect love and caring we hoped for as children. We're terrified that even if we risk changing, we won't be good enough to please the new parents, just as we weren't good enough to please the original ones. Better to stay helpless, loveless, hopeless, and ill; then we may at least attract caring.

CONCEPTS OF HEALING

Many people have concerned themselves with the nature of the healing force. It's the same as the illness force: it comes from within the client, a client connected to her universe. That part of the client prepared to accept responsibility for having caused the illness can now take responsibility for curing it. If 85 percent of illness is acknowledged as self-caused, the same 85 percent becomes available for self-cure. "Wow, I can cure 85 percent of my illness myself!" If factors beyond the individual's control are deemed to have caused 85 percent of the illness, then only 15 percent becomes available for self-cure. We then put ourselves in the hands of an expert, relying on her to cure the remaining 85 percent of our illness. This is a sobering thought in view of the fact that she'll be looking after her interests first and ours, if we're lucky, second. Those interests center on her views of illness, health, and the world. Financial and professional interests are powerful, but secondary to her need to be relevant, and to be "right."

By being willing to accept a large portion of our disease as of our making, created in order to take care of ourselves as best we can, we make available an equally large portion about which we can choose to do something. This makes us responsible and in charge of our own healing process. It doesn't matter what other people, experts or friends, regard as a reasonable percentage of the disease to acknowledge as our own. We can vary the percentage according to how much we want to take responsibility for ourselves at any point in our lives. Understanding that we've made ourselves ill in order to care for ourselves, and to congratulate ourselves for so doing, is an early step to feeling good about saying, "Yes, I made myself ill, and now I'm going to explore becoming well."

Taking responsibility for the future requires that we take responsibility for the past. That means accepting that even though we were in a position where we had few options, our reactions were our own. When we can accept the old hurts, we can drop them and our old anger. We changed the way we were in order to survive. Now we must change back in order to survive. These are the two changes of life. The first was made under duress and with few or no options. The second change, the change back, is entirely up to us. We need not undergo the laborious process of altering every decision we've taken. Why should we? We're happy enough with the very large part of us. There may be a few of our personal idiosyncrasies which result in us not getting what we want. Some of these will be causing illness. The change back to the way we were need not be either agonizing or profound. It may be slow, incremental and unremarkable.

Watch a weight lifter. Watch his face as he contemplates the lift, wondering if he'll make it. Watch his struggle and the stress on his frame as he uses every fiber of his body to effect the lift, drawing on his hours of physical and mental training. Notice the hope and the fear as he reaches upward in the last final thrust. See the exhilaration on his face as he feels the straightening of his arms as he achieves his goal. See his moment of peace and fulfillment as he walks from beneath his weight and sees it crash onto the mat.

We've struggled to lift a large and cumbersome burden onto our shoulders, because we were told to do so. It took us about six years of hard labor, lifting it bit by bit. We've struggled to live while carrying it around. Our back hurts, and our head aches. We daren't lean forward, and we daren't lean back. We don't have to lower it inch by inch in the same way that we raised it. We don't need to consider each painful decision we made all those years ago as we were raising it. We don't need to break our backs lowering it as we lifted it. We can walk out from under it. It will fall to the ground with no effort and no pain on our part. We can drop it.

As a therapist, I cast myself in the role of (and am often cast in the role of) a surrogate parent. We all use surrogate parents, until we no longer need them. Whenever clients consult therapists, transference occurs. When the client no longer needs a surrogate parent in order to feel safe, he'll no longer need to attend the therapist. That's cure. This may be a problem for a therapist who only feels safe when she's looking after people. She may not regard the client curing himself and leaving therapy to be in her best interests. She may be tempted to maintain the transference and counter-transference and keep the client in therapy. This happens in psychotherapy more often than therapists care to admit. Clients cast their therapists into roles that are purely for the benefit of the clients' needs ("you're wonderful, doctor"), and they in turn are cast as clients ("I can fix you") for the benefit of the therapist. This can be a pitfall of therapy, since neither the client nor the doctor ever leaves it.

THE ILLNESS CYCLE

If childhood didn't provide an environment in which to learn that we were loved, and it didn't equip us for adulthood by a gradual and safe handing over of the responsibility of looking after ourselves, then we tend to look for surrogate parents to cover the transitional period between leaving home and becoming self-responsible. During this period, people often seek therapy, among other things. I'm of the belief that this is a period of transition that, for the future peace of mind of all of us who needed therapy, we must pass through.

There's an added bonus to walking away from this transition period and leaving therapy. It comes in the form of effective partner selection. If we select a partner while we're in the transition period of diminished personal responsibility, our partner will be chosen as a surrogate parent. He'll only be available if he's in the same stage, that is, denying that people are responsible for themselves. He expresses this belief by taking care of his partner. Although partners respond differently, one taking care of, the other being cared for, they have the same belief system. These partnerships last only as long as both partners remain in the transition phase. When one moves on, the other will feel unsafe. They'll often move along together, in which case they report a growing and maturing of their relationship. If one partner refuses, through fear, to take responsibility for himself, and the other moves through the transition phase, the relationship collapses. Alternatively, two people who form a partnership, both from a position of self-responsibility, will be able to choose their partners unshackled by the above complications. They're likely to make wiser choices.

One of the major reasons a client attends a practitioner is to have his needs recognized. If a busy doctor spends five or ten minutes with the patient, with most of that spent looking at her computer and much of the remainder searching for the latest drugs, the patient is very likely to go away feeling that he's been dealt with perfunctorily. The treatment prescribed may be enough to relieve his symptoms, but the underlying psychological states have not been addressed and, since they're a major component of any illness, the condition is unlikely to resolve. The client may become angry at such a dismissal of his real needs and, as many a doctor finds out, makes himself worse and then threatens to sue the doctor for failing in her duty of care.

Those practitioners who spend more time with clients tend to be sued less. Sometimes clients only need to be seen for a short time, but these cases are in the minority. The repetition of a drug prescription is an example. If he wants a repeat prescription, however, then it would appear that both parties have settled for palliative (non-curative) treatment, and a review is perhaps warranted. If the client has a new complaint, one hour is the minimum time necessary to establish the client's needs, how the complaint is meeting those needs, and what alternative options are available. The five-minute consultation, followed by the routine prescription of a drug, is virtually the only medicine the vast majority of doctors practice. This, of course, reflects the vast majority of people's wishes.

Unless a consultation occupies a substantial amount of time, the doctor and the client never enter the "trance" state necessary for comprehension and cure of the problem. The trance state is simply a state of total focus. When I'm in the middle of an interview with a client and the telephone rings, for example, I become aware of just how deeply in trance I am. I've been totally occupied by what he's saying and by my observation of how he's saying it. I'm aware of nothing else. I realized many years ago that I'd better not arrange to do anything else during interviews, such as turning off an appliance or making a phone call, since I'd always forget. At other times my memory for such tasks was fine, but during a session with a client I've turned my mind to engaging her and her problem totally. Diagnosis and treatment is guesswork without having engaged the client's subconscious; otherwise the therapist is still dealing with the client's defended intellectual appreciation of her gout or his Crohn's disease.

By treating the convenient and safe version of his illness, both practitioner and client remain in the same defended frame of reference: that is, the condition is beyond the influence of the individual. Symptom relief is often the only acceptable treatment to the conscious mind. The trance state allows the therapist to diagnose the needs and advantages behind the client's decision to have the illness. The doctor allows her own subconscious to diagnose for her. This frees her from having to sift through a great deal of irrelevant material that both practitioner and client will raise in order to feel safe. The client's investment in remaining superficial about his disease is his fear of change, while the doctor will be tempted to keep the client sick in order to feel needed. The trance state is not the deep trance that many of us associate with the antics of stage hypnotists; rather, it is a presence and focus that excludes all else beyond the immediate task at hand.

We've all experienced the hypnotic state, perhaps the most obvious example being when we're watching a movie or reading a book. When something else demands our attention, we "snap out of it" and are often surprised at how occupied we've been. A long time may have passed of which we're unaware. "Gracious, is that the time?" we say to ourselves, having sat up for hours longer than we intended watching a thriller on TV. We experience the trance state at the moment of falling asleep and waking each day or at work when our mind "wanders" — the well-known state of reverie. These are all self-induced, hypnotic states and are similar to the frame of mind in which my client and I engage each other. If either of us is afraid of the other, the state of trance will not be achieved, and we'll both know that the majority of the problem remains. In a few more sessions we may risk entering the healing state.

PICKING A GOOD DOCTOR

This is easy, since there's no such thing as a good or a bad doctor, just doctors who are right for you at a particular time. When, or if, your original choice no longer suits you, you can change your original contract with the doctor, or change doctors. If you allow yourself to follow your feelings and intuition, you'll automatically pick someone whose appreciation of your disease complements your own. If you're too frightened to pick a doctor by such a method, stay where you are until it's safer for you to move. Then risk a little.

If the doctor believes that tonsillitis is caused by a streptococcus and that penicillin will cure it, and you also choose to believe that, then you'll be attracted to each other. After your child has suffered three attacks of tonsillitis during one winter and has had three courses of antibiotics, and your doctor still maintains that upper respiratory tract inflammations are caused by organisms and that the solution is to take more antibiotics, you may decide to seek a second opinion. Most likely the doctor will offer you the opportunity to discuss the matter with an ear, nose, and throat surgeon, who will give you the same explanation but with a different treatment—namely, removing the tonsils or, if the middle ear is a complication, inserting tubes through the child's tympanic membranes. If you say "Wait! I no longer trust your assessment of my child's disease, so I'm going to seek an alternative approach," then you may find a clinical dietitian, who will remove all dairy products from the child's diet and supplement it with calcium-containing vegetables. In addition, the dietitian may add more raw green vegetables, increase the fiber in the child's diet to regulate the bowels, make sure sufficient bacteria provide foods in the diet, and remove some of the simple, rapidly absorbed sugars from the diet, along with corn syrup. If you trust this person, and believe that this treatment makes sense, then you'll pass that belief on through your words and actions to your child, who, if he or she similarly chooses to believe, will recover and stop having tonsillitis or middle ear infections.

Or you may decide that since the child develops the ear infections only when his father returns to his job on the oil rig, where he's away for two months at a time, the basis of the problem is psychological. The child is giving himself ear infections in order to keep his father at home or perhaps to attract greater support from his mother while his father is absent. In this case, you may take the family to see a family therapist, who will reassure the child that even though his father is away from home, he still loves him, and that his mother will care for him while he's gone. Dad may choose to call home or use some other technological means to contact the boy more often. When the child no longer needs the ear infections, he'll stop having them.

Medical practice is a supply-and-demand industry. If more people require dietetic advice, then more dietitians will become available. If more people require naturopathic treatment, then naturopaths will proliferate. Similarly, people will patronize those treatment options they find appealing, including osteopathy, chiropractic, radionics, radiesthesia, herbalism, Gestalt, primal scream, transactional analysis, radix, neo-Reikian bodywork, drug therapy, surgery, bioenergetics, hypnotherapy, acupuncture, Rolfing, homeopathy, color therapy, massage, psychoanalysis, transpersonal psychology, cognitive behavior therapy, electroshock therapy, ayurvedic healing, visualization, flower remedies, behavior modification, and encounter. It's wonderful to have a choice.

Many therapies flourish despite attempts by the medical profession to criminalize them, attempts which of course are always framed as being in the public interest. Courts of Law are part of the problem and not part of the solution, since they always defer to orthodox medicine, and there's little legal support for alternative therapies however effective they may be, and however much the discerning public may want them. Orthodox medicine has monopolized the law for the benefit of doctors, much to the detriment of the health of populations.

This is in the process of changing with the evolution of the aforementioned PROMs (as you'll recall, "patient reported outcome measures"). These questionnaires give weight to what the patient says—not what doctors say—about how effective an investigation and treatment is. They have the potential to shift the focus of healing from healers of all persuasions back to the patients themselves. Not everyone will welcome this development. Whilst doctors are still the main source of health information, some 70 percent of people research health on the Internet, and many seek out other people suffering from the same diagnosis by accessing the Forums and Notice-boards. Health is the most researched topic on the Net. Communication technology, particularly smart phones, means that patients are playing a greater role in the health process and health outcomes than ever before.

LEARNING FROM ILLNESS

When I attend a practitioner, my main concern is to find out the extent to which her particular discipline is capable of teaching me how to care for myself. Will I need to attend this practitioner regularly for the rest of my life, with no insight into my illness, or will I learn from her how to keep myself well in the future? If she offers no insight as to how I prevent my current illness from recurring, or how I prevent other illnesses from developing, then I'm not interested to keep attending her. In my quest to be responsible for myself, I don't want to remain dependent upon the expertise of a practitioner who cannot or will not explain what's happening, and who won't teach me how to take care of myself. Illness is to be learned from, and if the health modality you first choose to treat a problem fails to enlighten you, and you wish to know why you've made yourself ill and how to increase your options for becoming well, I advise you to seek an alternative.

People exploring self-discovery and self-responsibility will find little joy in contemporary orthodox medical practice. You can't learn much in the ten minutes it takes to have a drug prescribed. The drug simply suppresses the physical and psychological symptoms, thereby decreasing rather than increasing awareness of the problem. Those not wishing to care for themselves will, however, find excellent symptomatic relief, and, if they're intent on losing any organs, willing accomplices. If they hurt themselves in a vehicular accident, they'll be helped by modem medicine's greatest technical achievements, including emergency medicine and perhaps reconstructive surgery.

Illness provides an opportunity for us to grow. I've postulated that we give ourselves illnesses in order to take care of more frightening psychological needs. If we discard the usual medical model that there's something "wrong" with us, and the offending organ or psychological state should be treated with a drug, or cut out with a knife, and instead regard illness as an integral part of the growth process, we'll have a clearer notion of its value.

By the indiscriminate removal of a disease process, we've not removed something that was making us unhappy, we've removed something that was taking care of us.

When we realize this, we can begin to use illness effectively. One can no more abandon an illness than one can abandon a part of our experience. We can no more cure illness by denying it than we can deny that we were once five years old. We cure ourselves by accepting it and by then exploring other options, different from the illness we originally chose. The disease then becomes part of our experience, able to be drawn upon at any time. We can revive it if necessary, or leave it dormant. Imagine going to a surgeon and saying, "I want you to cut out my experience between the ages of two and four, since it was a particularly traumatic time for me, and I want to forget it." Disease and learning are part of life.

Have you related any of what you've read to your own situation?

Perhaps you've been adopting the position of a detached observer, learning how other people "give themselves illness" while you "contract" yours. Or perhaps you've felt guilty at having given yourself a disease, and consider yourself weak to have been afraid to ask for the caring that you wanted directly, rather than suffering.

I repeat, everything you've done so far has been to care for yourself, and is sensible, honorable and, if need be, remediable. Everything you will do, is equally honorable. If you want to examine any illness from which you're currently suffering, or from which you've suffered in the past, using the frame of reference with which you're now familiar, ask yourself the following questions.

HOW HAS YOUR ILLNESS CHANGED?

o The way you're feeling? (what were you feeling before becoming ill, and what are you feeling now?)
o The way you're thinking? (what were you thinking before becoming ill, and what are you thinking now?)
o The way you're feeling about yourself?

○ The way you're feeling about life generally?
○ Your feelings toward others?
○ The relationship between you and your spouse, lover, partner, children, father, mother, siblings, other family.
○ Your ability to work?
○ The way you feel about work?
○ Your relationship with your workmates?
○ Your relationship with your boss or immediate supervisor?
○ Your employment prospects?
○ Your mobility?
○ Your financial state?
○ Your ability to play sport?
○ Your ability to travel?
○ Your self-worth?
○ Your ability to have sex with your partner?
○ Your ability to have sex with others?
○ Your ability to care for yourself, your spouse, your children and others.
○ Your need to be looked after?
○ Your ability to be independent?
○ Your ability to be happy?
○ Your willingness to be adventurous?
○ Your willingness to make it?
○ Your will to live?

Now that you're aware of how your illness is responsible for changing the way you feel, think, and act, turn the whole notion of cause and effect upside down. "How has your illness caused the way you feel, think, and act?" becomes "How has the way you feel, think, and act caused your illness?"

The way you feel, think, and act, as well as your illness, are both a consequence of your personality. They're both the result of early-childhood decisions — one does not "cause" the other. The notion that because we're ill, certain things take place, serves the purpose of

- Removing responsibility from us
  ("If it weren't for this cold, I would...")
- Confirming our fears
  ("Damn chlamydia—it'll be a long time before I have sex again...")
- Justifying our feelings, thoughts, and actions to ourselves and to others
  ("I'd really love to go to Bavaria next Christmas, but the cold climate doesn't suit my bronchitis.")

If we consider the end result of our being ill, we'll discover what we've set out (mostly in our subconscious) to achieve. We have changed our lives, using the illness to do it. We create the illness and in turn invest in it the power to change our lives. Illness, alone, is impotent. For example, a cold is not some unlucky event that prevents us from working. We give ourselves a cold in order to stop work. Arthritis is not some unfortunate disease which destroys our independence. We're scared to be independent so we give ourselves arthritis. Cancer is not something we develop by chance. It's something we give ourselves when we're too scared to live, or need to give ourselves a serious wake up call. Sometimes having illness *is* the best way of getting what we want. Health involves a willingness to take responsibility for the decision to be ill.

The following exercise in guided imagery will clarify some of the advantages of your being ill. Either read it yourself or have someone read it to you, pausing where appropriate.

Quiet your mind, release those things you've been concentrating on in this room, make yourself comfortable in your chair, take three or four deep breaths, breathe out the tensions from your body, and relax. Cast your mind back to the last time that you were ill, to the place where you were ill, to the house or hospital and to the room you were lying in, and be there for a moment in that place, lying quietly. See that place and the things around you as you lie there; hear the sounds, smell the smells, notice the movements of the trees outside the window or the cars in the street.

See yourself lying there or sitting in your chair, and become aware of this ill person who is you. As you lie there, let yourself be aware of how you're feeling: if you have pain or discomfort; whether you're quiet or restless, hot or cold; breathing easily or with difficulty; or any other bodily sensations you may have. And as you lie there, let yourself become aware of your feelings: whether or not you're sad, or afraid, or angry, or bitter and resentful; and whether you're joyful, excited, or anything else you're feeling or thinking in your state of illness.

Now become aware, if you haven't already done so, of the other people who are there with you while you're ill, either with you continually or intermittently. See their faces, see who's there, and hear what they're saying to you or to others who may be in the room. And as you become aware of their presence, be aware of anyone else whom you'd like to be there who is not present. If there's someone whom you'd especially like to be with you while you're ill, put that person there. Allow yourself to experience what that person is doing and saying and how you're feeling about him or her and others who are either present or absent. And as you experience being ill and seeing the people in your life who are important to you at this time, be aware of what you're telling yourself about this illness (or others you've had) and how you're reacting to being unwell. Become aware of what you think about being ill, how you regard yourself as a person now that you're ill, and what you know about people who are ill.

Leaving your illness for the moment, find yourself on a beautiful day with the sun shining, walking across a green meadow with the air fresh and the sky blue. At the end of the meadow is a path leading toward a small house, and as you walk through the meadow along the path toward the house, you can see something written on the door of the house. As you get closer you can see the words "ADVANTAGES FROM BEING ILL." Now open the door and let come out just one of the advantages in being ill that are within the house, knowing that the ones which are just inside the door, and which come out first, are the safest for you to consider. Now talk to the advantage which you've let out and get to know it, letting the advantage tell you how this illness that you have has really been helping you in some way. And as you talk with it, find out about the good things you've been getting, which may be anything at all, for the house has thousands of different advantages.

Now thank your illness for looking after you so well. And as you thank your illness, you may like to ask how else you could have come to get the good things for yourself without needing to go through the uncomfortable things like the aches and pains and miseries of the illness. Be aware that at this point in time you may be willing to get what you want in other ways, or you may choose to not remove the illness at this time, and do so later. The decision is yours.

Allow yourself to experience some of the things you're not getting in your life at the moment that you'd like, and see if they're related in any way to your illness, or if your advantage in having the illness gets those things for you. Consider this awhile. And now say goodbye to the advantage that you took out of the house and know that it, and the illness, will be there, within the house, if you want them. And as you walk back down the path through the meadow with the sun shining warmly down upon you, and the breeze blowing warmly and gently, let yourself feel the new power of the things you've discovered. Be with yourself for a few moments longer, feeling what you will, and then come back here to this room, to the book you're reading, and relax a moment with yourself.

When you're ready, you may like to turn back a few pages and reconsider the questions on page 307. How has your illness changed?

ILLNESS AND SOCIETY

Illness is partly an anthropological matter. Societies need illnesses in similar ways to individuals, that is, they're the result of social scripting as well as personal scripting.

The role that illness plays will vary between and within societies, as in individuals, with their needs. Historical, geographical, genetic and social factors all determine that diseases of one society will differ from diseases elsewhere. The significance of the various factors will vary. Poor hygiene, nutrition and a dusty environment will be more important in the development of trachoma in the Australian Aboriginal than a racial need for an eye complaint. Similarly, working in coal mines may be more causative of anthracosis, and working in asbestos plants more causative of asbestosis, than a need on the part of the workers for a lung condition. And yet many people are exposed to these environmental pollutants and don't develop diseases. This book addresses our ability to impact any condition by looking at who we are. It doesn't claim that you can, or should, control everything. We've discussed previously how individuals protect themselves against disease by having no need for illness. Collectively, as in the case of the miners, they may force management to improve the working environment. Societies may also live under similar conditions, but have different illness profiles. It's well documented in medical literature that the incidence of diseases differs across societies, and although environmental and dietetic explanations exist for these differences, I believe that the condoning of various diseases and the rejecting of others is an equally powerful factor.

Would you rather tell someone that you were suffering from arthritis or venereal disease? Would you rather tell someone you had a cold sore on the lip or genital herpes? They are virtually the same organism. Which illness do you have that you're willing to tell others about, and do you have others that you're less willing to discuss? Your answer is likely to reflect the image you have of yourself as well as the social pressures that condone certain diseases but not others. If you kill yourself, then a vehicle accident or cancer is more socially acceptable than suicide. If you want people to respect your suffering, then arthritis is more effective than IBS, since it is more visible. Society condones minor upper respiratory infections (they're a national pastime) and rejects people who choose to go insane instead, even though they may have the same needs: time out with caring. As governments and their social services take more responsibility for us—the carrot we're offered in order to accede to their wishes—diseases are increasingly being used by authorities to facilitate the handover of power to them. Many health programs are not in the public interest, but in the interests of vested interests. Many of us are willing to be relieved of the burden of self-responsibility as quickly as possible.

Governments foster an atmosphere of non individual responsibility which actively encourages people to become unwell and dependent. By so doing, Governments increase their stranglehold on people's lives. Imagine what would happen if people decided that they were not going to become seriously ill. The medical hierarchy, the drug companies, the hospital workers, the helping professionals, the insurance companies, and a large part of the public service would all be out of work. Consider the massive financial investment as a society in the early detection of breast cancer, prostate cancer, and bowel cancer, to name a few. Collectively, the medical agencies of Government are among the most influential organizations in our society. Your health may not be their first concern.

Illness is commonly deployed to avoid unwanted emotions. The less willing a society is to outwardly express anger, sadness, joy and fear, the more common this particular usage of disease will be. Take the following situation.

The foreman on a busy production line is genuinely concerned about the dangerous working environment. Driven by his own scripting to be responsible for others, he works at improving conditions on the factory floor. Management treats him warily, realizing both his potential to increase production and to stop it altogether. The workers use him to improve both their pay and conditions. Despite achieving considerable headway, he finds he's no happier than before. The workers never seem satisfied and management distrusts him, blaming him for poor productivity and industrial unrest. He has no natural base of support. He becomes very frustrated, has increasing doubts about his self-worth, becomes chronically afraid, develops kidney failure and is forced to retire. Both management and workers make speeches about his great work, and both pay special attention to his efforts in the field of industrial relations. He receives a golden handshake and, much to the relief of everyone, invalids himself out of their lives. He shifts house so that he may be further from them and nearer the dialysis machine at the hospital.

Illness has facilitated the resolution of a difficult social situation. In other societies, the workers and the management may have had a more respectful relationship; as a child the foreman may not have been raised to care for others; the retirement through illness may not have attracted a financial reward; the wife may have not been interested in caring for a sick partner; the hospital may not have had money donated by a drug company with which to buy a dialysis machine; and the foreman may have been prepared to withstand the attempts of both parties to exploit him. In that case this scenario wouldn't have developed. All of the factors influencing the expression and timing of this man's illness were, to a degree, socially determined. To that same degree the illness itself was socially determined.

In the capitalist world, money is often behind one group of people encouraging others to become ill. The drug companies are uniquely poised to exert pressure on governments to spend money in one area or another. The drug companies, however, are no more responsible for what's happened in the world than anyone else. It's nonsense to blame them. They've responded to the marketplace: to the people's call for more and more powerful symptom-relieving drugs. In this they've been aided by a medical profession ready and willing to promote any system of medicine that effectively maintains the status quo: that is, patients lose their symptoms, keep their diseases, learn nothing, and pay dearly for all three. Doctors remain overworked, defensive, powerful, and, if they so desire, wealthy. Mostly, as I've noted earlier, they get to be authoritative, or "right."

Economically, it's better in the long run for people to take responsibility for themselves and to stop regarding illness as bad luck (and therefore warranting of financial reimbursement). Illness is such an integral part of our society, and such a pillar of our financial system, that I don't hold much hope of changing it; nor do I necessarily want to. I raise it here as an option. Take, for example, the average course of events in family medical practices all over the Western world.

Thousands of family medical practitioners see hundreds of thousands of patients superficially every day. They may send a tenth of these people to specialists, often not because the general practitioner lacks skills, but because they don't have the time to diagnose and treat the patient properly. If a doctor sees many patients in a day, he can earn about four times as much money as he can if he sees fewer people but deals with them in depth. Very few doctors choose the latter option. Those patients sent off to medical specialists, for which the insurance funds, that is, you and I, pay, are likely to be further investigated, since that's part of specialist medical practice. ECGs, MRIs, blood tests, X-rays, scans, endoscopies, surgical procedures and so on are all generated by the specialist practitioner. Then hospitals, paramedical care, recovery and rehabilitation all add to costs, not to mention the drugs which are almost invariably prescribed. The income generated by one client attending a family medical practitioner, and being superficially dealt with, can be enormous. If the family medical practitioner, or the practitioner of first contact, were remunerated for doing the job properly in the first place, there would be minimal expense. In addition, the client could be taught how to avoid future illness in himself and his family, and even greater savings made.

To effect such changes in medical practice would mean an enormous change in thinking on the part of the public, the government and the medical fraternity, including alternative practitioners. As it stands, governments are pressured by doctors into buying the latest technological advances which keep the powerful hospital specialists happy, and are of little or no benefit to the majority of people paying for them. The cost of new medical technology is phenomenal. With each new multimillion dollar "advance" comes a decrease in the reliance that the public puts on common sense and its own ability to heal itself. The fear generated by the implication that "anyone who doesn't have a yearly scan is running the risk of cancer" causes far more deaths than it saves lives. Multiphasic screening is making some people very rich and contributing to the illness of the gullible. We can believe that the machines, laboratory tests, drugs and medical insurance will keep us well, or believe instead that we can make and keep ourselves well. The former belief will eventually bankrupt us all. The latter will result in cost-effective technical and psychological support for people intent on healing themselves.

As society evolves, so does its appreciation of those things which ail it. It's a mistake to believe that because we understand anatomy, physiology and biochemistry better than we ever have, we understand more about human beings and our diseases. Rather do we understand them differently. Our explanation of the things which happen to our minds and bodies will depend on the metaphor of the day.

The metaphor of the day depends on the general direction of society. Let me give an example.

Since the Industrial Revolution, our metaphor has become increasingly mechanical. The heart isn't pumping properly. The liver, which is like a complex chemical factory, is malfunctioning. The acid erosion of the protective layer of the stomach results in a stomach ulcer. With increasing technological sophistication, particularly since the Second World War, the tendency to attribute malfunctions of the body to mechanical breakdown has increased. This means that the origins of disease, and the treatment of disease, will also be regarded as mechanical. We now think of illness in technological, mechanical terms. The mechanical concept of disease isn't the only concept of disease, nor the correct concept. Neither is it incorrect. It's simply one way of looking at disease, based on the current metaphor. It happens to be the concept of disease which suits, or has suited, the industrial society. Knowing the basis of our notions of disease, it isn't difficult to see how our two major therapies, chemical therapy (drugs) and mechanical therapy (surgery), have arisen. It's also easy to see why other concepts of illness are rejected, using fear and ignorance masquerading as logic. The logic holds only within the narrow, mechanical frame of reference.

The technological revolution has resulted in more computing analogies to describe medical complaints. The loss of memory as we age can be explained as the hard drive filling up, resulting in delayed recovery of data, or the RAM being less agile or powerful.

The application of quantum mechanics to medicine will herald the next evolution of how we view disease. As I've noted earlier, doctors currently cite scientific principles that are now at least a century out of date. The medical profession hasn't adopted concepts of complex and interrelated systems, subatomic particle physics, entanglement or the uncertainty principle. As a consequence, many doctors reject the tenets of distance healing, energy-field healing, and multiple other healing modalities that make use of physics beyond the standard model. Because many less orthodox healing modalities have failed the "evidence based" test of contemporary orthodox medicine, they are often dismissed by their detractors as "unscientific." This becomes disingenuous when viewed alongside the incomplete science quoted by orthodox medicine to support their own model.

Another view of disease can be seen through the lens of dis-association. We lose contact with the sun, animals, fresh air, other people, microorganisms in the soil, and the billions of organisms on the surface of our skin and in our gut. We apply chemicals to everything. In losing contact with other life, we become separate; our own physiological mechanisms then become unable, in isolation, to keep us well. We need every other life form to be flourishing around us. In this model of disease, remedies are directed towards re-association, such as getting more sunlight, allowing kids to get dirty, ceasing the application of skin creams, stopping our practices of washing our hands all the time and sterilizing our houses, and re-asserting physical intimacy between people in order to transfer healthy organisms.

Every single event since the big bang (or the "big bounce," as some theorists posit) affects who we are. Everything. While we don't need to know what these influences are, having gratitude for the privilege of being alive would mean availing ourselves of these influences, whatever they are.

People hope, as they always have, that the current metaphor, and the notions stemming from it, would make them happy. Technological medicine was to have healed the world of all disease by now. Instead we've simply replaced the old diseases with new ones, or revived those that we temporarily shelved. The belief that drugs will save us is passing. Our belief that the technologists will heal us is lying in tatters on the surgery floor.

The Industrial Revolution has been replaced by the Technological Revolution, itself to be replaced by the Personal Revolution. The notion of disease as the mechanical failing of a machine under duress is being replaced by the notion that disease is the manifestation of imbalance, both internal and external. The change from one idea to the other isn't new. It's happened many times before and will happen again. Those in the forefront of medicine are not those who devise something new, but those who see change as inevitable, and see it early. Disease will come to be regarded as a whole person event. This change is made more necessary by the financial strictures of the technological revolution. It's simply impossible to continue funding the current style of medicine.

People have to take more responsibility and therefore more care of themselves. When society has made the next great leap forward, my concept of disease, depending as it does on emerging metaphor and my own internal processes, will be archaic. Then it will be the broken idols of psychotherapy which lie gathering dust on the group room floor.

EPILOGUE

At the start of the wet season above the plains a long way from the coast, a tiny rivulet is given life. Gathering every available tributary, it struggles in those harsh regions for survival. The trees, unable to sustain themselves from such a small creek, have not established themselves along its barely green edges. Nor do fish or animals rely on the meager water supply for their own needs, knowing its inconstancy. The sun makes moderate demands, evaporating a small portion of that water which hasn't sought refuge by running underground.

The terrain is a dominant influence in the infancy of the creek. The fledgling waters, in order to keep gathering, must satisfy the dictates of the land. In the early stage of its life, every rise, no matter how small, must be negotiated. Every dip, no matter how shallow, must be filled, before the waters, fed slowly by those following, can begin to move toward the ocean. In such a climate is the small waterway nurtured, fed by the land and, in order to guarantee its survival, aware of all the land exacts.

As the creek becomes surer with time and distance, accumulating the experience of its many tributaries, it begins to acquire its own strength. Larger watercourses join its course, and before long it begins, tentatively at first, to support life about it. Small trees adorn its banks, tadpoles breed in its quiet reaches, and the sun, attesting its permanence, places heavier demands upon its waters.

The landscape, once complete master over the course it must flow, is now bargained with. Sometimes the creek defers to the strength of a mountain range, turning back the way it came in order to find an opening, but as it gains in maturity and becomes a river, it makes its own mark upon the countryside.

Forging its way along valley floors and through gorges and canyons, the river changes the face of the land which spawned it. No longer needing to acquiesce for survival to every whim of the terrain, and aware of their mutual need, the river rejoices in its independence by supporting large trees, fish, birds and animals, and supplying small creeks and rock pools with clear water. The sun's ever-increasing demand for evaporation is met with ease.

When the last of the ranges has been negotiated, the river celebrates its course toward the sea, free of the need to rely upon others for its survival. Some of the early meanderings made in order to continue gathering water and appease the terrain are replaced by a graceful and powerful flow toward the ocean. Thankful for having followed the early directions of the land, the river blends with the ocean, feeling the power of achievement, the warmth of co-existence and the exhilaration of freedom. Born of the ocean and travelling the long journey back to the place where they first began, the waters know themselves for the first time.

He who understands paradox understands illness. When I say that an individual needs or wants an illness, and ensures that he suffers from it, I'm speaking of the paradox inherent within the words need and want. If you ask the person with cancer why he needs cancer, he will tell you that he doesn't need it, want it or like it. And of course, to his knowledge, he's being completely truthful. Nobody likes the aches, pains and anguish of being unwell. If the same person with cancer is offered the option of surviving by confronting his greatest fears, in many cases he will choose the cancer. He needs the cancer to avoid the fear. His decision either way is entirely honorable.

Fear is the basis of illness. Fear necessitates the early childhood adaptations that result in illness. We're afraid to take responsibility for ourselves. We don't trust our own parent to look after our own child, the grown-up part of us to look after the little kid in us. We try and get someone else to do it for us, for we were never taught in childhood that we could do it ourselves and do it successfully. Our illness confirms our frailty and our need for a caretaker. If, in addition, we don't like our little kid much, then even if we have the skills we may be disinclined to care for him or her. With either attitude we're likely to attract people to us who agree with our dismissal of our own parenting abilities, or don't like the little kid in us much either. Continuing confirmation of our own inadequacy requires continuing incapacity. Chronic illness serves the purpose well.

To cure ourselves we need to take back the responsibility of loving and caring for our little kids from whomever we have entrusted the task. We need to accept ourselves whoever, whenever and however we are. That means accepting that we have made ourselves unwell in order to care for ourselves the very best we know how. When we've taken back full responsibility for our little kids, we can find another grown-up willing to help us look after him or her. Our little kids can play with each other, while the grown-ups share the joys and burdens of responsibility.

We can make use of those healing professionals, orthodox or alternative, who make themselves available. We can pass through the transition stage of partial responsibility while under the umbrella of their care. When we're ready we can risk leaving the nest and taking off on our own, knowing that we can return if we want.

It's not for me, with my own needs, to tell you how, when or where you do it. I've suggested a program for recovery, a program for growth and discovery. Ultimately, your universe is beyond me.

Use this as you will. From here on there's room for one person only. From a distance I see you standing at the gate of your soul, looking in. You like very much what you see.

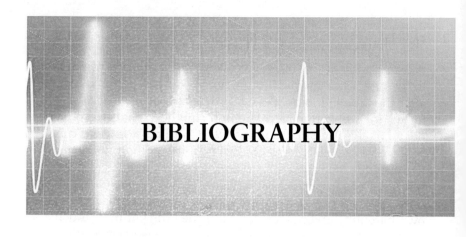

BIBLIOGRAPHY

Berne, Eric. *Games People Play*. New York: Penguin, 1964.

Berne, Eric. *What Do You Say after You Say Hello?* New York: Grove Press, 1972.

British Medical Journal, 23 (1982): 284.

Darby, David N., Stan Glasser, and Ian Frederick Wilkinson. *Health Care and LifeStyle: A Study of Self-Medication in Australia*. Sydney: New South Wales University Press, 1981.

Goulding, Mary, and Robert Goulding. *Changing Lives through Redecision Therapy*. New York: Brunner/Mazel, 1979.

Goulding, Mary, and Robert Goulding. *The Power Is in the Patient*. San Francisco: TA Press, 1976.

James, Muriel, and Dorothy Jongeward. *Born to Win*. New York: Addison-Wesley, 1971.

Karpman, Stephen. "Fairytale and Script Drama Analysis." *Transactional Analysis Bulletin* 7, no. 26 (April 1968): 39–43.

Kitzinger, Sheila. *The Experience of Childbirth*. Harmondsworth, UK: Penguin, 1978.

Lankton, Stephen R. *Practical Magic*. Cupertino, CA: Meta Publications, 1980.

Leboyer, Frederick. *Birth without Violence*. London: Wildwood House, 1975.

Mann, Felix. *Acupuncture: The Ancient Chinese Art of Healing.* New York: Vintage, 1973.

Perls, Fritz. *Gestalt Therapy Verbatim.* Moab, UT: Real People Press, 1969.

Rosenbloom, Art. *The Natural Birth Control Book.* Philadelphia: Aquarian Research Foundation, 1977.

Shears, C. Curtis. *Nutritional Science and Health Education.* Stroud, UK: Downfield Press, 1976.

Simonton, O. Carl, Stephanie Matthews Simonton, and James Creighton. *Getting Well Again.* New York: Bantam Books, 1980.

Spitz, Rene. "Hospitalism Genesis of Psychiatric Conditions in Early Childhood." *Psychoanalytic Study of the Child,* 1 (1945): 53–74.

Steiner, Claude. *Scripts People Live: Transactional Analysis of Life Scripts.* New York: Bantam Books, 1974.

Woollams, S., and M. Brown. *Transactional Analysis.* New York: Prentice Hall, 1979.

INDEX